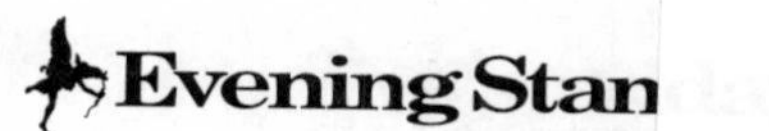

The London Fashion Guide

Mimi Spencer

For Paul, the world's least dedicated shopper

Particular thanks are due to Deborah Tilley, whose tireless research unearthed some little-known shopping gems, and to Charlotte Coleman-Smith for long hours and good sense.

First published in Great Britain in 1997 by
EVENING STANDARD BOOKS
Northcliffe House, 2 Derry Street, London W8 5EE

Reprinted in 1997

ISBN 1 900625 40 7

Associate editor and researcher Deborah Tilley

Publishing manager Joanne Bowlby
Editorial manager Charlotte Coleman-Smith
Production manager Roger Hall

Designed by Nick Cave

Illustrations by Tamasin Doe

Typesetting by Sally Blackmore
Copy-edited by Tracey Beresford
Index by Isobel McLean

Printed and bound in Great Britain by Redwood Books

A CIP catalogue record of this book is available from the British Library.

This book may be ordered by post direct from the publisher, but please try your bookshop first. Please send information about new London shop openings to Evening Standard Books, or fax us on 0171 376 2909.

Corporate editions and personal subscriptions of any of the Evening Standard Guides are available. Call for details, tel: 0171 938 6774

Also published in the series:

London Restaurant Guide, London Pub Guide, Wine Guide, Children's London, Best of... London, Good Food Shop Guide.

Contents

As anyone who regularly reads the fashion pages of the *Evening Standard* will know, I love to shop. I adore the sheer naughtiness of a splurge, the indulgent pick-me-up of a posh carrier bag, the crisp rustle of tissue wrapping, the buzz of a bargain culled from a boot sale. It seems I am not alone. In a recent *Evening Standard*/Mori poll, Londoners agreed that shopping was their favourite feature of the capital; more than a quarter of respondents said it was what they like most about their home town – better than the bars, the clubs, the music or the theatre. As London swings into pole position as the world's hippest city, its shops are leading the way.

You need only saunter down some of our most famous streets to be convinced of a renaissance. Not so long ago, the boards were up and no one was at home in Bond Street as rent hikes and recession did their damndest to bring the capital's principal shopping street to its knees. Now an international invasion is well under way, with American and European designers elbowing each other aside to grab the best bits of real estate.

Sloane Street is similarly packed with the kind of high-cachet boutiques that two years ago could only be accessed with a ticket to Paris and a steely shopping nerve; now sunglasses hold back glossy hair come rain come shine, as high-heeled shoppers glide from window to window, ending up at Harvey Nichols for a spin around label-land. In fact, London's department stores have all sharpened up, offering the kind of polish and service that was once the sole preserve of Manhattan.

The newest stores are vast and creamy, or temples of aluminium and plate glass; they are cool white establishments where a single jacket is placed in the window like a prize display at the V&A. The façades are imposing, the buildings palatial, the stock within the stuff of dreams.

At the other end of the spectrum, London boasts the best vintage and second-hand shops in the world. The Continent has nothing to compete with our lucky-dip shops, where seasoned hunters scrum down to emerge triumphant with a bargain. There are dark cubbyholes where original Pucci shirts lurk in the shadows, market stalls heavy with ark-old denim, and warehouses piled high with ancient cords that last saw the light of day when the price was in shillings and pence.

Our hang-out shops are unrivalled too, where the foot-sore perch on high stools and drink café latte through straws. Along with all the high-street names, whose stylish designs have made the British shopping experience so sought-after, there are the off-the-wall shops in out-of-the-way streets where everything and anything is possible. In London, you can buy an authentic Hussar's costume, a Victorian wedding dress, an original Japanese kimono. You can visit the crooked boutique that inspired Dickens' *The Old Curiosity Shop*, or call a charity to have your unwanted clothes carted away. You can wake up with a design idea and wear it within a fortnight, or invest in a Savile Row suit that will still be going strong when you are bundled up in a bath chair.

Introduction

For sheer choice, London cannot be beaten. In effect, the capital's shopping areas are much like a collection of villages. The only problem is knowing where and when to go. Hampstead and Highgate, for instance, is Nicole Farhi territory, all berry colours and sloppy Joe sweaters; the South-west stays open on Sunday afternoons to service weekend walkers and passers-by. If you want menswear or vintage clothes, make Covent Garden your first port of call; if you want shoes, don't go to Notting Hill – there's not a shoe shop in sight – but you will find the best antique clothes and incomparable street and clubwear outlets.

West Soho has a particular flavour – funky, fast and smart – while somewhere like Clerkenwell Green has a different feel, with the emphasis on crafts, jewellery and textiles. To make it easy, this book features seven of the city's best-loved shopping streets, each with enough personality to fill an entire afternoon in glorious reverie. These are streets of character: Walton Street is great for jewellery and for flaunting new purchases from Joseph; Jermyn Street specialises in top-notch men's shoes and shirts; spend a happy hour in Ledbury Road, around the corner from Portobello Market, where the shops are special and the atmosphere soothing. Or, for the polar extreme, make a beeline for Newburgh Street for cool, clubby clothes with a true London flavour.

If you want to shop wisely, handpick your destinations from these pages and plot a course across the capital (the 20 shops that have won an Eros Award are the prime starting points, see page 8). If you want to shop cannily, do some homework and uncover the unusual places where the best buys are just waiting to be discovered. But if you want to shop for England, without wisdom or circumspection but just for the sheer entertainment value of it all, pull on your walking shoes, grab hold of your Guide and buy...

Mimi Spencer, 1997

How to use this Guide

All entries are arranged alphabetically by area. All Over the Shop refers to a mixed bag of areas not covered within well-known shopping catchments.

(m) **denotes a shop which stocks only menswear**

denotes a shop which sells men's and womenswear

Where there is no symbol, the shop stocks only womenswear.

Lavazza has developed a reputation for producing the finest quality coffee since its humble beginnings from a small grocery store in the heart of Old Turin, Northern Italy.

Luigi Lavazza, the founder of the company, had no idea that the business he started in 1895 would one day become Italy's number one coffee brand with growing interests around the world. Today, Lavazza remains family-owned and run by the latest generation of the Lavazza family.

Lavazza for the

Coffee is the second most valuable trading commodity in the world — sales are only exceeded by oil. It's hardly surprising that people feel so passionate about the 'perfect cup of coffee' and that the discerning palate in the UK puts Lavazza, the real Italian coffee, at the top of their shopping list.

As 'Café Society' develops in the UK, along with our interest in good food and quality wine, so has the opportunity to serve authentic Italian espresso in the home. Lavazza's range of ground coffee blends makes the perfect cup of cappuccino or espresso and each blend is suitable for use in any type of coffee-making equipment.

Lavazza has a range of blends, all of which have an intense flavour, full aroma and a truly distinctive taste.

Lavazza Qualità Rossa
A strong, robust coffee and the leading Italian blend

Lavazza Caffè Espresso
A premium blend of 100% Arabica beans carefully selected for a smooth flavour and intense aroma

Lavazza Qualità Oro
A truly refined blend, for the discerning coffee drinker, who enjoys a strong but well-balanced cup of coffee

Eros Awards

Agent Provocateur 196
cheeky and cool; lingerie lovers won't shop anywhere else

Anya Hindmarch 219
whose deeply desirable bags are well worth saving up for

The Cross 165
a perfect little shop with a big personality, for special, idiosyncratic buys

Erickson Beamon 202
because a girl can never have too much beautiful jewellery

Jigsaw 42, 50
for superior, clever fashion for men and women at an affordable price

Joseph 20
the buying, marketing, service and atmosphere here is second to none

Koh Samui 24
a shop that consistently predicts trends before they happen

The Library 21
an intelligent and welcoming environment for top names in menswear

Low Pressure 84
an unbeatable place for the best surf and snow gear around

Office 211
the shoe store that always gets the trends first

Oxfam No Logo 115
high-quality names unite in one outlet at this unique charity shop

Paul Smith 24
a designer who sells in bulk but makes it all seem so personal

Richard James 195
who has brought menswear bespoke tailoring into the Nineties

Rigby & Peller 187
for underwear that fits like a dream

Selfridges 101
which has picked itself up and pushed itself forward over the past year

Shop 92
the funkiest shop in town, for clubbing clothes and bags of attitude

Space NK 25
London's most fashionable beauty spot

Steinberg and Tolkien 105
a real rummage ground for second-hand and vintage clothes

Tutta La Moda 25
a suburban shopping oasis for hand-picked designer names

Whistles 47
for brilliant, design-led fashion and a cache of innovative labels

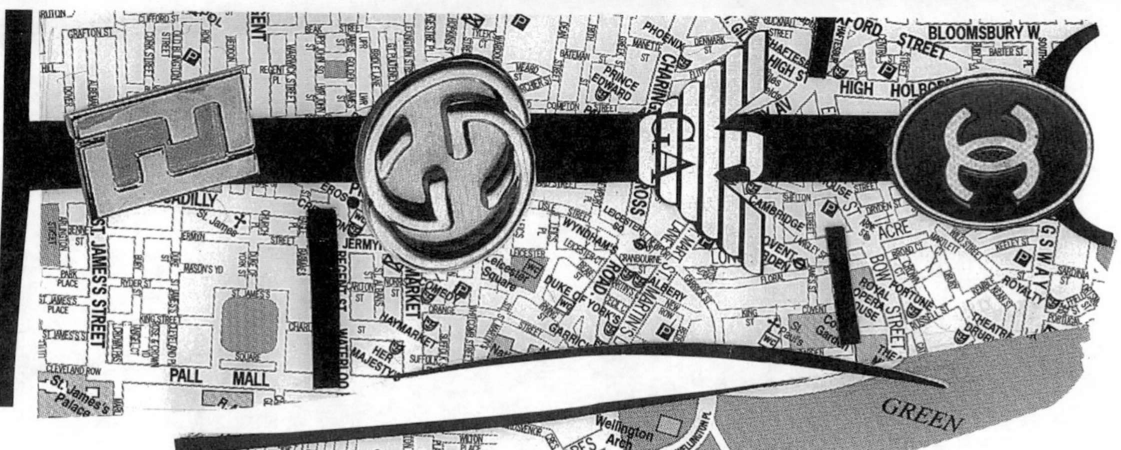
BLOOMSBURY W.
OXFORD STREET
HIGH HOLBORN
CHARING CROSS
PHOENIX
PRINCE EDWARD
WYNDHAM'S
LEICESTER SQ
Leicester Square
ROAD.
ST. MARTIN'S
DUKE OF YORK'S
ALBERY
COVENT GARDEN
BOW STREET
ROYAL OPERA HOUSE
FORTUNE
ROYALTY
THEATRE DRURY
ACRE
GSWAY
HAYMARKET
HER MAJESTY'S
MARKET
REGENT ST
WATERLOO
JERMYN
PALL MALL
ST. JAMES'S STREET
St. James's Palace
St. James
GREEN
Wellington Arch
DUKE OF WELLINGTON PL.
GROSVENOR CRES
WILTON CRESCENT
St. Paul's Knightsbridge
SLOANE

Designer

Bond Street

Anna Molinari

11a Old Bond Street W1
Tel: 0171 493 4872
Open: Mon–Sat 10am–6pm

One of Italy's most successful labels – adored by fashion editors, models and Milanese babes alike – Anna Molinari is a vital stop on any trawl down Bond Street. She specialises in sex-kitten clothes, steering clear of retro pastiche in favour of modern glamour. Her prints are without equal, copied (albeit badly and blatantly) by the British high-street chains. The collection owes much to Lolita and Vespa-riding through the cobbled streets of Milan. Cute, clingy knits, fragile lace dresses and pale, buttery leathers, as worn by Isabella Rossellini are at its core. Blumarine is the marginally cheaper, younger range, sold alongside the main line from this mosaic-lined store. Take a walk through the outsize mannequin legs over the door to get at some of the best Italian imports in the capital.

Aigner

119 New Bond Street W1
Tel: 0171 499 4041
Open: Mon–Sat 10am–6.30pm and late night Thurs till 7pm

See page 152.

Armando Pollini

35 Brook Street W1
Tel: 0171 629 7606
Open: Mon–Sat 10am–6pm and late night Thurs till 7pm

Italian Armando Pollini is known for his footwear – in all its simple glory. His discovery and use of "Elast", a fine stretch fabric originally made for use in ladies' corsetry, caused a stir in the footwear industry and has been copied up and down the high street ever since. Recently, Pollini took these fabric developments into a capsule collection of low-maintenance clothing that includes maxi coats, knee-length dresses and semi-tailored knitwear, all with the signature angular silhouette and minimal detailing.

Betty Barclay

99 New Bond Street W1
Tel: 0171 409 2880
Open: Mon–Sat 9.30am–6pm and late night Thurs till 7pm

If mix-and-match fabrics (leather, knitwear and synthetics) are your style then this is the place for you. The Barclay look is classic mother-of-the-bride stuff. Someone has to do it.

Also at: 96 Kensington High Street, W8, tel: 0171 795 6555.

Bruce Oldfield Ready-to-Wear

31 Brook Street W1
Tel: 0171 491 3222
Open: Mon–Sat 10am–6pm and late night Thurs till 7pm

In May 1996, Bruce Oldfield embarked on the first phase of an important departure away from couture – the opening of this three-storey ready-to-wear outlet in the West End. The focus of the store, as in his couture business, is sophisticated occasion and evening wear (as favoured by Marie Helvin and Charlotte Rampling); but there are still plenty of the elegant jersey separates and dresses with which Oldfield originally made his name. Designed by Patrick Reardon, the store also houses the wedding collection on the fairy-tale top floor – a range of standard-size dresses (from £1,400) which can be altered to fit – and a "resort collection" of beachwear, designed for holidaying in the playgrounds of the *beau monde*.

Couture at: 27 Beauchamp Place SW3, tel: 0171 584 1363, *see page 28.*

Cerruti 1881

ⓜ

76 New Bond Street W1
Tel: 0171 493 2278
Open: Mon–Sat 10am–6pm and late night Thurs till 7pm

A big hit with the football fraternity – Newcastle's David Ginola is the house model – this menswear store, with its calm, beige interior and helpful shop assistants, has been open since 1986, although the original company was founded in 1881 (hence the name). Nino Cerruti, grandson of the original owners and a Hollywood favourite, is now at the helm and believes in relaxed, comfortable clothing. This means plenty of softly tailored suits, plus T-shirts and shirts with blue as a strong central theme. Prices average at £650 for overcoats, £495 for jackets.

Cerruti 1881

106 New Bond Street W1
Tel: 0171 495 5880
Open: Mon–Sat 10am–6pm and late night Thurs till 7pm

Cerruti's womenswear has enjoyed something of a renaissance with the arrival of young Cuban Narciso Rodriguez (fêted designer of Caroline Kennedy's wedding dress) to assist Nino Cerruti on his top-level Arte line. The upshot is that the catwalk collections have been accruing accolades from the fashion pack, though the range stocked here is the more conservative 1881 line, produced on licence under the Escada umbrella. What you get is modern, masculine tailoring in go-anywhere navy, ecru or sand; for spring 1997, the shifts, trouser suits and fitted knits take a dip into Escada's colour palette, in fuchsia, orange and turquoise. A few pieces from the magnificent Arte range can be unearthed here, but for a more comprehensive range of stunning chiffon dresses and pretty suits, head instead for the wider selection stocked at Harvey Nichols and Harrods.

Chanel

26 Old Bond Street W1
Tel: 0171 493 5040
Open: Mon–Fri 9.30am–5.30pm and Sat 10am–4pm

The twinset, the tweed suit, the little black dress and the strings of pearls: these are seminal moments in twentieth-century fashion, all the brainwaves of the acid-tongued Mademoiselle Coco Chanel. The spirit of adventure and innovation lives on in Bond Street, under the canny stewardship of Karl Lagerfeld, who has succeeded in pushing the label beyond the traditional and into the wild, sometimes weird, frontiers of modern fashion. This store re-opened in October 1996, designed to reflect the style of the Chanel boutique at 31 rue Cambon in Paris, with black lacquer fittings, luxurious suede furniture and signature beige carpeting. On the ground floor, Chanelites will drool over the full line of cosmetics and fragrances, watches and accessories, while the lower ground is home to the ready-to-wear collection and the second floor houses leather goods including the gilt-and-quilt handbags. A place to breath in the refined, rarefied air at the top of the fashion pile. Or buy a bottle of No. 5.

Also at: 31 Sloane Street SW1, tel: 0171 235 6631.

CK Calvin Klein

53-55 New Bond Street W1
Tel: to be confirmed
Open: Mon–Sat 10am–6pm

This is the first of Klein's massive European expansion, brought to the UK by Tricia Earl, wife of Planet Hollywood's Robert Earl. The store opens in March 1997; another glitzy party is sure to be laid on as befits any American designer who has bagged a bit of Bond Street before his competitors can lay claim to it. (Tommy Hilfiger opens next door soon). CK is the kid sister of the mainline Calvin Klein range, aimed at a younger, slightly less expensive crowd; the designs are brilliant, taking classic US sportswear for a spin and ending up with something wearable, alluring and very welcome on these shores.

Comme des Garçons

59 Brook Street W1
Tel: 0171 493 1258
Open: Mon–Fri 10am–6pm, late night Thurs till 7pm and Sat 10am–5pm

Designer Rei Kawakubo is to fashion what Marco Pierre White is to restaurants – an essential ingredient that no one in the know would be able to do without, but no one knows quite what to do with, either. Comme spearheaded the Japanese wave of design influence in the Eighties, with serious, conceptual collections and a good dose of hype. These are clothes as intellectual exercise, worn by architects and media types. The minimalist interior is no place for giggling, even if the spring 1997 collection of stretch gingham dresses with cushioned hips and rumps looks like a dog's breakfast: think of it as a way to wear your art on your sleeve. The diffusion line and the perfume, in a lozenge-shaped, shrink-wrapped pack, are far more wearable.

DKNY

27 Old Bond Street W1
Tel: 0171 499 8089

Open: Mon–Sat 10am–6pm and late night Thurs till 7pm

Overpriced, over-exposed and over here? Perhaps, but DKNY's store (complete with juice bar and video banks) is routinely packed with Donna wannabes. The label has recently – and confusingly – fractured into five different groupings, for sportswear, designer wear and so on. But this is still a place to see, be seen and try on the unmatched logo sportswear in the upbeat, vaguely clinical environment. That's if you can squeeze past the security guards during the busiest times.

Donna Karan

19 New Bond Street W1
Tel: 0171 495 3100

Open: Mon–Sat 10am–6pm and late night Thurs till 7pm

One of the new US imports to arrive, with much fanfare, on our shores, the Donna Karan flagship is as serene as DKNY across the way is rowdy. The clothes are special – beautiful suits, terrific evening wear – from the designer who has a global reputation for understanding and flattering the female form. For spring, you'll find superb suiting and the best devoré evening dresses in town in this most engineered of shopping environments. A little slice of New York for a huge slice of your salary.

Equipment

26 Brook Street W1
Tel: 0171 491 3130

Open: Mon–Sat 10am–6.30pm and late night Thurs till 7pm

The place for shirts – in a rainbow of the season's colours and an array of the season's styles: T-shirts at £65, jersey shirts from £100 and velvet shirts from £150. Equipment shirts are always neatly folded, never on hangers, never in boxes. Don't be put off by the Eighties-style suspended shelving and the sober atmosphere. The interior and the stock are focused and precise. Delve in.

Also at: 21 Sloane Street SW1, tel: 0171 235 9896.

Escada

66–67 New Bond Street W1
Tel: 0171 629 0934

Open: Mon–Sat 9.30am–6.30pm and late night Thurs till 7pm

Flashy, glitter-struck womenswear is the forte of this hugely successful German label. The consultant designer here is Todd Oldham, who has been hired to put some Gucci-style top spin on an ageing label. Shrinking violets, walk on by – but if you are in the market for well-cut suits in potent colours, you are in luck.

Also at: 194–195 Sloane Street SW1 from September 1997.

Gianni Versace

34–36 Old Bond Street W1
Tel: 0171 499 1862
Open: Mon–Sat 10am–6pm

One of the most impressive, and intimidating, sites in the Bond Street line-up, the Versace store is a shrine to Gianni's rock'n'roll dream. Be prepared to out-pose the door-staff (a pair of Versace shades is indispensable) as you sashay on perilously high heels towards the rails of party frocks and body-conscious day wear. Alongside the main-line collection, there are the Versus and Istante lines (more reasonable, more wearable), menswear and the ever-expanding Versace fragrance range – all requiring the same degree of brash self-confidence to pull them off.

Versus available at: 92 Brompton Road SW1, tel: 0171 581 8407.
Istante available at: 183–184 Sloane Street SW1, tel: 0171 259 5700.
Versace Jeans Couture opens soon at: 110 New Bond Street W1.

Guy Laroche

65 New Bond Street W1
Tel: 0171 493 1362
Open: Mon–Sat 9.30am–6pm

Since the Laroche launch in 1961, the ready-to-wear and couture collections have been designed by Angelo Tarlazzi, Michel Klein and most recently Alber Elbaz. Today, the label is out of synch with the thrust of fashion, but the fragrances (Drakkar Noir, Horizon, Fidji) continue to sell well in department stores.

Joan and David

150 New Bond Street W1
Tel: 0171 499 7506
Open: Mon–Sat 10am–6pm and late night Thurs till 7pm

The world of New Yorkers Joan and David Helpern encompasses shoes (the original venture), bags, scarves, belts and now ready-to-wear. The store, designed by Eva Jiricna, is a perfect modern framework in which to show the collections, which are as balanced as the shop itself. Says Joan of her company, which turned over £75 million last year, "Everything mixes and matches, and works with the last collection, and will carry through into the next." Footwear remains at the forefront of the business, and is well thought out, comfortable and cool. A real find.

Lanvin

108 New Bond Street W1
Tel: 0171 499 2929
Open: Mon–Sat 10am–6.30pm

John Stephen – an initiator of the peacock fashion revolution of the Sixties and the man who introduced Levi's jeans to the UK – brought the Lanvin name to this country 16 years ago. The top-drawer French label, now designed by Dominique Morlotti (ex-Dior), is known for subtle, precise suits in superlative fabrics. Don't miss the Espace Tradition designer collection, or the deeply glamorous womenswear, designed by Ocimar Versolato, available in Harrods.

Also at: 94 Brompton Road SW1, tel: 0171 581 4401.

Laurèl

105–106 New Bond Street W1
Tel: 0171 493 1153

Open: Mon–Fri 9.30am–6pm, late night Thurs till 7pm and Sat 10am–6pm

Laurèl is the little sister of Escada, and the more elegant and understated end of the business. The label produces its own slant on whatever is currently in fashion, although a few loud accessories and trimmings are thrown in for good measure. Also stocked: the Laurèl jeans range.

Loewe

130 New Bond Street W1
Tel: 0171 493 3914

Open: Mon–Sat 9.30am–6pm

Spanish leather brand Loewe (pronounced Low-ay-vay) is a market leader in luxury luggage, handbags and accessories. It looks, smells and feels expensive – so no surprises that the suede, leather, cashmere and silk have a heavy-weight price-tag attached. The bag collection rivals Prada's for quality if not quirkiness, and there are no desperate queues of fashionoids here, either.

Louis Féraud

73 New Bond Street W1
Tel: 0171 491 2339

Open: Mon–Sat 9.30am–6.30pm and late night Thurs till 7pm

There are changes afoot at Louis Féraud with the appointment of designer Alistair Blair, the Scottish St Martin's graduate who boasts a distinguished career at Dior, Givenchy, Chloe, Lagerfeld and most recently Valentino. Now the head of the prêt-à-porter collections at Louis Féraud, he is taking the label in a new direction, promoting a free, more spirited style. Jackets drape the body and seductive dresses accentuate the figure in textural fabrics and versatile colours. Suits from £650; long, luscious coats start at £1,250.

Mulberry

41–42 New Bond Street W1
Tel: 0171 491 4323

Open: Mon–Sat 10am–6pm and late night Thurs till 7pm

The flagship Mulberry store is the first to house the entire range, including men's and women's ready-to-wear, accessories, the home collection – and not forgetting the famous Filofaxes. The traditional English name, having recently celebrated its twenty-fifth anniversary, is moving in a new direction, combining the Mulberry county-set heritage with an injection of humour, innovation in fabric and an approach that hovers at the periphery of fashion.

For branches, call: 0171 491 3900.

Nicole Farhi

158 Bond Street W1
Tel: 0171 499 8368
Open: Mon–Sat 10am–6.30pm and late night Thurs till 7pm

The most popular designer label in British women's wardrobes, Nicole Farhi epitomises the hackneyed but helpful fashion phrase "understated elegance". French-native Farhi (the original "French Connection" behind the high-street name) delivers clothes that last and are beautiful to boot, although originality is hardly her middle name. Trends of the season are apparent here and there, perhaps in the cut or colour. The relaxed store also includes menswear, accessories and Nicole's – the chic stop for breakfast, lunch, afternoon tea or supper, where inveterate shoppers flock to swap stories of the day's purchases.

Also at: 27 Hampstead High Street NW3, tel: 0171 435 0866, 193 Sloane Street SW1, tel: 0171 235 0877, 25–26 Sloane Street W1, tel: 0171 486 3416, and 11 Floral Street WC2, tel: 0171 497 8713.

Polo Ralph Lauren

143 New Bond Street W1
Tel: 0171 491 4967
Open: Mon–Sat 10am–6pm and late night Thurs till 7pm

It may be British style served up the American way, but whatever Ralph Lauren does is lapped up by UK customers with an unceasing appetite for his "lifestyle" clothes. Polo Sport is popular across the board, with street kids, off-duty bankers and the urban style tribe alike – and you'll find them all in this tiny store on a Saturday morning. Ralph addicts: watch out for the immense Ralph Lauren British headquarters and largest international store (45,000 square feet), opening at 1 New Bond Street in early 1998.

Teenflo

28 Brook Street W1
Tel: 0171 629 6077
Open: Mon–Sat 10am–6.30pm and late night Thurs till 7pm

Teenflo is a Parisian family-run label, introduced to this country by retail genius Joseph, which gradually began to deserve its own store as its popularity grew. The name is offputting, but the clothes are spot-on: the cotton/Lycra trousers are a must-have purchase, at £99, as are the cashmere coats. Add to this an adventurous use of colour and a reasonable price range, and Teenflo becomes a necessary stop on your way down Bond Street.

Vivienne Westwood

6 Davies Street W1
Tel: 0171 629 3757
Open: Mon–Sat 10am–6pm and late night Thurs till 7pm

One of the UK's foremost fashion exports, Westwood designs are eclectic and witty, tailormade for moments when only a grand entrance will do. More moderate tastes will discover classy tweeds, scalpel-cut suiting and covetable shirts here – accompanied by the bizarre accoutrements that have made

Westwood the country's best-loved and most original designer. This summer, her historical tastes stretch to the nipped-in waists of the Forties, without a care that the rest of the fashion world is knee-deep in Seventies styling. The Gold Label tailoring is sold in Davies Street; the Man collection and the Red Label diffusion line can be found in Conduit Street; or visit World's End for the more street-oriented pieces – if you can squeeze past the bustle-and-bodice Japanese visitors to gain access.

Also at: 43 Conduit Street W1, tel: 0171 439 1109, and World's End, 430 King's Road SW10, tel: 0171 352 6551.

Wardrobe

Sfera House, 42 Conduit Street W1
Tel: 0171 494 1131
Open: Mon–Sat 10am–6pm and late night Thurs till 7pm

We've all encountered the snotty sales assistant who refuses to offer any help unless we look likely to spend a month's salary. When it happened to Susie Faux in 1973, she fought back by opening her own shop, billed as the problem-solving centre for working, and weekending, women. Faux is well known on the fashion circuit, dispensing flattering clothes (from little-known labels such as Antonio Fusco, Joop! and Kiton) and expert advice to women who are short on time but long on style. Staff also advise on hair, make-up and general health, with a Shiatsu practice and a Nutritional Therapist on site.

Yves Saint Laurent Rive Gauche

135–137 New Bond Street W1
Tel: 0171 493 1800
Open: Mon–Fri 9.30am–6pm, late night Thurs till 7pm and Sat 10am–6pm

Thirty years at the top have done nothing to dent the reputation and retailability of YSL, and here, you'll discover why: sharp suiting for sophisticated tastes is the message. Today, the main collections – shown in a salon atmosphere after the designer decided that the Paris fashion circus was out of control – are re-runs of great Saint Laurent moments, but who can argue with that?

Also at: 33 Sloane Street SW1, tel: 0171 235 6706.

Amanda Wakeley

80 Fulham Road SW3
Tel: 0171 584 4009
Open: Mon–Sat 10am–6pm and late night Wed till 7pm

Having won the Glamour title at the British Fashion Awards twice in a row, Amanda Wakeley is firmly placed at the top of her profession. Her pale, interesting outlet and studio in the Fulham Road is designed to mirror her quietly glamorous designs. Here, customers indulge in shimmering column dresses, slinky knits and some of the most luxurious lounge wear in London. Chelsea's ball-going girls will find it, literally and metaphorically, right up their street.

Anouska Hempel

2 Pond Place SW3
Tel: 0171 589 4191
Open: Mon–Fri 9am–6pm by appointment

It's dark, disguised and known only to those in the know. Anouska Hempel – aka Lady Weinberg, aka owner of the maddeningly modern Hempel Hotel – makes beautiful couture evening- and day-wear collections for Chelsea hostesses, which can be adapted in colour and fabric to suit the requirements of her her well-heeled customers. The workmanship is some of the finest you'll come across, and prices start at an appropriate £2,000.

APC

124 Draycott Avenue SW3
Tel: 0171 225 0364
Open: Mon–Tues and Thurs–Fri 10am–6.30pm, late night Wed till 7pm and Sat 10am–6pm

APC (Atelier for Production and Creation) was created four years ago by French design guru Jean Touitou. Preferring to sit towards the back of the fashion theatre (he says the APC design team is as important as he is), he designs clothes that are understated and reliable, and his audience comprises people who steer clear of obvious labels. Staples include corduroy fitted jackets and hipsters, A-line knee-length skirts, slim Shetland wool twinsets, industrial denim jackets, and some of the best-cut jeans on the planet.

Betty Jackson

311 Brompton Road SW3
Tel: 0171 589 7884
Open: Mon–Sat 10am–6pm

Betty Jackson has survived two decades in which countless other designers have folded, perhaps because she routinely serves up clothes that, while remaining intrinsically stylish, refuse to date. She caters for women who have a lot more to think about than their wardrobes – so expect stress-free dressing (comfortable but cool sloppy Joes, easy-to-wear separates) at middle-ranking designer prices. Jennifer Saunders is a friend and fan; newcomers will go a bundle on Jackson's gentle coats, slim-line trouser suits and knockout knits.

Catherine Walker

65 Sydney Street SW3
Tel: 0171 352 4626
Open: Mon–Sat 10am–6pm

Princess Diana's favourite dress designer produces enviable gowns at top-of-the-heap prices at this elegant showcase of a shop. Many designs are inspired by the rich colours and textures of Walker's native Provence. The impeccably tailored couture day- and eveningwear collections feature sumptuous fabrics and intricately embroidered details with a drop-dead feminine silhouette – long and lean, dramatic and demure. This is one place where you get exactly what you pay for

Bridal wear available at: The Conservatory, 46 Fulham Road SW3, tel: 0171 581 8811, see page 226.

Claudia Sebire

136 Fulham Road SW10
Tel: 0171 835 1327

Open: Mon–Sat 10am–6pm and late night Wed till 7pm

This must be Fulham Road's Best Kept Secret. OK, so it's a cliché, but the clothes inside this enticing boutique are most certainly not. For nine years now, Claudia Sebire has boasted a committed customer base of expensive Chelsea ladies, who drop by after lunch for enduring wardrobe basics from Strenesse, Mani (part of the vast Giorgio Armani empire), Georges Rech, Comma, MaxMara and René Lezard. Accessories courtesy of Cole Haan, Osprey, Liberty and Giorgio Armani – together with fine service and a brand new wooden floor – complete the look.

Galerie Gaultier (&)

171–175 Draycott Avenue SW3
Tel: 0171 584 4648

Open: Mon–Sat 10am–6pm and late night Wed till 7pm

Fashion's favourite luvvie, Gaultier must hold the record as the most enduring *enfant terrible* in town. When he's not camping it up on TV or partying hard on both sides of the Channel, he comes up with mad-cap designs that are always expertly cut and workable. This spring's jumpsuits that tie up at the back like surgeon's gowns are one of his less likely endeavours, but at Galerie, there are plenty of other JPG specials that make more sense. The shop, designed by Chalaner and Clark with a Parisienne courtyard in mind, houses the main-line collection, the JPG line, the jeans range and some one-offs (soon to include his new couture line), exclusive to the shop. It also carries Gaultier's growing band of fragrances and skin and bodycare products. The staff – as eye-catching as the interior design – are enthusiastic and friendly enough to keep you coming back for more.

Irie

130 Draycott Avenue SW3
Tel: 0171 584 1252

Open: Mon–Tues and Thurs–Fri 10am–6.30pm, late night till 7pm and Sat 10am–6pm

Former design assistant to Kenzo, Irie was born in Osaka, Japan, where he studied at the Sogo School of Fashion before setting up his own label in 1983. His eclectic ideas – inspired by his passion for Fifties films and brought to the UK by Joseph – range from clean-cut trouser suits to bold animal prints in opulent jewel colours. Pleasant and perfectly in tune with the times.

Issey Miyake

270 Brompton Road SW3
Tel: 0171 581 3760
Open: Mon–Sat 10am–6pm

Architects wear Issey Miyake. So do artists, media and stage old-timers, novelists and sculptors; in short, people with the strength of character to carry off the costumes he creates. Over 30 years Miyake has become a phenomenally successful designer, best known for his sculptural, folded fabrics. Every season, he canters off at a tangent, producing shows that make a great picture but rarely a great outfit. Pleats Please, the functional diffusion line launched in 1990, is still going strong with its concertina construction and adaptability – easy to store and perfect for travel. If only everything in life were as simple. Eau D'Issey was the first "ozonic" perfume to hit the counters, and still has a huge following.

Joanna's Tent

289b King's Road SW3
Tel: 0171 352 1151
Open: Mon–Sat 9.45am–6pm and late night Wed till 7pm

After more than 21 years in the business, Joanna's Tent has just had a major refit. The names that Joanna Pittacas has become known for include Ghost, John Rocha and G Gigli. The Stephen Jones hats alone make a visit worthwhile. Downstairs, a kids' department specialises in DKNY and Paul Smith.

Joseph

77 Fulham Road SW3
Tel: 0171 823 9500
Open: Mon–Tues, Thurs–Fri 10am–6.30pm and late night Wed till 7pm, Sat 10am–6pm and Sun 12pm–5pm

For almost a decade, Joseph Ettedgui has been the dominant figure at Brompton Cross. With a nose for new talent, an eye for a retail opportunity and a taste for stubby cigars, he is without doubt the most effective personality in British fashion. And all the while, the Moroccan-born dynamo maintains his own enviable position as one of the country's most influential designers. Where do you go for trousers with a terrific cut? Cool coats in luxe fabrics? Avant-garde knitwear? Dresses to get you noticed? The best grilled vegetables in the capital? The answer is Joseph, every time.

For branches, call: 0171 629 4774.

Le Coin

315 Brompton Road SW3
Tel: 0171 591 0022
Open: Mon–Sat 10am–6.30pm and Sun 12pm–5pm

Two floors – on a corner, of course – of womenswear from new and established designers such as Rifat Ozbek, Plein Sud, Pearce Fionda and Strenesse, with shoes from Robert Clergerie and Emma Hope. The staff are extremely helpful, and there is a constant supply of wine should you require that extra bit of Dutch courage to part with your hard-earned.

The Library

268 Brompton Road SW3
Tel: 0171 589 6569
Open: Mon–Sat 10am–6pm and late night Wed till 7pm

What owner Peter Siddell doesn't know about menswear retailing probably isn't worth knowing. After partnering Stuart Malloy during the early years of Quincy and heading up the menswear division at Joseph, Peter set up The Library. This shop should be the first choice for any narcissistic male, with feisty fashion from Dirk Bikkembergs, Martin Kidman, Alexander McQueen, Raf Simons and Carol Christian Poell. A selection of books provides a reference-library backdrop. Plans are afoot for a womenswear store... The sooner the better.

Roland Klein

7–9 Tryon Street SW3
Tel: 0171 823 9179
Open: Mon–Thurs 9.30am–5.30pm and Fri 9.30am–5pm

French-born Klein is one of the best-loved designers in London, gentle in nature and gentle in his fashion outlook. He designs not only his own label (aimed at a mature audience, though lacking in fashion fizz), but also for MaxMara and Marina Rinaldi; the uniforms at BT and the Stock Exchange are his too.

Sarah Spencer

3 Motcomb Street SW1
Tel: 0171 235 1125
Open: Mon–Fri 10am-6pm and Sat by appointment

Mary Jane Atkinson-Willes took over the Sarah Spencer label four years ago, designing bright and bold prêt-à-porter for the ladies of the royal circle.

Skala

307 Brompton Road SW3
Tel: 0171 584 6553
Open: Mon–Sat 10am–6pm

Sabrina Lorenz, who has a doctorate in medicine, an economics degree and her own pathology lab, opened Skala to introduce German designers to this country. Labels include Suzanne Bommer, who sculpts lean pieces from experimental fabrics, Joop!, and Skoda Attendance knitwear.

Tokio

309 Brompton Road SW3
Tel: 0171 823 7310
Open: Mon–Sat 10am–6.30pm and Sun 12.30pm–5.30pm

You can always rely on Tokio to know exactly what's relevant in fashion now. It currently carries Clements Ribeiro, Lawrence Steele, Martin Kidman, Stella McCartney (Paul's daughter and London's brightest new design talent) and Tocca, with shoes and clothes from Costume National and Miu Miu. Downstairs is a constant stock of last season's ranges at knockdown prices.

City and East End

Amen

80 St Stephen's Road E3
Tel: 0181 983 6767
Open: Mon–Sat 10am–6pm

Amen traditionally means "so be it", but in this case, it is also stands for "a men's shop", although the store is now gradually moving into womenswear. The main labels are Jasper Conran, Kenzo, Ted Baker, Limehouse, Full Circle and Roger Dak Suiting, a successful combination of sports, casual and smart clothing. Women get clubwear from Sub Couture, together with PND suits, Shelton Miranda shirts, and shoes from Red or Dead, Hudson, Lionheart and Jeffrey West.

Zee and Co

434 Roman Road E3
Tel: 0181 981 3333
Open: Mon–Sat 9.30am–6pm

Label addicts going cold turkey in the East End will find respite here, where high-profile names such as Dolce and Gabbana, Versace, Iceberg, John Richmond, Patrick Cox and DKNY exist in harmony. The men's shop up the road at number 416 has the same labels, plus Paul Smith and Stone Island.

Also at: 416 Roman Road E3, tel: 0181 980 2122, and 36 Upper Street N1, tel: 0171 354 5855 (also open Sun 11am–4.30pm).

Covent Garden

Agnès B

35–36 Floral Street WC2
Tel: 0171 379 1992
Open: Mon–Sat 10.30am–6.30pm, late night Thurs till 7pm and Sun 12pm–5pm

Imagine the simplest of black T-shirts, the most perfectly proportioned suit, a sweater that gets noticed without making a fuss : this is the essence of Agnès B, a designer with an ability to make the most basic garment look like a cool French classic. Her first shop opened 20 years ago in the fashionable rue du Jour in Paris and quickly multiplied to take over the entire street. Now, Agnès has taken on New York, Amsterdam, Tokyo, Brussels and London, with her famous pearl-snap cardigan leading the way. The range here includes clothes for women (very Jean Seberg), men (very Alain Delon) and children, plus Lolita for teenagers and a line of cosmetics (brilliant) and perfume. And Agnès runs an art gallery – in the rue du Jour, *quel surprise*! – in her spare moments.

Also at: 111 Fulham Road SW3, tel: 0171 225 3477, 235 Westbourne Grove W11, tel: 0171 792 1947, and 58–62 Heath Street NW3, tel: 0171 431 1995.

The Changing Room

Thomas Neal's Centre, Earlham Street WC2
Tel: 0171 379 4158

Open: Mon–Fri 11am–7pm, Sat 10.30am–7pm and Sun 12.30pm–5.30pm

A calm and collected retailer stocking Tehen, John Rocha, Workers For Freedom, Georgina von Etzdorf and Pleats Please by Issey Miyake. A free styling service is available, plus accessories by Van der Straeten and interior design ideas (sculpture and lighting) to access that all-important lifestyle approach.

Also at: 10a Gees Court W1, tel: 0171 408 1596.

Dexter Wong

17 Monmouth Street WC2
Tel: 0171 240 7692

Open: Mon–Sat 11am–7pm

Born in Penang, West Malaysia, Dexter Wong moved to London in 1975, and studied at St Martin's before starting his own label. He is a trend merchant – responsible for originating the overshirt in the early Eighties and the tight Lycra Tee for men, which heralded the body-conscious era of the early Nineties. Spring's collection is entitled "Blue", drawing inspiration from the elements, with tonal and photo-prints on chiffon, Lycra and denim. Prettiness itself.

Emporio Armani

57–59 Long Acre WC2
Tel: 0171 917 6882

Open: Mon–Sat 10am–6.30pm, late night Thurs till 7.30pm and Sun 11.30am–5.30pm

Armani, bless his beige socks, declared that fashion was dead in 1996, but a visit to the Emporio flagship store gives the lie to his theory. Sure, the clothes are on the quiet side, but they never miss a beat when it comes to keeping up with trends. After nearly 25 years in the industry, Mr Armani has generated an international reputation as a perfectionist, discounting the superfluous to concentrate on the detail. Emporio is aimed at young-ish professionals, for whom the perfectly cut trouser suit – with an Armani label and a matching price tag – is the last word in chic. For more modest incomes, there's the Armani underwear and accessories lines. And for the tired and hungry, the Emporio Armani Express Restaurant on the first floor at the Brompton Road branch serves raviolo of wild mushrooms from beige plates, *naturalmente*.

Also at: 187–191 Brompton Road SW3, tel: 0171 823 8818, and 112a New Bond St W1, tel: 0171 491 8080.

Jones

13–15 Floral Street WC2
Tel: 0171 240 8312/379 4299

Open: Mon–Sat 10am–6.30pm and Sun 1pm–5pm

Stocking future fashion from some of the world's finest "frontier" designers, Jones has established itself in ten years of business as a showcase for both young and well-known names, such as Hussein Chalayan, Costume National and Martine Sitbon. Owner and founder Stuart Malloy is a master at tipping a trend, so for spring 1997, men will get their hands on Dolce and Gabbana doing the Italian *Vogue* look, Dirk Bikkembergs dressing pirates in leather, W< (masses of black) and Helmut Lang's signature androgynous lines. Women, next door, are treated to Alexander McQueen, Dries van Noten, Jean Colonna, Corinne Cobson and Jones Own Label, plus shoes by Wannabe, Dirk Bikkembergs and Armando Pollini. Go in to buy, or to spy what's coming next in high style.

Koh Samui

65 Monmouth Street WC2
Tel: 0171 240 4280
Open: Mon–Sat 11am–7pm

Partners Paul Sexton and Talita Zoe track down the most talented young British graduates and support them on their road to success, making Koh Samui a unique and respected venture. They also provide a platform for commercially successful designers. This season, Anthony Gibson, Joley Nian and Clements Ribeiro join Abe Hamilton, Stephen Fuller, Justin Oh and Fabio Piras to supply ground-breaking cuts and fabrics, combined with experimental techniques and print methods. You saw it here first.

Paul Smith

40–44 Floral Street WC2
Tel: 0171 379 7133

Open: Mon–Fri 10.30am–6.30pm, late night Thurs till 7pm and Sat 10am–6.30pm

While Paul Smith prefers not to call himself a "designer", he could validly refer to his work as one of British fashion's biggest and best exports. Smith is this country's most successful menswear maestro, recently celebrating 25 years in business with an exhibition at the Design Museum – the first dedicated to a single fashion designer. The oft-repeated phrase "classic with a twist" (coined by the man himself) does indeed sum up his approach. Today, he dominates Floral Street, with four connecting shops selling a bizarre concoction of kitsch disposable knickers and 3D cameras alongside his marvellous but pricey womenswear and men's suits. Upstairs you can find shirts, underwear, accessories and casual clothes; downstairs is the suit and shoe room, with old-fashioned polished wood fixtures and old-fashioned service and attention.

Paul Smith jeans available at: 7–9 Langley Court WC2, tel: 0171 240 5068. *For discount Paul Smith, see page 223.*

Question Air

38 Floral Street WC2
Tel: 0171 836 8220
Open: Mon–Sat 10.30am–6.30pm and Thurs 10.30pm–7pm

Residents of Dulwich Village already know that they boast one of the best clothes shops around, but for strangers to SE21, Question Air might be a surprise. The company has been going for seven years and now has three shops in London, carrying Ghost, Betty Jackson, Lacroix Jeans and Patrick Cox for women. The Dulwich shop has an extended repertoire, including Nicole Farhi, Paul Smith, Kenzo and Stephane Kélian shoes and a strong menswear line-up. The ever-cheerful, ever-helpful staff also design and sell their own range of leather and suede jackets and trousers (in jean- and hipster-cut), with prices from £195. The WC2 store doesn't do it nearly so well.

Also at: 78 High Street Wimbledon SW19, tel: 0181 946 6288, and 85–87 Dulwich Village SE21, tel: 0181 299 4252.

Space NK

(&)

Thomas Neal's Centre, Earlham Street WC2
Tel: 0171 379 7030
Open: Mon–Sat 11am–7pm

Space, because it feels like an art space, all clean lines and white light. NK, because it is the brainchild of Nicola Kinnaird, one of the UK's most inventive and inspirational retailers. She gets new products first, and she gets them exclusively: Philosophy, Kiehl's, Antonia's Flowers, Shu Uemura and Benefit beauty products were all introduced to London by Kinnaird, whose terrier-like capacity to go after and bring back a trend is known and loved by London's most fashionable. Her beauty concept has proved so successful that the designer fashion (from Copperwheat Blundell, Rifat Ozbek and Vivienne Westwood, among others), has recently taken a back seat. While beauty products are the backbone of the business – so much so that Kinnaird has opened another three Space NK Apothecary stores in the capital – there remains a deeply fashionable feel to the whole place.

Woodhouse

(m)

138 Long Acre WC2
Tel: 0171 240 2008
Open: Mon–Sat 10am–6.30pm, late night Thurs till 8pm and Sun 12pm–6pm

Big-attitude menswear store that focuses on structured suiting, sports-influenced casuals and Fifties styling. For spring, colours take a departure from the city palette, with cornflower-blue, lemon, pea-green and tangerine, and shapes are more relaxed, with flat-front trousers, Harringtons and ribbed towelling tops. The store also stocks Stone Island, Kenzo, Victor Victoria, Donna Karan, Iceberg and, new for this season, Katharine Hamnett, Romeo Gigli and Antonio Miro.

For branches, call: 0171 629 1254.

Greenwich

Tutta La Moda

(&)

32 Tranquil Vale, Blackheath SE3
Tel: 0181 297 1162
Open: Mon–Sat 10.30am–6pm

The decadently decorated Moda is a delicatessen in a world of supermarket-style designer shopping. Purposefully avoiding the mega-store theme that has become big business among top names, owner Michael Patsalou has created his own little atelier in Blackheath, more akin to visiting an old friend than a clothes shop. The stylish stock combines Italian elegance with a modern feel and includes a mouth-watering own-label collection. Added to this is a constantly changing range of designers that have included in the past Rina da'Prato, Equipment and Jeffrey West. If you've got time to engage in a bit of long-distance travelling, a visit here is thoroughly recommended.

Hampstead and Highgate

Europe

64 Hampstead High Street NW3
Tel: 0171 431 9804
Open: Mon–Sat 10am–6pm and Sun 11am–6pm

Jo and Gordon Drennen's thriving business is a favourite designer outlet in the leafy glades of Hampstead, and its success has warranted a second branch at Oriel Place, around the corner, to house the more casual ranges. The main lines include MaxMara, Victor Victoria, Romeo Gigli, Synonyme by Georges Rech and Cerruti 1881 in the High Street store, and laid-back labels Polo Ralph Lauren for women, Kenzo Jungle and Cerruti Sport in Oriel Place.

Also at: Oriel Hall, Oriel Place NW3, tel: 0171 435 6251, and 41 Heath Street NW3, tel: 0171 431 5577.

John Barry

39 Heath Street NW3
Tel: 0171 435 8928
Open: Mon–Fri 9.30am–5.30pm and Sat 10.30am–6pm

An institution in Hampstead, John Barry has been on site for 45 years, offering a personal service to customers by creating a versatile wardrobe from a select series of names such as Escada, Miss Valentino, Jean Muir and Mimmina. The atmosphere is relaxed and the staff are decidedly more friendly than in the average Escada boutique.

Midas

58 Rosslyn Hill NW3
Tel: 0171 431 3547
Open: Mon–Sat 10am–7pm and Sun 12pm–6.30pm

In the eight years Midas (formerly Kumagai) has been trading, it has built a reputation as one of the largest Ghost stockists in London. La Perla's day, evening and swimwear, Transit casualwear and Ben de Lisi's covetable evening dresses make the shop a hot stop – especially on Sundays, when strollers from Hampstead Heath can drop by and buy. The store also operates a personal shopping service for anyone in need of a little extra help, and a pager number (0941 147 529) operating round-the-clock for deliveries anywhere in the world. There's dedication for you.

Highbury and Islington

Paradox

(&)

321 Upper Street N1
Tel: 0171 226 8530
Open: Mon–Sat 11am–7pm

One of the first fashion boutiques to appear in Islington, heralding an influx of design-led stores, Paradox is still growing; recently, womenswear was introduced to accompany its already successful men's lines. Key names to expect include Joseph, Helmut Lang, Issey Miyake, Alexander McQueen, Patrick Cox and Wannabe, Bella Freud and Jones Own Label. In short, it is a fine local stop for top designer clothes that are usually impossible to find outside the polished establishments of the West End and Knightsbridge.

Kensington

Bonpoint

17 Victoria Grove W8
Tel: 0171 584 5131
Open: Mon–Fri 9am–5pm and Sat 10am–4pm (closed for lunch daily 1pm–2pm)

Any shop that closes for lunch cannot be too serious about sales, but French designer label Bonpoint still stays afloat. Nothing here is worth a lunch-hour trek, anyway, but the weekend wear has the odd unexpected touch – a fake-fur collar and cuffs and matching accessories including bags, gloves and shoes. A suit will set you back around £400 and a winter coat £450.

Childrenswear available at: 35b Sloane Street SW1, tel: 0171 235 1441.

M

15 Victoria Grove W8
Tel: 0171 838 1128
Open: Mon, Tues and Thurs–Sat 10am–6pm and late night Wed till 8pm

M stocks a range of evening, cocktail and wedding outfits (billed by the owner as ideal for town weddings and registry offices) from German-born, United Arab Emirates native Mariam El-Accad. The fabrics used in the elaborate designs are all rich and lustrous, and the just-opened shop includes all those little extras that make a trip here worthwhile: you are served unlimited coffee while you browse through the rails, sizing goes from 8 to 26, a remodelling service is available to transform those past purchases if you've had one too many calorific cappuccinos, and hand-made hats and luxury lingerie give a finishing flourish.

Knightsbridge

A La Mode

36 Hans Crescent SW1
Tel: 0171 584 2133
Open: Mon–Sat 10am–6pm and late night Wed till 7pm

A rich and rare boutique, run in style by husband-and-wife team Peter and Josephine Turner, who between them possess the most finely honed buying antennae in the business. The shop has been a mecca for fash-aholics for a decade now, and the current batch of labels is as mouthwatering as ever: plenty of American greats from Isaac Mizrahi, Marc Jacobs and Richard Tyler; the banded dresses of Herve Leger; evening wear from John Galliano and Ben de Lisi. The personal service includes free alterations and worldwide delivery. The windows alone let you know exactly where high style is going next.

Alberta Ferretti

205–206 Sloane Street SW1
Tel: 0171 584 8984
Open: Mon–Sat 10am–6pm

The annual rent alone nudges half-a-million pounds, but if you are a player in international fashion right now, you have to have a pitch in Sloane or Bond Street. Italian designer Ferretti produces some of the most covetable clothes on the catwalk, and a more affordable diffusion line of gorgeous gear called Philosophy. The whole lot is available at this spanking new outlet.

Bruce Oldfield

27 Beauchamp Place SW3
Tel: 0171 584 1363
Open: Mon–Fri 10am–6pm and Sun 11am–5.30pm

Oldfield creates stunning couture gowns for his San Lorenzo fan club, and in the meantime he has raised over £300,000 for Barnados through fashion-related events. His first shop, open since 1984, offers a personal service for delicious dresses in draped crepe, chiffon and satin. There is also a couture wedding service, very popular with overseas brides, starting at £3,500.

Ready-to-wear at: 31 Brook Street W1, tel: 0171 491 3222, *see page 11.*

Caroline Charles

56–57 Beauchamp Place SW3
Tel: 0171 225 3197
Open: Mon–Sat 10am–6pm and late night Wed till 6.30pm

Caroline Charles's boutique is a double-fronted 1830s house, where her well-cut but uninspired collections are sold to celebrities and working women. Charles is one of the longest-serving designers on the UK fashion scene, and it's a tribute to her resilience that she is still in style after three decades.

Also at: 170 New Bond Street W1, tel: 0171 493 4733.

Christian Dior

22 Sloane Street SW1
Tel: 0171 235 1357
Open: Mon–Fri 10am–6pm and Sat 10.30am–6pm

With British designer John Galliano at the helm, the venerable House of Dior is due for a shake-up. The jewel in the Moët-Hennessey-Louis Vuitton crown, the company celebrates its fiftieth anniversary this year. In 1947, Christian Dior's New Look changed the face of fashion for ever, and caused riots on the streets of Paris into the bargain. The man himself died after only a decade at the top, and the title went first to Yves Saint Laurent (for three years), then to Marc Bohan (until 1989), then to Gianfranco Ferre. Half a century after the first big stir, Dior is set to shine again as Galliano settles into the top job in international fashion. Watch the windows here to witness the transformation.

Christian Lacroix

8a Sloane Street SW1
Tel: 0171 235 2400
Open: Mon–Fri 10am–6.30pm, late night Wed till 7pm and Sat 10am–6pm

It may be Eddy from *Ab Fab*'s favourite label, but Lacroix has more to offer than the clichéd reputation for mix-match-mad designs with which he has been saddled. His couture and ready-to-wear lines are meticulously researched, cleverly historical and constructed with panache. The colours are beautiful and the eclectic styles are more in line with modern fashion than some critics will allow. The diffusion line, Bazar, is the best of the lot, with clash tweeds that will keep London's bohemian population amused for hours.

Also at: 29 Old Bond Street W1, tel: 0171 409 1994.

Dolce and Gabbana

175 Sloane Street SW1
Tel: 0171 235 0335
Open: Mon–Fri 10am–6pm and Sat 10.30am–6pm

One of the most successful and recognisable labels in the world, Dolce and Gabbana takes Anna Magnini – all curves, wilfulness and pout – as its starting point. The main-line collection always has a lingerie theme, always includes a leopard print or two, and clings like a long-lost friend. On slender, sexy bodies, it is sensational. D&G services the wannabe customer, with logo Tees and bags, although Domenico Dolce and Stefano Gabbana are all for phasing out the lettering in the name of good taste – and, no doubt, to stump the counterfeiters.

Emanuel Ungaro

36 Sloane Street SW3
Tel: 0171 259 6111
Open: Mon-Fri 10am-6pm and Sat 10.30am-6pm

Mr Ungaro has won every major French fashion award, has dressed films starring Catherine Deneuve, Isabelle Adjani and Anouk Aimée, and specialises in bright, curvy clothes for the woman who has left her twenties behind.

Sharon Stone and India Hicks are loyal customers, but his newest fan is Princess Diana, who often wears his £10,000 couture creations to grand events (she orders a couple of outfits each season and the *directrice* Madame de Limur travels to London to supervise fittings). His flattering peplum suits take her to engagements during the day.

Feathers

40 Hans Crescent SW1
Tel: 0171 589 0356
Open: Mon–Sat 10am–6pm and late night Wed till 7pm

Feathers is a classy boutique, arranged in easy-access sections with each designer's name clearly labelled, allowing you to head straight for your favourite. Choose from a selection including Jean Paul Gaultier, Rifat Ozbek, Alberta Ferretti or Moschino (both couture and Cheap and Chic). For new talent, look out for Maria Grachvogel, Lawrence Steele and Barbara Bui.

Georges Rech

181–182 Sloane Street SW1
Tel: 0171 235 3343
Open: Mon–Sat 10am–6pm and late night Wed till 7pm

Dry and bright would be a decent enough description of Georges Rech's decent enough clothes. For spring, the label boasts a rainbow of pastel colours, slender jersey dresses, optic-print shirts and evening wear in pale aqua and purple, camel and espresso-brown. If you prefer a little more direction, head for Synonyme, the funkier diffusion line featuring florals and pinstripes, or Georges Rech Sport for sweatshirts and jeans.

Gianfranco Ferre

37 Sloane Street SW1
Tel: 0171 838 9576
Open: Mon–Sat 10am–6pm and late night Wed till 7pm

Ferre is big business, with boutiques in Moscow, Tokyo, Seoul, Palm Beach and, of course, his home town of Milan. This London shop sells the expected but agreeable range of show-off wear for the rich and the round. The Pavarotti figure of Ferre was behind the Dior label for seven years, where he specialised in frills, furbelows and grand gestures of fashion. That's what you'll find at his London store, all inspired by his training as an architect. Visit the Dior boutique to witness the changes wrought by new boy John Galliano.

Giorgio Armani

178 Sloane Street SW1
Tel: 0171 235 6232
Open: Mon–Sat 10am–6pm and late night Wed till 7pm

Who cares if it's simple? Who cares if it's ecru? When it's got a bona fide Armani label nestling in the collar, you know you've got something special. Armani has an unmatched talent for producing precise fashion for women and men who want personal perfection rather than public display. Needless to say, this store offers solace from cabbies and brouhaha outside – it's refined and rich, and so are its customers.

Gucci

17–18 Sloane Street SW1
Tel: 0171 235 6707

Open: Mon, Tues, Thurs, Fri 9.30am–6pm, Wed 10am–7pm and Sat 10am–6pm

If you aren't aware of Gucci's renaissance – it has re-emerged Lazarus-like since Tom Ford took over in 1994 – then you should put this book down and admit that fashion is passing you by. Gucci is the label of the moment. It is worn by global style setters – but, more to the point, the design, marketing and advertising are without equal. The British high street is overloaded with cringe-making copies, but there are only two places to go for the real thing. The celebrated snaffle loafer is ever present (along with a further 150 styles of shoe; watch *Vogue*'s People pages to see what's hot), as is the bamboo-handled handbag and the Gucci watch. For spring, the fashion collection is bronzed and beautiful, with tube dresses, collarless coats and the skinniest pants in town, sold from a store which is about to quadruple in size making it the largest Gucci boutique in Europe.

Also at: 32–33 Old Bond Street W1, tel: 0171 629 2716.

Guess?

171–175 Brompton Road SW3
Tel: 0171 823 8008

Open: Mon–Sat 10am–6pm and late night Wed till 7pm (phone to check first)

Guess? brings a little of its West Coast cool to London with this just-opened flagship store; the changing rooms come complete with self-positioning cameras (if you are desperate to see how your butt looks in your Guess? blue jeans) and a self-serve juice machine lets you rejuvenate before an onslaught on the rails. The merchandise here doesn't approach the high-energy look of the provocative ad campaign (featuring schoolgirl Loneke Engel), but it is hardy and hip. The same could be said of the store's steely interior, where you can dream of Venice Beach while you buy your stock of summer T-shirts.

Hermès

179 Sloane Street SW1
Tel: 0171 823 1014

Open: Mon–Sat 10am–6pm

The "H" loafer and belt are the latest way to wear the understated label that has been the ultimate in elegance and style since 1837 – leave the silk scarves to the horsey set. Hermès's craftsmanship and product quality attracts the most graceful names in the world; Marlene Dietrich and Ingrid Bergman were both fans, and when Grace Kelly used an Hermès bag to disguise her pregnancy in Monaco, a cult accessory was born. Today, a Kelly bag is virtually impossible to buy here. Orders are placed years in advance, and the precious stock is only sufficient to service the waiting list (or should we say lust?).

Iceberg

82 Brompton Road SW3
Tel: 0171 225 0515
Open: Mon–Fri 10am–6.30pm, late night Wed till 7pm and Sat 10am–6pm

American designer Marc Jacobs has turned this once-staid label on its head, making it one of the priority viewings in the Milan collections schedule. Where once Iceberg specialised in novelty knitwear (the kind that had Mickey Mouse staring gormlessly out from your chest), the current look is sharp and sweet with plenty of techno fabrics and lots of attitude. A sign on the door here says "Open by appointment", so don't bank on the retail side being as customer-friendly as the clothes.

Isabell Kristensen

33 Beauchamp Place SW3
Tel: 0171 589 1798
Open: Mon–Fri 10am–6pm and Sat 11am–6pm

Ms Kristensen is huge at Ascot (she comes each day in a different vast concoction of a hat to play to the paparazzi), and she maintains a client list of equal impact: the Duchess of York is a big devotee, and Cher, Tina Turner and Mica Paris all have Kristensen in their closets. She also designs for film and television (the evening wear in *Damage* was hers). Not for wall-flowers, obviously.

Katharine Hamnett

20 Sloane Street SW1
Tel: 0171 823 1002
Open: Mon–Fri 10am–6.30pm, late night Wed till 7pm and Sat 10am–6pm

Hamnett is back showing in London after a brief sojourn in Milan and Paris – not a bad thing, given that her collections are so influenced by the London look. The shop was designed by David Chipperfield as a shrine to minimal styling, with functional touches such as the glass shelving and a grey stone floor. It acts as an "exhibition space" for the complete Hamnett look (curvy, sexy clothes that have traded in their cutting edge for retail appeal), including the latest addition, Katharine Hamnett shoes.

Kenzo

15 Sloane Street SW1
Tel: 0171 235 4021
Open: Mon–Sat 10am–6pm and late night Wed till 7pm

Kenzo is a national institution in France and, although available in most major department stores, this is the only stand-alone Kenzo boutique in London. As well as carrying the Paris main line, burdened with the bold blossoms that are the Japanese designer's signature, there is also a comprehensive selection of pieces from the Jungle range, the impressive diffusion line of colourful shirts, gilets and jackets. The menswear is available in department stores.

For menswear stockists, call: 0171 229 7993.

Linea

4 Harriet Street SW1
Tel: 0171 235 8881
Open: Mon–Sat 10am–6pm and late night Wed till 6.30pm

The chief label carried at Linea is Vestimenta, one of those classic Italian labels that few people have heard of. You can also pick up the Fendi collection (beware: the fur bites), and a curious range of cartoon knitwear from Castelbajac.

Also at: 8 Heath Street NW3, tel: 0171 794 1775 (for Moschino, Versace, D&G and Thierry Mugler)
Childrenswear at: 8 Perrins Court NW3, tel: 0171 794 4408 (for Moschino and Versace for 0–12 year-olds).

Lucienne Phillips

89 Knightsbridge SW1
Tel: 0171 235 2134
Open: Mon–Sat 9.30am–6pm

With 22 years to her credit in her Knightsbridge store, Lucienne Phillips has seen trends, as well as customers, come and go, and admits that business is not what it used to be. Her speciality is to select fine British ready-to-wear from designers such as Jasper Conran, Jean Muir, Jean and Martin Pallant, Charles and Patricia Lester, and hats by Rachel Trevor-Morgan. The shop looks ark-old, but go inside – you won't regret it.

Margaret Howell

29 Beauchamp Place SW3
Tel: 0171 584 2462
Open: Mon–Sat 10am–6pm

Margaret Howell's collections have developed over 28 years along classic lines, always rooted in a retro feeling from the Thirties and Fifties. Colours and fabrics are comfortable – with linen and cotton a constant – and the cuts are mannish. Howell's pyjamas and bathrobes hang on the most fashionable bathroom pegs, with prices from £135.

Also at: 24 Brook Street W1, tel: 0171 495 4888, and 7 Paved Court Richmond TW7, tel: 0181 948 5005.

MaxMara

32 Sloane Street SW1
Tel: 0171 235 7941
Open: Mon–Sat 10am–6pm and late night Wed till 7pm

Sane, serene and responsible for some of the most gorgeous coats on earth, MaxMara never fails to come up with a collection that is exquisitely cut and subtle. There are so many diffusion lines and dovetailing ranges (SportMax, Weekend, Penny Black, Marina Rinaldi, up to 16 lines in all) that it can be difficult to keep up, but, as they say in the business, never mind the label, feel the quality.

Also at: 153 New Bond Street W1, tel: 0171 491 4748.

Ninivah Khomo

5 Beauchamp Place SW3
Tel: 0171 591 0112
Open: Mon–Sat 10am–6pm and late night Wed till 7pm

A St Martin's student of the Seventies, Khomo has a thing about leopard print, which should put her in the picture for a fashion revival. You can dress in spots (on chiffon, Lycra or satin), or decorate your home with some of the many "extras" in the shop (tissue boxes, lampshades, bedspreads and that all-important leopard-print shopping trolley). Rifat Ozbek loves it, and I bet Dolce and Gabbana would faint at the sight.

Pallant

19a Motcomb Street SW1
Tel: 0171 259 6046
Open: Mon–Fri 10am–6pm

This boutique stocks smart day and evening wear from the couture end of the Pallant business. Recently a diffusion line (called, brilliantly enough, pallant...) has been added to attract that elusive younger audience. It is available at the second branch.

Also at: 162a Sloane Street SW1, tel: 0171 245 1145.

Paul Costelloe

156 Brompton Road SW3
Tel: 0171 589 9480
Open: Mon–Sat 10am–6pm and late night Wed till 7pm

A grand store for Irish-born Costelloe, with a weekend-in-the-country feel and expressionless clothes. Natural fibres, with a particular bias towards traditional Irish linen, are abundant, but the design hand is all too often clumsy and ill-considered. The Dressage diffusion line is zippier, with jeans and separates ideal for... a weekend in the country.

Prada

44–45 Sloane Street SW1
Tel: 0171 235 0008
Open: Mon–Sat 10am–6pm and late night Wed till 7pm

When Miuccia Prada gave up banner bearing for the Italian socialist party and turned her hand to fashion design, the world was blessed with the most precise, engaging clothes imaginable. The clothing – now including the ultra-successful Miu Miu diffusion line, so called because it was Miuccia's nickname as a child – is an off-shoot of the original leather ventures of her forebears Fratelli Prada. Today, even if you smirk at the hype and hoopla surrounding Prada's "ugly chic" philosophy, you will be hard put not to admire, covet, even buy the brilliant leather shoes and wallets, or the nylon macs and bags. The shop, a celery-green art space with an eerie atmosphere, is routinely packed with Prada junkies. But, go on, buy a key ring.

Red or Dead

1 Sloane Street SW1
Tel: 0171 235 1335
Open: Mon–Sat 10am–6.30pm

Red or Dead wins the Street Designer of the Year Award with monotonous regularity. Is this because the competition is nil, the judges are short-sighted, or the collections are magnificent? A bit of each, perhaps. After a turbulent 1996, when the company nearly sank, was sold, bought back and sold again, Red or Dead has weathered the storm under the parental gaze of Wayne Hemingway and his wife Geraldine, who set up shop from Camden Market in 1982. It is almost an impostor in the spit-and-polish of Sloane Street (another of Wayne's little jokes?), with a summer look poached from a bad Bollywood movie. Combined with hippy wedgies, wallpaper-print loafers and Dr Scholl sandals, the ensemble could only be Red or Dead. Cheesy Designer of the Year would be nearer the mark.

Also at: Thomas Neal's Centre, Earlham Street WC2, tel: 0171 240 5576 (shoes and clothes), and 33 Neal Street WC2, tel: 0171 379 7571 (shoes only).

Stewart Parvin

14 Motcomb Street SW1
Tel: 0171 838 9808
Open: Mon–Sat 10am–6pm

Parvin specialises in luxury kit for mothers-of-brides, Ascot fillies and the Scandinavian royal family. The service is personal and polished, and the fluid lines are flattering. Expect to pay up to £1,800 for a complete outfit; couture bridalwear starts at £3,000.

Tomasz Starzewski

177–178 Sloane Street SW1
Tel: 0171 235 4526
Open: Mon–Sat 10am–6pm

Poor old Tomasz must be bored silly with press references to his "ladies-who-lunch" clientele. But lunch they do, in his bright, breezy suits and wow dresses. They dine in his cocktail dresses and dance in his ballgowns. Tania Bryer and Ivana Trump probably wear Tomasz to prune the roses – and why not? His bold little store opened last year, with a couture and bridal service on the first floor. You won't find a more friendly, fun-loving couturier this side of the Gare du Nord.

Valentino

174 Sloane Street SW1
Tel: 0171 235 0719
Open: Mon–Fri 10am–6pm and Sat 10.30am–6pm

Mr Valentino is the glamour king of Rome. He has a "red" of his own, which appears on the catwalk every season, a fondness for black-and-white and a pug called Oliver, to whom a diffusion line has been dedicated. He also has a mind-bogglingly successful fashion empire, from top-level couture (the old-fashioned kind, that understands how to flatter and disguise the vagaries of the female form, particularly the female forms of some of the richest women in the world) to Valentino shades, as worn in the via Spiga. It's all very *Dolce Vita*, tailor-made for frollicking around in the Trevi fountain. The Miss V diffusion line is big on ruffles and the lingerie look for spring.

Miss V at: 160 New Bond Street W1, tel: 0171 493 2698.

Notting Hill

Graham and Green

10 Elgin Crescent W11
Tel: 0171 727 4594

Open: Mon–Fri 10am–6pm, Sat 9.30am–6pm and Sun 11am–5pm

An atmosphere of calm and general well-being surrounds Graham and Green, making it a delight to visit for shoppers and browsers alike. The company started 20 years ago and deals mainly in "alternative" interiors for its Notting Hill clientele. The introduction of clothing five years ago was a natural addition to the "lifestyle" concept that Graham and Green was among the first to pinpoint as the retail opportunity of the Nineties. Labels here are spot-on for the customer who comes in for home ideas: Comme des Garçons for arty types, Ghost for working mothers, John Rocha and Irene Van Ryb for expensive eclecticism. Fred Bare, Phillippe Model, Hervé Masson and Jo Gordon make for a strong accessories team. The mix is imaginative, with an emphasis on the unusual, which means you can't *quite* leave without buying something.

Oxford Street and Regent Street

Browns

23–27 South Molton Street W1
Tel: 0171 491 7833

Open: Mon–Sat 10am–6pm and late night Thurs till 7pm

See page 216.

Ghost

13 Hinde Street W1
Tel: 0171 486 0239

Open: Mon–Sat 10am–6pm and late night Thurs till 7pm

Don't leave home without it: Ghost's hallmark crinkled viscose fabric travels like no other, and the shapes and colours are as trend-conscious as they come. Easy to wear (they hide all the bumps) and easy to wash (they don't even need ironing), each piece is as individual and feminine as the customers Ghost attracts – including Nicole Kidman, Amanda Donohoe, Andie McDowell, as well as batallions of fashion editors, photographers and stylists. Practicality need not be dull, and Ghost proves it.

Also at: 36 Ledbury Road W11, tel: 0171 229 1057.

Hugo Boss

(m)

184 Regent Street W1
Tel: 0171 734 7919

Open: Mon–Sat 9.30am–6.30pm and Thurs 10am–8pm

The Boss flagship store provides the full range of Boss merchandise including suits, casualwear, bodywear and accessories.

Paddy Campbell

8 Gees Court W1
Tel: 0171 493 5646

Open: Mon–Sat 10am–6pm late night Thurs till 7pm and Sat 10.30am–6pm

"Timeless classic" is the kind of phrase that makes fashion writers wince, but it just so happens that it sums up Paddy Campbell's work perfectly. The collections are principally day wear in natural fibres – tweeds, linens and wools – although there is a slim evening wear section too.

Also at: 17 Beauchamp Place SW3, tel: 0171 225 0543.

Pellicano

63 South Molton Street W1
Tel: 0171 629 2205

Open: Mon–Sat 10am–6pm and late night Thurs till 7pm

See page 218.

Soho and West Soho

Ally Capellino

95 Wardour Street W1
Tel: 0171 494 0768

Open: Mon–Fri 11am–6pm and Sat 10.30am–6pm

Are you a fan of concrete grey, sludge blue, algae green? Do you like to slip through a crowded room unnoticed? Are you looking for clothes that don't shout their pedigree or announce their arrival at parties? If so, you are a Capellino customer in the making. This British designer's fêted utilitarian approach to basic fashion (plenty of linen, boxy shapes, easy pants) is reflected in the refined interior of both her shops. AO is the new diffusion line, a tad looser, louder and more of a personality at parties.

Also at: 66 Sloane Avenue SW3, tel: 0171 591 8201.

Idol

15 Ingestre Place W1
Tel: 0171 439 8537
Open: Mon–Fri 10.30am–6pm and Sat 11am–5pm

There is a very definite Idol image that carries through from season to season: ingredients include acres of crushed or bleached velvet, heavily beaded bodices, Empire lines and medieval styling. The label was set up in 1989 by Penny Meachin (also noted as New Zealand's first woman to qualify as an electrician) and Kerrie Hughes. Look out for the pair's cleverly textured fabrics, feathered sleeves and web-like weaves, the kind of unusual details that have made this label a favourite with London's individualists.

South-west

L K Bennett

32–38 High Street, Wimbledon Village SW19
Tel: 0181 944 8822
Open: Mon–Sat 9.30am–6pm and Sun 11am–6pm

L K Bennett began seven years ago as an accessories boutique, and rapidly expanded to its present set of five shops, now selling clothes too. This – the main clothes shop – sells Teenflo, Regina Rubens, Philippe Adec, Kenzo, Ben de Lisi and Margaret Howell. The accessories shop sells bags by Mulberry; jewellery by Dinny Hall and Wright and Teague, hats by Fred Bare, Gilly Forge and Bailey Tomlin, and scarves by English Eccentrics. The own-label shoes, however, are the best seller: designed and made in Italy, the collection includes classic evening shapes and seasonal styles all within an intelligent price range.

Also at: 239 King's Road SW3, tel: 0171 376 7241.
Footwear at: 29–30 High Street, Wimbledon Village SW19, tel: 0181 944 8822 and 83 King's Road SW3, tel: 0171 352 8066.
Accessories at: 66 High Street, Wimbledon Village SW19, tel: 0181 947 2038.

Matches ®

34, 37, 38 and 39 High Street, Wimbledon Village SW19
Tel: 0181 947 8707
Open: Mon–Sat 10am–6pm and Sun 12pm–5pm

In a street takeover to rival Chanel's in Paris's rue Cambon or Agnès B's in the rue du Jour, Matches has put Wimbledon Village firmly on the fashion map. At number 34, you can find directional and contemporary labels including Paul Smith Women, John Rocha, Prada, Moschino (both main line and Cheap and Chic), Victor Victoria, Future Ozbek and Clements Ribeiro. The MaxMara shop is at number 37, while 38 and 39 stock menswear from Ralph Lauren, Paul Smith, Prada and Versace. In short, if you don't find it in Matches, it probably isn't worth buying.

Also at: 13 Hill Street, Richmond TW9, tel: 0181 332 9733.

Noble Jones

7 Hill Street, Richmond TW9
Tel: 0181 332 2151
Open: Mon–Sat 9.30am–6pm and Sun 12pm–6pm

The world paper shortage prevents us from listing every label stocked here, but try this for starters: Mani (from the Giorgio Armani stable), Ben de Lisi, Kenzo Jungle, John Smedley and Trussardi for women, and Gianfranco Ferre, Versace, Exte and Romeo Gigli Sport for men. Downstairs, the shoe room carries Wannabe by Patrick Cox, Robert Clergerie for women and Grensons for men, and a well-considered own-label collection of footwear – all set against a cool, cast-aluminium interior, provided by interior designer Paul Andrews.

Silver

56b High Street, Wimbledon Village SW19
Tel: 0181 944 5995
Open: Mon–Sat 10am–6pm and Sun 12pm–5pm

Matches again, but this time, it's the more casual end of the business, concentrating on the jeans lines of Armani, Guess?, Katharine Hamnett and Ralph Lauren. Joseph, Artwork, Romeo Gigli and Equipment allow you to put together a total look all in one go.

View

17 Hill Street, Richmond TW9
Tel: 0181 332 2726
Open: Mon–Sat 10am–6pm and Sun 12.30pm–5.30pm

View is Richmond's strongest designer dealer, a real A to Z of top fashion names, from Anna Sui to Valentino, Armani jeans to Versace V2 – and everything else in between. Newly acquired and highly desired names include Donna Karan for men and Nicole Farhi's diffusion line, the fairly unremarkable Diversion.

Yvonne Damant

13 Richmond Hill, Richmond TW10
Tel: 0181 940 0514
Open: Tues–Sat 10.30am–6pm

Yvonne Damant's subtly eccentric style is a rare treat and one that we were almost tempted to keep to ourselves. Her all-white shop, originally located in The Square nearby, is the sort of place that exudes calm and reminds you that shopping for clothes should be a pleasure not a chore. The brilliant designs of Belgian deconstructivist Ann Demeulemeester set off Damant's own collection of minimal wraps, evening dresses and refined wedding outfits in luxurious velvet and crepe. Among the clothes are a few home ideas and some jewellery – from Jacqueline Rabun, among others – that gets more space around Christmas time. These added extras have little to do with fashion but everything to do with the beautiful way the shop looks and feels.

All Over the Shop

Bizoo

27 Fife Road, Kingston-upon-Thames KT1
Tel: 0181 541 5000
Open: Mon–Sat 10am–5.30pm and late night Thurs till 6.30pm

Bizoo is one of the few places to shop in Kingston if you want to avoid the high street and track down designer labels such as Iceberg, Versace, Cerruti, Tehen, Cotton Club underwear and Gottex swimwear. Not only do the staff pride themselves on their attentive service, they also offer "off-street parking" and a privilege discount card with 15% off main-line and 10% off jeans collections. As if this weren't enough, on Sundays the girls are on the road transporting clothes to people who can't make it to the shop during the week.

Collection

198 Chiswick High Road W4
Tel: 0181 995 1942
Open: Mon–Fri 10am–6pm and Sat 9.30am–6pm

Collection is part of American Pie, whose original menswear shop (selling Armani jeans, Nicole Farhi and Versace) is located next door at number 200. Womenswear buyer Michele Betzner caters for all ages and tastes, with an emphasis on casual, comfortable clothes including Katharine Hamnett, Betty Jackson and Calvin Klein and the insipid Paul Costelloe. D&G belts and Dyberg Kern silver jewellery round off the stock.

For branches, call: 0181 995 1942.

If

32 Clifton Road W9
Tel: 0171 289 0866
Open: Tues-Sat 10am-6pm

The delightful Francine Khanna has been looking after the ladies of Warwick Avenue for the past 15 years and provides them with a selection of French and Italian labels such as MaxMara, Synonyme and Krizia. The basic interior, smart lines and friendly service make for an unintimidating shopping environment.

Larizia Too

78 St John's Wood High Street NW8
Tel: 0171 586 4530
Open: Mon–Sat 9am–6pm

Such are the demands of the residents of St John's Wood (including Liam and Patsy) that their local high street has more designer names per square metre than anywhere else in suburban London. Larizia Too stocks D&G, DKNY, Iceberg, Anna Sui and Paul Smith, and masses of logo'd accessories.

Also at: 74 St John's Wood NW8, tel: 0171 722 5999 (shoes), and 7 Church Road, Wimbledon Village SW19, tel: 0181 944 5751 (clothes and shoes).

Mid-range

Bond Street

Designworks

19 Avery Row W1
Tel: 0171 495 5846
Open: Mon–Sat 10am–6pm and late night Thurs till 6.30pm

The compact Designworks shop is Tardis-like, packed with accessible menswear that is among the best of its kind. The strength of the designers (brother-and-sister team Max and Tamara Plaskow) comes from their ability to cover all bases, a plus for men allergic to the long-haul shopping experience. Designworks' suits come in light-weight, high-tech fabrics but with a seductive, Fifties feel; shirting is either structured with a cut-away collar or casual with Western-style front; "softwear" (casual clothes to you and me) covers velours, cotton and towelling pieces – ideal for hanging around at home. For wearable, unfamiliar, label-less clothes, look no further than Avery Row.

Gant Store

107 New Bond Street W1
Tel: 0171 629 3313
Open: Mon–Sat 9.30am–6.30pm late night Thurs till 7pm and Sun 12pm–5pm

The label stocked here is Gant USA, an American-branded sports/casual range, which started out as a shirt collection, designed by Bernhard Gant in 1949. It now runs the gamut from heavy cotton shirts, twill trousers and mariners' jackets to "rugger" tops, Bermuda shorts and caps. All of it is inspired by a very marketable New England look. Invest in a Sluggercoat or a Salty Dog sailor's coat or go all-American – if you have to – with a stars-and-stripes sweater. There are more formal ranges too, with blazers, Newport chinos and club-stripe ties. Preppy paradise.

Jigsaw

126–127 New Bond Street W1
Tel: 0171 491 4484
Open: Mon–Wed, Fri 10.30am–7pm, late night Thurs till 7.30pm and Sat 10.30am–6pm

No other store fills so shrewdly the gap between high street and high design. Jigsaw's flagship, designed by John Pawson, is a sublime shopping space, resembling nothing so much as an art gallery. But the clothes are no museum pieces: they combine practicality and value with a pride in fine fabrics and detailed design. The Jigsaw team works out of a vast, cathedral-like space in Kew, where some of the best ideas of the season are dreamt up and executed. Prices range from £35 to £250, making this one of the strongest middle-range shops in Britain. This outlet features capsule collections from "discovery" designers (Gautschi and Myriam Soritue), and the new children's range. Be advised: no shopping foray is complete without a tour of the rails here.

For branches, call: 0171 491 4434.

Lord's

70 Burlington Arcade W1
Tel: 0171 493 5808
Open: Mon–Sat 9.30am–6pm

Lord's is the largest and oldest shop in the Burlington Arcade, although it is no longer a family business (it's owned by the N Peal group). The three narrow floors cater for the quintessentially English gentleman, with shoes by Grenson, ties by Dunhill, Leonard and Givenchy, and pure silk dressing gowns by Daniel Hanson. Don't leave without visiting the top floor, which carries every shade and shape of cashmere imaginable.

Pal Zileri

38 New Bond Street W1
Tel: 0171 409 2188
Open: Mon–Wed, Fri 10am–6.30pm late night Thurs till 7pm and Sat 10am–6pm

Cashmere, fine merino wool and camel hair are the highlights from this Italian menswear company. Pal Zileri Sport is the diffusion range – street-influenced PVC, nylon and leather – while a made-to-measure service, an "alternative" wedding collection and an extensive selection of large sizes are also on offer.

Ronit Zilkha

34 Brook Street W1
Tel: 0171 499 3707
Open: Mon–Sat 9.30am–6.30pm

Ronit Zilkha stocks the tailored suit in all its glory – some bright, some piped, some plain. Cherie Blair is a Zilkha devotee, and so, ironically enough, are the society hostesses who while away their days lunching, chatting and shopping. A good stop for christening, wedding and Ascot outfits, if you like peplums.

Also at: 17 Hampstead High Street NW3, tel: 0171 431 0253, and 99 Marylebone High Street, tel: 0171 486 6785.

Savoy Taylors Guild

164 New Bond Street W1
Tel: 0171 408 1680
Open: Mon–Sat 9am–6pm and late night Thurs till 7pm

Catering for every male wardrobe requirement, from tailored suits and evening wear to weekend casuals and accessories, the Guild also boasts an extensive range of designer brands including Yves Saint Laurent and Valentino.

Squire

17 Clifford Street W1
Tel: 0171 287 5029
Open: Mon–Sat 10.30am–6.30pm

A new addition to London retailing, Squire aims to revolutionise the way we shop. Here is a space in which to hang, to kick back and chat as only

Londoners know how, under the supervision of Italian-in-London Carlo Brandelli. The shop, with acid-green walls and ambient lighting, features sleek covert coats – now in London's Design Museum as a "classic" exhibit – and slick suits (with a nod to the mod look of Italy in the Sixties). A gallery of Pop Art originals makes the backdrop. Squire is located slap-bang in the middle of London's art-land and fashion world. How could it go wrong?

The White House

51–52 New Bond Street W1
Tel: 0171 629 3521
Open: Mon–Fri 9am–5.30pm and Sat 10am–5pm

Away from the hustle of the Street, the White House is quiet. Very quiet. But then, so is its stock of Hanro and Tavernier underwear, Scottish cashmere and accessories. The service is old-fashioned (read, efficient) and the own-label underwear and children's collections – including christening robes worn by royal babies all over the world – are well worth perusing.

This site will be the first London home to Tommy Hilfiger by next year. Hilfiger started out peddling bell-bottom jeans to his hometown friends back in 1959, and his heavily logo'd sportswear is now worn by Bill Clinton, Snoop Doggy Dogg, Goldie – hell, everyone from college kids to the hip-hop crew. Hype knows no bounds.

Timberland

(&)

72 New Bond Street W1
Tel: 0171 495 2133
Open: Mon–Sat 10am–6pm and late night Thurs till 7pm

Step into Rockies territory, where all is wild and adventurous. Apart from the clothes, that is, which play it remarkably safe given the company's penchant for the great and glorious outdoors. As many a Londoner will bear witness, the boots are unbeatable. Last season, Timberland for kids arrived – an adorable collection of miniature battle boots, guaranteed waterproof for puddle-splashers, and warm enough for winter walks home from school. The new Sports Series of "active apparel" is great too, whether you're off to the tundra or to Tunbridge Wells.

Also at: 125 Long Acre WC2, tel: 0171 240 4484.

Camden

Anna

126 Regent's Park Road NW1
Tel: 0171 483 0411
Open: Mon–Sat 10am–5pm and Sun 11am–4pm

This is Anna Parks's second retail venture (her first is in Norfolk), located in the serene suburban surroundings of Primrose Hill. The beautifully converted former antique shop stocks Nicole Farhi, Paul Costelloe, Sara Sturgeon,

Marc Cain, Resource and Sand. Anna's success is derived from buying selected pieces that co-ordinate well, giving women with little time access to a one-stop shop. Very Nineties.

Chelsea

Bruce Jeremy

(&)

71 King's Road SW3

CLOSED

Almost an institution on the King's Road, Bruce Jeremy is known for his strong tailored suits for both men and women, mixed with some slinky clubwear and now a range of clothes for children. He backs his own-label collections with names such as Jeffrey West and Mario Omar.

Escapade

Antiquarius Centre, 141 King's Road SW3
Tel: 0171 376 5767
Open: Mon–Sat 10am–7pm and Sun 1pm–6pm

Escapade is a cool Parisian label that concentrates on occasion suits, shirts and dresses. There is also a range of suede trousers and shirts that can be made to your measurements, with prices from £129.

Hampstead Bazaar

138a King's Road SW3
Tel: 0171 581 2005
Open: Mon–Sat 10am–6.30pm and Sun 12pm–6pm

While the King's Road aches to be in fashion, Bazaar is more interested in free-and-easy comfort clothes. All garments are sized from an 8 to an 18 and come in a wide range of colours so you can integrate them into your existing wardrobe. Prices from £80; available at seven branches in London.

For branches, call: 0171 431 3343.

Made on Earth

(m)

97 King's Road SW3
Tel: 0171 376 3981
Open: Mon–Sat 10am–7pm and Sun 12pm–5.30pm

This boutique stocks an own-label range of menswear, together with small independent French names in both formal and casualwear. Upstairs is devoted to knitwear, shirts and accessories, while downstairs you can pick up an off-the-peg suit from £285. If you don't see the size you need, there is a special order service in a range of fabrics with your suit ready in two to three weeks.

Also at: 2 Upper St Martin's Lane WC2, tel: 0171 240 6286.

Mary Quant

3 Ives Street SW3
Tel: 0171 581 1811
Open: Mon–Sat 10am–5.45pm

Quant's current business is a far cry from the old days of "no rules" fashion on the King's Road. The signature daisy is still being stuck on everything that moves, from mini skirts (she did invent them, after all) to crop tops. More successful is the make-up range, which comes in every colour under the sun: 101 lipsticks, 80 shades of nail polish, and 120 eye colours that can be mixed and matched in Quant's cute compacts. When you've finished experimenting you can swipe it all off with the perfume-free skincare range. Run your eye over the sweet little knits before you head, shiny faced, for home.

Reiss

114 King's Road SW3
Tel: 0171 225 4910
Open: Mon–Sat 9.30am–6.30pm, late night Wed till 7pm and Sun 11.30am–5.30pm

In May 1996, Reiss opened its flagship store on the King's Road. Designed and created by Stuart Lever (architect) and Four 1V (interior designers), the shop boasts a transparent frontage and a clean style of visual merchandising that effectively showcases the increasingly modern collections. Although the name has been around for over 20 years, it is only recently that Reiss has edged itself to the forefront of British menswear design, creating suits, jackets, knitwear, jeans and shirts that are unrivalled in price and a pleasant surprise in quality. Also new is AccessoReiss, a range of ties, belts, socks, shoes and underwear to complement the core collection.

Also at: 245 Regent Street W1, tel: 0171 499 9987, and 116 Long Acre WC2, tel: 0171 240 7495.

Voyage

115 Fulham Road SW3
Tel: 0171 823 9581
Open: Mon–Sat 10am–6.30pm and late night Wed till 7pm

You cannot admit to being a true Fulham fillie until you own your quota of Voyage clothes. They look distressed and agitated (that's the point), and immediately mark the wearers out as Sloanes-turned-bohemians. The signature at this unassuming shop is ancient velvet trim – as worn by Jemima Khan throughout her pregnancy – and the anonymous, earthy colours and crumpled linens favoured by Emma Thompson, Melanie Griffith and Serena Linley. Donna Karan and Calvin Klein frequently drop by for inspiration, from the wooden shelves stacked with creased silks and the bamboo rails stuffed with one-offs. According to the manager Antoine, the idea behind the look is "not too much, not to match", and each piece is practically an original, since colours change every week. The price is original too, from £350 for a dress. The couple behind the store, Italian Tiziano Mazzilli and his Belgian wife Louise, are former designers for Valentino, but these days they're delighted that their clothes go unrecognised. You might well be too.

Whistles

27 Sloane Square SW1
Tel: 0171 730 9819

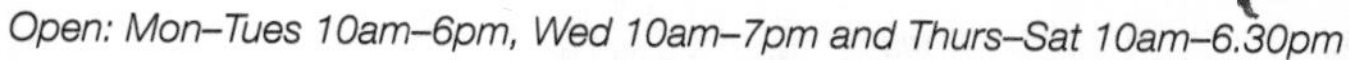

Open: Mon–Tues 10am–6pm, Wed 10am–7pm and Thurs–Sat 10am–6.30pm

No London shopping trip is complete without a whizz around Whistles, one of the most popular and professional outfits on the fashion map. Whistles was started by Richard and Lucille Lewin in 1976 and began trading from a small shop in George Street W1. Now the company boasts 11 retail shops and ten concessions, and an annual turnover in excess of £10 million. Its success is founded on a canny philiosophy: to bridge the gap between high street and high design, and to do it with one eye on trends and the other on value for money (expect to pay between £270 and £445 for a Whistles own-label suit). To top it off, Lucille sources the most forward-looking designers in the world: current in-store designers include SportMax, John Rocha, Philosophy by Alberta Ferretti and Ghost. Fresh for spring is Amaya Arzuaga, Paul & Joe, Jean Colonna and the stunning Martine Sitbon.

For branches, call: 0171 730 9819.

City and East End

424

Roman Road E3
Tel: 0181 980 4500
Open: Mon–Sat 10am–6pm

David Rosenburg describes his business as an "independent", which means he does his own thing, looking further than transient trends and obvious labels and focusing instead on fabric and styling details. Current names include John Richmond, Hope and Glory, All Saints and Nick Coleman.

Austin Reed

13–23 Fenchurch EC3
Tel: 0171 283 3347
Open: Mon–Fri 8.30am–6pm

This is the original Austin Reed shop, on site since the turn of the century, and still selling clothes of the same premium quality. The outlook has evolved, away from sturdy shirts and towards sleek suits and comfortable classics. Womenswear came along in the Eighties, cutting through the competition with its fearful power shoulders. Today the mood has calmed down and the company has again responded to demand with "Look the Business" collections, "Austin Reed Sportsman" shops and the division of the main line into Blue (classic), White (contemporary) and Green (traditional) labels. The Regent Street branch (at number 103–113) is the best of the lot, complete with an art deco barber's shop in the basement and Cerruti 1881 and KL on the rails.

For branches, call: 0800 585 479.

C'est What

The Arcade, Liverpool Street EC2
Tel: 0171 623 3556
Open: Mon–Fri 8.30am–6.30pm

Professional women on their way home from the City will find wearable labels at this run-of-the-mill boutique. There's no big pull (the main label is the safe, reliable Fenn, Wright & Manson, available all over the capital), but for convenience alone C'est What scores points.

Also at: 805 High Road N12, tel: 0171 343 9238, and Baker Street station (discount store) W1, tel: 0171 935 2820.

Madeleine Hamilton

14 Chichester Rents, Chancery Lane WC2
Tel: 0171 404 8484
Open: Mon–Fri 9am–6pm and Thurs 10.30am–7.30pm

Catering for a niche market of lawyers and bankers, and the odd bod from the hunting, shooting, fishing crowd, Hamilton provides her customers with work and after-office wear that includes tailoring and shirting in high-quality fabrics. Her own label is complemented by Paul Costelloe jeans from his Dressage range and Jean Muir classics.

Redds Active

475 Roman Road E3
Tel: 0181 980 1963
Open: Mon–Thurs 10am–5.30pm and Fri–Sat 9.30am–6pm

With three shops on the Roman Road, Redds has the area sewn up for sports, casual and designer clothing. The "active" store at number 473 stocks the usual suspects (Nike, Adidas, Reebok, Converse, Vans; Farah trousers), and that hardy perennial, the Naf Naf puffa. At number 483, the labels go upmarket – Depart, Red or Dead, Bazaar, Out of Xile and Sticky Fingers – and number 475 houses Redd's one-stop sale shop, with permanent reductions on last season's stock.

Also at: 25 Chapel Market N1, tel: 0171 278 8915.

Zobia

6 Bishopsgate Arcade EC2
Tel: 0171 638 7498
Open: Mon–Fri 10am–6.30pm and Sun 10am–3pm (closed Sat)

It started out as a City-boy suit shop, but Zobia has now moved into weekend and after-office clothes too, directed at the same customer. Replay, Ted Baker, Diesel, Armand Basi, Gallagher, Urban Stone and Richmond Denim make up the (very worthwhile) mix. There are also shoes by Hudson, Jeffrey West and Berliners.

Also at: Centre Court Shopping Centre, 4 Queen's Road SW19, tel: 0181 944 7931.

Covent Garden

Armand Basi

12 Floral Street WC2
Tel: 0171 379 3843

Open: Mon–Sat 10am–6.30pm, late night Thurs till 7pm and Sun 12pm–5pm

Spain's most successful fashion export, Armand Basi has been creating avant-garde knitwear since 1986 – as worn by Antonio Banderas, *olé*! The collections have now expanded to include leather, tailoring, womenswear and a capsule "clubwear" range. Be advised: it's raunchy, it's raucous and it's very, very Spanish.

Augustus B

Thomas Neal's Centre, Earlham Street WC2
Tel: 0171 240 8729

Open: Mon–Sat 11am–7pm and Sun 12pm–5.30pm

Be sure to keep an eye on Augustus B, as his own label should prove a huge success if his already thriving menswear business is anything to go by. To fill in any gaps, he buys labels that combine modest tailoring and practical casuals, such as Full Circle jackets and jumpers, and Shelton Miranda novelty-button shirts for lager lads, as well as Jo Y Jo refined knitwear for Martini men.

Catherine Byrne

28a Floral Street WC2
Tel: 0171 240 7220

Open: Mon–Sat 10am–6pm and late night Thurs till 7pm

This is a refined, modern shop with zesty, colourful clothes co-designed by Catherine Byrne and Andy Shorten. The silhouette is long and slender, with hand-stitched details and contrasting yarns. B Byrne is the street diffusion range, exactly the kind of clothes the Byrne man would wear when he takes off his slender suit at the end of the day.

D A Lilliard

44 Monmouth Street WC2
Tel: 0171 379 8399

Open: Mon–Sat 11.30am–7pm and late night Thurs till 8pm

Lilliard takes lush velvet, luxe crepe, pure silk and fine wool and spins them into deliciously detailed classic suits for the kind of men who put style above fashion. He keeps a low profile, allowing the clothes to speak for themselves – although his made-to-measure service (which caters for women too) recently kitted out every one of the Spice Girls, an eyebrow-raiser indeed. Men's suits from £400, shirts from £80; women's suits start from £650.

Ermenegildo Zegna

42 Shelton Street WC2
Tel: 0171 497 0001
Open: Mon–Sat 10.30am–6.30pm and late night Thurs till 7pm

Covent Garden has more menswear outlets per square metre than any other part of London – and Ermenegildo Zegna is as good a place as any to start, particularly if you practise the straight-in-and-make-a-get-away shopping method. The 85-year-old Italian family business has had plenty of time to establish itself as a brand leader, and the symmetrical, spacious store in WC2 houses unstructured collections with an emphasis on fabric construction and superior tailoring.

Also at: 37 New Bond Street W1, tel: 0171 493 4471.

Galicia

24 Wellington Street WC2
Tel: 0171 836 2961
Open: Mon–Fri 10.30am–6pm and Sat 11am–5pm

One of the oldest businesses in Covent Garden, Galicia has been in Wellington Street for 20 years, although the stock has, naturally, evolved over the years. Now you can find a good selection of working-womenswear, from MaxMara, Georges Rech and Paul Costelloe.

Gordon Happs

28–32 Shelton Street WC2
Tel: 0171 240 7767
Open: Mon–Sat 10am–7pm and Sun 12pm–5pm

For the past two years, the Gordon Happs shop has been thriving just off the beaten fashion track in Shelton Street, quietly selling classic English tailoring and casualwear. The two British designers behind the label concentrate on quality and fabric, not forgetting price: shirts from £45, suits from £350. There is always a vast array of shoes, bags, ties and even a Gordon Happs aftershave for complete good taste.

Jigsaw Menswear

9–10 Floral Street WC2
Tel: 0171 240 5651
Open: Mon–Wed 10.30am–7pm, Thurs 10am–8pm and Sun 12pm–6pm

What joy when Jigsaw celebrated its 20-year anniversary by introducing menswear in 1993. In just three years, its deeply fashionable suits, perfect knits and sleek shirts have become the backbone of many a male wardrobe. These are confident clothes, stylish enough to compete with the imported chic of the Italian manufacturers, reasonable enough to be available to all. This store is the Big One, though new stores seem to spring up regularly – the latest additions are in Fulham Road and Brook Street. Even style no-hopers can't go wrong here.

For branches, call: 0171 240 5651.

J Simons

2 Russell Street WC2
Tel: 0171 370 7353
Open: Mon–Sat 10am–6pm

If the street entertainers are getting your back up, make a break for J Simons and enter a world frozen in time, circa 1965. The three assistants (of which J, for John, is one) are experts on a period that may have slipped your memory, but is rekindled with button-down shirts, chinos, Sebago loafers and Sero shirts.

Karen Millen

17–19 Neal Street
Tel: 0171 240 4401
Open: Mon–Wed, Fri 10am–7pm, late night Thurs till 8pm, Sat 10am–6.30pm and Sun 12pm–6pm

See page 209.

Les 2 Zebres

38 Tavistock Street WC2
Tel: 0171 836 2855
Open: Mon–Sat 10.30am–6.30pm

In France, "zebra" is the colloquial name for a man who dresses to impress. This shop was opened in the late Seventies by two designers from Lyons and specialises in French and Italian labels little known outside their native countries. The clothes appeal to unorthodox men, with a streak of the zebra in their blood.

Morning

20 Wellington Street WC2
Tel: 0171 379 8249
Open: Mon–Sat 10.30am–6.30pm

Long before Covent Garden became a magnet for tourists from Tokyo, the Italian-owned Morning was doing fine business in well-made clothes with staying power. Today, the monochrome shop is a retreat from the outside hoo-ha, great for sculpted suits and evening wear, with prices from £300 to £500.

Moss Bros

27 King's Street WC2
Tel: 0171 240 4567
Open: Mon–Sat 9am–6pm

Moss Bros is the nation's recognised authority on the hire and sale of men's formalwear. In Moss Bros's own words... "A reminder for those who are finding it tough: You should always show an inch of shirt cuff. The band of your tie should be kept out of sight – Keep it under your jacket or you'll look a fright. If in doubt with your dressing, you're bound to get cross, So for all types of dress etiquette, just call Moss Bros." Yes, indeedy.

For branches, call: 0171 447 7720.

Muji

39 Shelton Street WC2
Tel: 0171 379 1331
Open: Mon–Wed, Sat 10am–7pm, late night Thurs and Fri till 8pm and Sun 12pm–6pm

Sweep past Muji's racks of pencil pots and rice crackers to get at some of the best sofa clothes in town. The lines are soft and fluid, the fabrics warm and uncreasable – great for TV evenings and Sunday mornings. It may be generic, but it works.

For branches, tel: 0171 379 1331.

Nigel Hall

6 Shorts Gardens WC2
Tel: 0171 379 6966
Open: Mon–Fri 11am–7pm and Sat 10.30am–7pm

High on the feel-good factor, Hall has a hands-on approach to his compact and covetable collections for men. Knitwear is a forte: for spring, look out for fine-gauge pullovers in azure and coconut, with hipster pants and close-check shirts. Then keep your eyes peeled for his second store, opening soon nearby.

Rina da'Prato

Thomas Neal's Centre, Earlham Street WC2
Tel: 0171 240 8812
Open: Mon–Sat 11am–7pm and Sun 12.30pm–6pm

Vogue loves Rina. When the glossy featured her glam knitwear, she sold out within days. Since then, the Scottish designer has twice been nominated as knitwear designer of the year at the Lloyds Bank Fashion Awards, and now she is expanding the business to include tailoring, men's and children's ranges, all housed in her tiny shop. Go get them, before *Vogue* does.

Ted Baker

1–2 Langley Court WC2
Tel: 0171 497 8862
Open: Mon–Fri 10am–7pm, late night Thurs till 7.30pm, Sat 10am–6.30pm and Sun 12pm–5pm

Ray Kelvin – self-confessed East End barrow boy – believes his shirts are "made in heaven" and enjoys popping into his shops to introduce himself as "Ted" to surprise his bemused customers. Alongside the men's shirts that have made him famous, there are jeans, casual jackets, accessories and ties, with prices from £35 – in fact, Baker clothes are so popular that they have now taken over the former Chipie store next door. Popular with Blue Peter presenters, Jonathan Ross and Andy Peters... Nuff said, Ray, nuff said. His clothes speak to lads-about-town, off-duty city gents, and now to women too, with the launch of the Ted Baker Women line. Teddy Boy, a cute but cool kids' line is also new.

Also at: 7 Foubert's Place W1, tel: 0171 437 5619.

Fulham

Kit and Twentieth Century Frox

614 Fulham Road SW6
Tel: 0171 731 3242
Open: Mon–Fri 10am–7pm and Sat 10am–5.30pm

If you can forgive the cringing pun, Twentieth Century Frox is worth a visit for its good-looking evening wear from ten different designers – either for sale from around £150, or for hire (prices start at £65 for three days). Three years ago, Kit was added to provide a range of middle-of-the-road day and casualwear labels such as Jackpot, Sticky Fingers, Nougat, Jo Y Jo and Unisa shoes.

Moon

445 North End Road SW6
Tel: 0171 381 6362
Open: Mon–Sat 10am–6pm and late night Wed till 7pm

At the "right" end of the North End Road near Fulham Broadway, Moon is the kind of shop that you always mean to pop into and then you never quite get the time. Find the time, because among the cacti and ethnic wooden fixtures, you'll discover plenty of pretty and practical clothes from Great Plains (part of the French Connection group) and Switch, a label that does clever things with crepe.

Penhallow

115 Wandsworth Bridge Road SW6
Tel: 0171 371 5362
Open: Mon–Sat 10am–6pm

Linda Penhallow's shop is a good find for smart suits, knitwear and daytime separates from good quality but reasonably priced names such as Jo Y Jo (knitwear) and Unisa (shoes).

Greenwich

The Selection

15 Greenwich Market SE10
Tel: 0181 858 5130
Open: Mon–Fri 10.30am–5pm and Sat–Sun 10am–6pm

The understated Jo Y Jo is the mainstay in this small, friendly boutique that has been holding court in the lively atmosphere of Greenwich Market for the past decade. There are also easy-wear collections from Adini, Nougat, Solola and Kangol (for cool hats), plus hosiery and hair accessories. Black Sheep is a range of snug knitwear, just the thing for those country walks on Blackheath.

Stitches and Daughters

5–7 Tranquil Vale SE3
Tel: 0181 852 8507
Open: Mon-Sat 9.30am-6pm and Sun 12pm-5pm

Fashion, fabric, furniture, books and lamps, all housed in Julia Redfearn's lifestyle store. The clothing includes Great Plains (from French Connection), Fenn, Wright & Manson and the Scandinavian label Bitte Kai Rand. Larger sizes should keep an eye out for Sahara, which produces "proper frocks" in floral patterns for sizes 8-22.

Also at: 9a The Market SE10, tel: 0181 305 1396, and 36 Horseley Down Lane, Butler's Wharf SE1, tel: 0171 357 6905.

Hampstead and Highgate

Arc en Ciel

10 Heath Street NW3
Tel: 0171 794 6311
Open: Mon–Sat 10.30am–5.30pm and Sun 1pm–5pm (phone to check first)

The English translation of *arc en ciel* is rainbow, and it's easy to understand why when you see the clothes. The stock is made up of just one label – Chacok, a French company whose designer, Arlette Chacok, lives on the French Riviera, which no doubt influences her colour palette. The shop attracts a lot of American and Japanese visitors as well as locals, unfazed by the kaleidoscope of stripes, flowers and patterns in a multitude of mix-and-match fabrics. Not advised for hangover sufferers.

Callaghan's

9 Perrins Court NW3
Tel: 0171 433 3299
Open: Mon–Fri 9am–5pm, Sat 10am–6pm and Sun 11am–6pm

A legend in its native Dublin, Callaghan's has taken 200 years to reach London, but now that it has, it is set to become one of the leading names in traditional all-weather gear. The roots are in saddlery equipment and clothing, although the emphasis is shifting towards handknits, waxed jackets and practical shirts.

Jane and Dada

59 Hampstead High Street NW3
Tel: 0171 431 0708
Open: Mon–Sat 9.30am–6.30pm and Sun 10am–6.30pm

Jane and Dada are a pair of friends who one day decided to open a business (they make it sound so easy). Dada runs the Hampstead end, while Jane looks after the West End clients in her St Christopher's Place shop. Both carry cool classics from Fenn, Wright & Manson, In Wear, Jackpot, Penny Black, Marina Rinaldi and Sand.

Also at: 20-21 St Christopher's Place W1, tel: 0171 486 0977.

Palomino

5 Flask Walk NW3
Tel: 0171 431 9141
Open: Tues–Sun 10.30am–6.30pm

It's hard to categorise Palomino as anything other than the ultimate men's gift store. The clothes are basic (though unique from season to season) with a label list that includes Marco Polo, Tom Tailor, funky O'Neill sportswear and Original Blue. A diverse assortment of accessories includes watches from De Mathiesen (also in New York's Museum of Modern Art, no less), holdalls by Brics from Italy, and giftwear from Alessi. What more could a man desire?

Replay

44 Hampstead High Street NW3
Tel: 0171 435 4066
Open: Mon–Sat 10am–6.30pm and Sun 12pm–6pm

Mobile phone, big wallet and ego to match? This is the shop for you. Matinique is the leading label, along with Calvin Klein T-shirts and Ralph Lauren shirts. The visual merchandising – shirts and jackets with sleeves rolled up – should give a clue as to the customer the shop is trying to attract. Go get it boys.

Velo

32 Rosslyn Hill NW3
Tel: 0171 431 4767
Open: 11am–6.30pm seven days a week

It is rare to come across a menswear boutique that both knows what it's doing and does it in consummate style. However, the two ex-City boys who started the business to fill a glaring gap in the quality menswear market in Hampstead appear to have a pretty good idea of what men want to buy. The labels are not unique (Paul Smith jeans, Armani, CP Company, Cerruti and Ted Baker, and underwear from Calvin Klein) but the friendly, unintimidating atmosphere is.

Zana

6 Flask Walk NW3
No phone
Open: 11am–6pm seven days a week

It's hard to tell what is sold in this boutique, as the stock changes constantly from season to season. Investigations reveal that the winter emphasis is on beaded evening dresses and hand-made crushed velvet scarves, while summer's stock is a lighter weight, with silk scarves and suits. Waistcoats and ethnic jewellery feature all year round.

Highbury and Islington

Clusaz

56 Cross Street N1
Tel: 0171 359 5596
Open: Mon–Sat 10.30am–6.30pm

The best thing about Clusaz, apart from the clothes, of course, is the changing room, which is saturated with natural light. If you look good here, you'll look good anywhere. The two partners have been in business for nine years and buy ranges that are easily incorporated into existing wardrobes: French Connection, In Wear, Fenn, Wright & Manson, Sara Sturgeon, Betty Jackson, Jo Y Jo and Diversion by Nicole Farhi.

Diverse

286 Upper Street N1
Tel: 0171 359 0081
Open: Mon–Sat 11am–7pm and Sun 12pm–5.30pm

It lives up to its name: two floors of fashion, with a few gift and home ideas thrown in for good measure. For women there's Ghost, John Rocha, Diesel, Katharine Hamnett Denim and AO by Ally Capellino; men get Firetrap, Full Circle, John Rocha and the impressively tailored Mediterranea.

Jeanette Henry

8 Shillingford Street N1
Tel: 0171 704 9595
Open: Tues–Sat 10.30am–6pm

Word of mouth has made Henry's friendly shop a local favourite. Her strength lies in made-to-measure day and evening wear in clean, clutter-free fabrics such as silk, linen and Cupro, a synthetic silk. The service takes three weeks for a design in stock fabric, or up to two months if material has to be sourced. An off-the-peg collection follows the same sleek design principle at a down-to-earth price (skinny rib tops, £60; suits around £400).

Kensington

Amazon

19–21 Kensington Church Street W8
Tel: 0171 938 2993
Open: Mon–Fri 10am–6pm, late night Thurs till 7pm, Sat 9am–6pm and Sun 12pm–5pm

As swiftly as the Amazon rainforest dwindles, Amazon in Kensington goes on expanding. Currently running at nine outlets, with 12 floors of fashion, it sells a mix of high-street and designer labels at discounted prices. The bargains are sourced from surplus stock, bulk orders and regular buying trips, so no one ever knows what's coming next. A monthly visit will uncover some of the best bargains around, from French Connection, Naf Naf, Moschino, In Wear and Nicole Farhi.

Also at 1, 3, 7, 19 and 22 Kensington Church Street W8, and 3 The Quadrant, Richmond TW12, tel: 0181 940 9970.

Blazer

(m)

101a Derry Street W8
Tel: 0171 376 1234

Open: Mon–Fri 9.30am–6.30pm, late night Thurs till 8pm and Sat 9am–6pm

No great shakes in menswear, Blazer can be relied upon for safe casual and smart clothes for guys who like to blend in nicely with the crowd. Good for no-nonsense work shirts and suits at unassuming prices, and the odd jumper.

For branches, call: 0171 524 1717.

Phase Eight

28a Kensington Church Street W8
Tel: 0171 937 5498

Open: Mon–Sat 9.30am–6pm and late night Thurs till 7pm

A comfortable, welcoming place for comfortable, welcoming clothes. In 1979, Patsy Seddon opened her first branch of Phase Eight in the off-route location of Wandsworth Common, simply to satisfy a personal craving for a decent local fashion boutique. Today, with a grand total of 13 London branches, and several outside the capital, the Phase philosophy remains safe and amenable, but is no less successful for that. Jackets from £140, dresses around £120.

For branches or mail order, call: 0171 371 5656.

Pied à Terre Lifestyle

102 Kensington High Street W8
Tel: 0171 376 0296

Open: Mon–Sat 10am–8pm and Sun 12pm–6pm

See page 141.

Red Herring

6 Old Brompton Road SW7
Tel: 0171 581 0299

Open: Mon–Fri 10am–6.30pm, Sat 10am–6pm and Sun 12pm–4pm

A little bit of this and a little bit of that... Red Herring promises something for everyone in its semi-circular, stock-full shop – from inexpensive shoes to workaday suits and accessories. For discreet clubbers, there are Dollargrand bags and Drama separates; for working women there are suits and jackets, and a useful label called Switch, which specialises in crinkly crepe. Average prices: £40 for shoes, £25–£100 for clothes.

Sally Parsons

15a Bute Street SW7
Tel: 0171 584 8866
Open: Mon–Sat 10am–6pm

Sally knows her market well: following the initial success of her childrenswear shop, she introduced womenswear and has just opened a beauty salon in the basement. There is a distinctly Continental flavour here, from the Gérard Darel suits, the fluid lines of Tehen, Lamberto Losani cashmere and Robert Friedman shirts. Childrenswear from Cacharel, Petite Faune and Hummelsheim makes up the mix, with its glad-to-be-trad mood.

Twist

35 Kensington Church Street W8
Tel: 0171 938 3806
Open: Mon–Sat 10am–6pm

Using the phrase "classic with a twist" is a shooting offence in the fashion writers' instruction manual. But here, you'll find the twist more classy than classic. Comfort, versatility and practicality are the keynotes; all fabrics are a poly-viscose mix, making them easy care and easy wear. Twist's styling makes it a popular choice with pregnant women, as skirts and trousers all have elasticated waists, and come in a range of up-to-the-minute colours to ensure that comfort and cool go hand in hand. Prices start at £50 for tunics, £47 for trousers, £53 for jackets.

Knightsbridge

Anvers

193–195 Brompton Road SW3
Tel: 0171 581 3737
Open: Mon–Sat 10am–7pm and Sun 12pm–5pm

Anvers is a Belgian import – brought to the UK by Whistles' Lucille Lewin – which, although not remarkable in design, uses interesting textural fabrics to give it an edge. A suit costs £300–£500; dresses are around £155. A concise range of accessories (bags, belts and a very flattering selection of underwear) completes the picture in this flower-filled shop.

Egg

36 Kinnerton Street SW1
Tel: 0171 235 9315
Open: Tues–Sat 10am–6pm

Egg is an intense enterprise, arty and spiritual, never faddish. It operates from a nook in Knightsbridge Mews, where the whitewashed walls and direct light are all part of the experience. The boutique sources unique products from Asia – pottery, stoneware and hand-quilted cushions – and unusual sweaters, wraps and kaftans from another place, another time. Asha Sarabhai's textiles and

Eskandar's knits are weird and wonderful, and a favourite among high priestesses of style, most of whom live in Hampstead.

Esprit

6 Sloane Street SW1
Tel: 0171 245 9139
Open: Mon-Sat 10am-6.30pm and late night Wed till 7pm

As design codes go, Esprit's practical, reasonable philosophy is a winner. Over the past year, the trend element has been souped up, so there is the occasional must-have in among the might-haves (few fashion editors got through the winter without Esprit's boat-neck sweater and velvet trouser suit). Accessories are good too.

For branches, call: 0171 240 6969.

Hackett

(m)

137–138 Sloane Street SW1
Tel: 0171 730 3331
Open: Mon–Sat 9.30–6pm and late night Wed till 7pm

Hackett started on the New King's Road 13 years ago, selling clothes and accessories found in house clearances. What a difference a day makes. Now, it is one of the best examples of British menswear retailing in the country; it plays on our gentlemanly heritage, but has its tongue firmly in its cheek, so there's plenty of humour in there too. The suits are superlative, the braces, ties, shoes and cufflinks a laugh, and the casual clothes just right for weekending males. There is even a bespoke tailor on site, and a barber for a quick short-back-and-sides.

For branches, call: 0171 738 8666.

Hawa

37 Beauchamp Place SW3
Tel: 0171 225 0109
Open: Mon–Sat 10am–6pm and late night Wed till 7pm

Allow us to let you into a secret. One visit to this two-storey boutique in deepest Knightsbridge will have you coming back time and again. The stock is mainly French and Italian labels, such as Roberto Musso, Regina Rubens, Sophie Sitbon, Barbara Bui and Lawrence Steele. Yoneda Kasuko, who uses precious fabrics for very wearable day and evening wear, is an exclusive label. Liza Minelli and Jamie Lee Curtis already know about Hawa – and now you do too.

OuiSet

35 Brompton Road SW3
Tel: 0171 584 5439
Open: Mon–Fri 10am–6.30pm, late night Wed till 7pm and Sat 10am–6pm

A quiet German label with an annual turnover in excess of £250 million, OuiSet is aimed largely at the over-25s. There's plenty of tweed and dogtooth tailoring, plaid swing coats and shift dresses, leather, suede and just a touch of glamorous evening wear for party lovers.

The Scotch House

2 Brompton Road SW1
Tel: 0171 581 2151
Open: Mon–Sat 9.30am–6pm and Wed 10am–7pm

Hang on to your sporran, here's a revelation: The Scotch House, located on "Scotch Corner", sells all things Scottish. The cashmere, lambswool and Shetland collections are great to fill in the chilly gaps in a wardrobe, and there are hundreds of pure new wool tartans to peruse at your leisure. If Scottish visitors wish to see their clan tartan, the staff in the tartan room are only too happy to help.

Also at: 84–86 Regent Street W1, tel: 0171 734 0203, and 165 Regent Street W1, tel: 0171 734 4816.

Notting Hill

Natural Selection

57b Pembridge Road W11
Tel: 0171 792 2717
Open: Mon–Fri 11am–6.30pm and Sat 9am–6pm

Unsurprisingly, linen, wool and suede are the primary concerns at Natural Selection. Alison Roper, who was based at Camden Market for five years, has been developing her shop's range of products over the past 18 months, creating a careful balance of unique accessories and clothing. The eight other designers whose work can be found here each bring something special: linen dresses at £44, bright handknits from £35, and flower jewellery from just £8.

Oxford Street and Regent Street

Alfred Dunhill

30 Duke Street SW1
Tel: 0171 499 9566
Open: Mon–Fri 9.30am–6pm and Sat 10am–6pm

"Everything but the motor" says the slogan on the early Dunhill advertisements, reflecting Alfred Dunhill's original idea to supply accessories and clothing to the first motorists of this century. He was a pioneer of products such as wristwatches, cufflinks, pipes, hand-blended tobacco and cigarette lighters – all of which are still a feature of the shop today. In the Seventies the tailoring range was added, soon followed by knitwear, shirts and casualwear, completing Alfred Dunhill's wish to be the ultimate gentlemen's store. His maxim – "It must be useful, it must work dependably, it must be beautiful, it must last, it must be the best of its kind" – still holds true today. There's no better place to shop for Christmas presents for dads.

Aquascutum

100 Regent Street W1
Tel: 0171 734 6090

Open: Mon–Sat 9.30am–6pm, late night Thurs till 7pm and Sun 12pm–6pm

The Aquascutum name is derived from the term "watershield", from the company's use of waterproofing for wool coats in the 1850s. Since then, it has continued to incorporate technological advances in fabric in its trench coats and all-weather gear. In 1997 the company aims to design for a younger market, by introducing slim tailoring and knitwear, simple evening wear and nylon coats. If you have always walked on by, drop in: you may be pleasantly surprised. Café 100 is ideal for a quiet coffee.

For branches, call: 0171 734 6090.

Atelier

3 Gees Court W1
Tel: 0171 409 2855

Open: Mon–Sat 11am–6pm and late night Sat till 7pm

Atelier specialises in Italian labels such as Moschino and Versace alongside an own-brand line of tailored suits, dresses and separates. The attraction of the shop is that it imports stock direct, giving a saving of around 25%. Suits from £190 to £700; dresses from £99 to £300.

Burberrys

18–22 Haymarket SW1
Tel: 0171 930 3343

Open: Mon–Sat 10am–6pm and late night Thurs till 7pm

It's ever-so English, ever-so smart – and a big hit with street kids who know a quality purchase when they see it. With a 140-year history, two royal warrants and six Queen's Awards for Export, Burberrys is a national institution promoting a traditional way of life – although lately, the company has dragged itself into the Nineties with a more fashion-first approach. Beware the check cheats who sell rip-off Burberrys nearby. It ain't worth a thing if it ain't the real thing.

For branches, call: 0171 930 3343.

Episode

172 Regent Street W1
Tel: 0171 439 3561

Open: Mon–Tues 10am–6.30pm, Wed and Fri 10am–7pm, late night Thurs till 8pm, Sat 9.30am–7pm and Sun 12pm–6pm

Episode is a grown-up middle-market favourite with a loyal following of working women. Look for the lean trouser suits, the slim knits and the reliable separates in technically finished and traditional fabrics such as gabardine, tweed, wool, silk and cashmere. The colour palette, which is mainly cream, white, charcoal, navy and lilac, is easy and subtle. No prizes for stunning originality, but a good stop for simple stuff.

For branches, call: 0171 589 5724.

Grey Flannel

7 Chiltern Street W1
Tel: 0171 935 4067

Open: Mon–Sat 9.30am–6pm and late night Thurs till 7pm

This shop covers every base in the menswear business – from suits to shoes, hats to ties, formalwear to casualwear, made-to-order or off-the-peg. The location (off Baker Street) attracts a constant stream of media, advertising and music folk who want to look discreetly fashionable without being too way-out. Grey Flannel has its own label, with suits from £350, and a tailoring service with prices starting at £500 with a four to six week turnaround.

Jaeger

200–206 Regent Street W1
Tel: 0171 200 4211

Open: Mon–Sat 9.30am–6pm and late night Thurs till 7pm

Everyone's mother loves Jaeger, which is enough to put any fashion type off the scent of these high-quality, lasting clothes. Designer Jeanette Todd has pushed the edges of the label (adding a younger Jaeger London collection, JJJ Sport and an upbeat knitwear range) and has been so successful that the company won the coveted Contemporary Classics Award at last year's Lloyd's Bank Fashion Awards. As *Vogue* will tell you, style Jaeger up with modern accessories and you can't go far wrong. The Jean Muir collection (another mothers' favourite) is a permanent feature of this glossy flagship shop.

For branches, call: 0171 200 4000.

Kent and Curwen

39 St James's St SW1
Tel: 0171 409 1955

Open: Mon–Fri 9.30am–6pm and Sat 10am–5pm

Kent and Curwen deals in country weekend and outdoor clothing for the English gentleman – cricket shirts and jumpers, rugby shirts, striped blazers and club ties. The ranges are split into City (suits and formalwear), Country (sports jackets and casual shirts) and Sport. The company maintains links with classic sports such as golf, polo, rugby and tennis, and is the official UK apparel licensee for the Wimbledon Championships. If you can't make it to the store then all the merchandise is also available by mail order on 01483 426917.

Also at: 21 Copthall Avenue EC2, tel: 0171 374 8333.

Malcolm Levene

13–15 Chiltern Street W1
Tel: 0171 487 4383

Open: Mon–Sat 9.30am–6pm and late night Thurs till 7pm

Malcolm Levene is an unpredictable menswear shop that has built a reputation for the calibre of its personal service and stock. Customers who have watched the business grow over the past 15 years have come to expect a certain eccentricity from the clothes – and the shop's conventional exterior hides a sense of humour. Look inside the double-breasted jacket and you might just catch a glimpse of that lime-green lining shining through.

Racing Green

193–197 Regent Street W1
Tel: 0171 437 4300

Open: Mon–Fri 9.30am–6.30pm, late night Thurs till 8pm and Sat 10am-6.30pm

Racing Green started life as a mail-order concept selling down-to-earth, practical clothes to armchair shoppers. Director David Krantz, former founder of Blazer, believed that people were fed up with over-the-top fashion, so he applied the American "sportswear" theory to the design ideas behind Racing Green. With the phenomenal success of the mail-order catalogue (a Fulham coffee table is not complete without one), the demand for a retail outlet resulted in this, the flagship store.

Also at: The Bentall Centre, Kingston-upon-Thames KT1, tel: 0181 546 2234. For mail order, call: 0345 331177.

Thomas Burberry

191 Regent Street W1
Tel: 0171 734 4816

Open: Mon–Wed 10am–6pm, late nights Thurs and Fri till 7pm and Sat 9.30am–6.30pm

Thomas Burberry combines the quality and tradition that is associated with its parent company with a touch of youthfulness and fun. The outcome is lifestyle clothes: cotton jeans, polo dresses and tailored trouser suits are the mainstays for women, while men (or boys) can pick up casual tweeds, cords, Oxford cotton shirts and chinos. Equally at home on Daddy's country estate as they are in Chelsea.

Viyella

179–183 Regent Street W1
Tel: 0171 734 7524

Open: Mon–Fri 9.30am–6.30pm, late night Thurs till 8pm and Sat 9.30am–6pm

The name Viyella is most often associated with the cloth from which the company takes its name – a patented mix of Merino wool and cotton. Today, the company manufactures practical clothes that never dip a toe into the dangerous waters of high fashion.

For branches, call: 0171 200 2977.

Soho and West Soho

Beau Monde

43 Lexington Street W1
Tel: 0171 734 6563
Open: Mon–Wed, Fri 10.30am–6.30pm, late night Thurs till 7pm and Sat 10.30am–6pm

There is a Fifties feel to the feminine tailoring found in Beau Monde which ensures that girls look like girls "should", or should have 30 years ago. The majority of the fabrics are natural – such as Irish linen – and the silhouette is simple: lean lines for shift dresses and matching jackets. Prices start at around £159 for dresses and £300 for trouser suits, and any style can be made up in the colour and fabric of your choice. The boutique is also used as a permanent art space, with engaging displays which change every six weeks.

Etcetera Projects

7 Newburgh Street W1
Tel: 0171 287 2792
Open: Mon–Tues, Sat 10.30am–6.30pm and Wed–Fri 11am–7pm

See page 213.

Makmin

8 Ganton Street W1
Tel: 0171 494 0779
Open: Mon–Sat 11am–6pm

The two sisters behind this two-year-old shop trained as an actress and a dancer, so there is no fashion background to influence the way they work. On the hanger, the clothes need a little imagination, but on the body they flatter with uncomplicated outlines and adaptable shapes. Prices start at £40 and £100, depending on the season.

South-west

Anna

44 Hill Rise, Richmond TW10
Tel: 0181 948 0199
Open: Mon–Fri 10.30am–5.30pm, Sat 10.30am–6pm and Sun 1pm–6pm

If you've ever wondered where you can get hold of the Marina Rinaldi collection for sizes 16 and above – here's where. Anna's business also caters for sizes 10–14 with Moschino jeans, Mathilde, Happy (in sizes 10–18) and Tehen. To complete your wardrobe there's evening wear from La Perla and jewellery from Giorgio Armani.

Bazar

(&)

8 and 55 Barnes High Street SW13
Tel: 0181 876 9504/4540
Open: Mon–Sat 10am–6pm

Bazar is split into two separate shops selling clothes (at number 55) and accessories (at number 8), providing the ladies of Barnes with easy-to-wear fashion without the trouble of travel. Labels include French Connection, AO by Ally Capellino, Jackpot, Marco Polo, Sun and Sand and Great Plains, and accessories are provided by Dents (for leather gloves, bags and belts), Cara, Joseph Azagury (pretty, elegant shoes) and Robert Clergerie (fashion footwear). There is also a comprehensive lingerie and nightwear section with Wonderbras, Jockey for Her, Cacharel and the comfy Sloggi, delectable Japanese kimonos and pure silk nightdresses. Accessories for men are available too.

Betty Beeckman

8 Church Road, Wimbledon Village SW19
Tel: 0181 944 6429
Open: Mon–Sat 10am–6pm and Sun 2pm–5pm

Service is the name of the game at this pleasant shop in the increasingly fashionable glades of Wimbledon. If you need a hand getting to know what you ought to be wearing or what colour will suit you, you can rely on Betty Beeckman to point you in the right direction. She has what her customers call "an eye for putting an outfit together", and many of them shop with her for their entire season's wardrobe. The labels include Georges Rech, Synonyme by Georges Rech, Sara Sturgeon, Fenn, Wright & Manson and Mathilde, concentrating mainly on versatile trouser and skirt suits, knitwear and shirts.

Green and Pleasant

129 Church Road SW13
Tel: 0181 741 1539
Open: Mon–Sat 9am–6pm

You may be forgiven for thinking that Green and Pleasant is a florist at first glance, but once inside you will discover everything for the bathroom, bedroom and kitchen... and, yes, even clothes tucked in there somewhere. Expect to find Joseph, New York, 120% Lino and fabulous Neisha Crosland scarves.

Also at: 195 High Street Guildford, TU1 tel: 01483 38207.

Jacqueline Hammond

2 Church Road, Wimbledon Village SW19
Tel: 0181 946 7073
Open: Mon–Sat 10am–6pm and Sun 1pm–6pm

London's main stockist of Apostrophe – a wearable but sober womenswear range for work or evening wear.

Lizard

(m)

10 Hill Street, Richmond TW9
Tel: 0181 948 1383
Open: Mon–Sat 9.30am–6pm and Sun 12.30pm–5.30pm

After 17 years in business, Lizard is a well-established name in Richmond for easygoing menswear, although the shop is now so full of stock that it looks as though it could do with a bigger location to fit everything in. There's an enormous range of labels (too many to mention here) including Paul Smith jeans, Henry Lloyd, Lacoste, Diesel streetwear, YSL, Urban Stone, All Saints and Full Circle. Accessories are provided by Paul Smith and shoes are from Nicholas Deakins and Lacoste. Watch out for new labels appearing this year, such as the technical street- and sportswear designer Sergio Tacchini.

Stuff

2–2a George Street, Richmond TW9
Tel: 0181 940 8237
Open: Mon–Sat 10am–6pm and Sun 12pm–5pm

Despite such a dodgy name, Stuff sells decent clothes in a welcoming, unpretentious atmosphere. It is the leading British stockist of Sara Sturgeon (for simple womenswear), complemented by other understated names such as Ally Capellino and Amaya Arzuaga. Also available is a range of more commercial, bread-and-butter labels that includes Jo Y Jo, Mario Omar, Sticky Fingers, Resolve and Antonio Derrico, for what the owners call the "Saturday shopper". If you live in Ealing, visit the original store (established for 22 years) which carries John Rocha and Weekend by Max-Mara, too.

Also at: 7 The Green, High Street W5, tel: 0181 567 1385.

All Over the Shop

30 Lamb's Conduit Street

Lamb's Conduit Street WC1
Tel: 0171 404 3987
Open: Mon–Fri 10am–6pm, evenings and weekends by appointment

A peaceful, meditative shop where browsing is encouraged and the mood is serene – so laid-back, in fact, that the owners couldn't come up with a name for their new shop. The sound of running water plays gently in the background, and the clothes are to sigh for. The partnership is between ex-lawyer Bette Casey and Warren Griffiths, who designs much of the stock using unusual, textural fabrics. In addition to the own-label, Warren Griffiths, the shop stocks Carole Waller and accessories by Bill Amberg and Sally Gissing. A made-to-measure service is also available and all work is carried out in the design studio downstairs. Don't be afraid to ask if anything else in the shop takes your fancy – everything is for sale. And if you fancy popping in at the weekend or after hours, just give them a call.

Boden

Midland Terrace, Victoria Road NW10
Tel: 0181 453 1535
Open: Mon–Fri 9am–6.30pm and Sat 10am–3pm

Johnny Boden is a bit of a card in the fashion world. He employs his friends to model the Sloaney staples (Bedford cords, crew-neck sweaters, chinos, checkered waistcoats) in his ultra-successful mail-order catalogue. The socks are fantastic (they're called "Boring Socks" by Boden), and the outdoor kit is great for taking away to the country at the weekend. This is the warehouse shop for the basic range, including the adorable Baby Boden for budding Chelsea girls and boys.

For mail order, call: 0181 453 1535.

Katherine Bird

20 Battersea Rise SW11
Tel: 0171 228 2235
Open: Tues, Wed, Fri 10.30am–6pm, Thurs 11am–7pm and Sat 10am–6pm

In among the eateries and furniture shops of Battersea Rise, Katherine Bird caters for any occasion with her mix of own-label made-to-measure and off-the-peg clothing. More informal collections from Fenn, Wright & Manson, Sara Sturgeon and Marc Aurel plug any gaps. Accessories, should you want the full ensemble, are provided by Unisa (shoes), Victoria Ann Millinery (hats), and Shakira Caine and Mounir (jewellery).

Palmer

133 Northcote Road SW11
Tel: 0171 228 7233
Open: Mon-Sat 10am-6pm

Staff here are a dab hand at putting outfits together, so ask for advice. The buyers endeavour to source labels that combine quality and direction, and presently stock Victoire, Caractère and Mer du Nord. Suits from £350, knitwear from £85. There are also accessories, including Unisa shoes and bags by Cochinelle.

Menswear at: 125c Northcote Road SW11, tel: 0171 978 4588, and 771 Fulham Road SW6, tel: 0171 371 8130.

Schweizer

67 Westow Street SE19
Tel: 0181 771 1010
Open: Mon–Sat 10am–6pm

Schweizer is a classic mid-range store for some of the most popular, easy fashion in the country, as stocked in many a middle-ranking fashion boutique: there is Nougat and Sticky Fingers for women, while Method and Peter Werth service the male clientele. Prices start at an equally unthreatening £25. The comprehensive selection of grown-up accessories and costume jewellery rounds off the line-up.

Siena

18 Bellevue Road, Wandsworth Common SW17
Tel: 0181 767 1961
Open: Mon–Sat 9.30am–6pm and late night Thurs till 7pm

For busy South-west London mums, Siena is a welcoming shop that has baskets of toys on hand to keep the kids amused while they get on with the important business of shopping. Another feature is the twice-yearly fashion show featuring forthcoming collections. The clothes are weekend casuals and occasionwear, from names such as Gérard Darel, Marc Aurel, Part Two, Sticky Fingers, Kenzo Jeans and August Silk. From £39.95 for jeans to £340 for a two-piece suit.

Square One

43 St John's Wood High Street NW8
Tel: 0171 586 8658
Open: Mon–Sat 10am–6pm

The former proprietor of this shop was Mrs Vanger senior, who ran a "couture style" boutique for St John's Wood ladies of lunch and leisure. Son Gary is now at the helm and has marshalled the business towards the success it is today. He chooses to ignore current fashion trends in favour of timeless classics and mainstay pieces. His buying style is methodical and deliberate, with individual designers hand-picked for their specialities: Ralph Lauren for his signature navy and white, Patrick Gérard for suits, Zanone for knitwear and Mulberry for luxe accessories.

Street & High Street

Camden

Asi La

178 Camden High Street NW1
Tel: 0171 267 7153
Open: Mon–Fri 10am–6pm and Sat–Sun 9.30am–6.30pm

The first stall-shop encountered outside Camden Town Tube, Asi La stocks a mix of street and clubwear designed for women, but worn by the occasional brave male. Tight, stretchy hipster skirts and shirts get souped up with bright and directional ski wear in the winter and printed tees in the summer. Any item can also be made-to-measure, to ensure that all-important clubster fit. Prices from £10 to £60.

CCC

190 Camden High Street NW1
Tel: 0171 482 4019
Open: Mon–Fri 10am–6pm and Sat–Sun 10am–6.30pm

Cheap Clubby Classics is what this shop stands for – so no prizes for guessing what you get inside: cute, silly togs for boys and girls at bargain-basement prices (most of them are clearance lines), plus a small own-line range. The Ministry of Sound's street range is sold here, and down in the basement you'll find boots for the boys and wicked high heels for club-bound girls. There are even bargain buckets (50p and £1) to rifle through at your leisure.

Ground Zero

44 Parkway NW1
Tel: 0171 482 3003
Open: Mon–Sat 11am–7pm

Hailed as the world's smallest department store, Ground Zero is a brand-new concept shop that aims to turn the world of lifestyle shopping on its head – the cloudscape painted on the floor says it all. The stock is a marvellous mix of contemporary art, design, furniture and clothing from over 40 different designers, including Conscious Earthwear, Sub Couture, Knitted Dogs, Loaf, Dope, T'Art (T-shirts), Eastpak (rucksacks) and Catherine Newell (courier bags). Watch out for big things from this small store.

Larache

95 Parkway NW1
Tel: 0171 267 1097
Open: Mon–Sat 11am–6.30pm and Sun 12pm–6pm

If Omar, D'Influence and Carleen Anderson can find a little something here, then so should you. Leaders in street clothes and accessories, Larache has lately been concentrating on building up its own label, RAP. Brit-pop boys love the mad mix of semi-classic, sports and branded garments for men and women. Other labels: Gallagher, Spiewak, Free and Corgi socks.

Chelsea

AdHoc

153 King's Road SW3
Tel: 0171 376 8829

Open: Mon–Sat 10am–6.30pm, late night Wed till 7pm and Sun 12pm–5pm

AdHoc stocks everything for the conscientious clubber, from sparkling platform shoes and garish feather boas to tight, bright crop tops, hotpants and slinky skirts in any fabric – so long as it's Lycra. The jumbled stock and staff are as lively as each other, so be prepared to out-cool the till keepers. Great for combat trousers, drape jackets and bondage gear, great for tiny Tees, and better still for a good pose of a Saturday afternoon. The new branch in Kensington Church Street is brighter and whiter than its predecessor on the High Street, but the stock is just as funky.

Also at: 10–11 Moor Street W1, tel: 0171 287 0911, and Unit 4 Lancer Square, 28 Kensington Church Street W8, tel: 0171 938 1664.

Fly

(&)

352 King's Road SW3
Tel: 0171 376 7606

Open: Mon–Sat 10.30am–6.30pm

Fly started life in the now-extinct Bluebird Garage (currently another Conran restaurant, more's the pity) and carries the best American streetwear the market has to offer. Among labels such as Stussy, Fresh Jive, Droors and DC Shoes is a selection of ultra-hip skateboards, sold downstairs and dovetailing well with the fashion above. Fly can proudly lay claim to the title of "London's one-stop shop for urban gliders".

The Gap

(&)

122 King's Road SW3
Tel: 0171 823 7272

Open: Mon–Sat 10am–7pm and Sun 11am–5pm

It's not a shop, it's a lifestyle. There can be few Londoners who don't already own a pocket Tee or a skinny-rib poloneck from this arbiter of basic, brilliant taste. Gap is now the second-biggest branded fashion name in the world (after Levi's), and, with more shop openings in the pipeline, it is set to grow even stronger in the UK. The endless stacks of chinos and rows of denim that were once the name of the game at Gap, sold from table tops so that customers can really get stuck in, have been pepped up with direction-led lines. Very occasionally the look of the moment can be sourced at The Gap (last winter's velvet pieces were a sell-out). Now, with an extensive and aesthetic advertising campaign, the label promises everything that is important for the season at a credible price. The company has also become very good at providing bathroom and home accessories – and the new Campari-coloured Om perfume is a knockout.

For branches, call: 0800 427 789.

Johnson's La Rocka

406 King's Road SW10
Tel: 0171 351 3268
Open: Mon–Fri 11am–6pm and Sat 11am–6.30pm

The name sounds exactly like the clothes it sells: Sixties- and Seventies-inspired contemporary rock 'n' roll clothing aimed at London's peacock boys. From the outside, it looks like yet another retro vintage clothing store, but inside you'll soon realise that Johnson's is one of a kind. From highwayman brocade jackets to tonic suits, garish shirts to fake-fur trousers and full-length fun-fur coats, velvet trews to biker Tees ... this could be the start of a Whole New You.

Also at: Kensington Market, Kensington High Street W8, tel: 0171 937 4711.

Mandi

139 King's Road SW3
Tel: 0171 376 7491
Open: Mon–Sat 10am–7pm and Sun 12pm–6pm

Make sure you don't miss Mandi (spelt with a Y on the shop front, but Mandi herself tells us it's with an I) on your trawl down the King's Road. It offers a novelty in the now style-starved street: provocative clubwear, recycled suede and leather, PVC and stretch-satin jeans and brilliant hand-knits that are a step up from the owner's market-stall beginnings. The shop is no bargain basement, but you can be assured of eyebrow-raising, heart-stopping fashion for under £100. Buy a pair of killer snakeskin platforms and hobble home happy.

One Nation

674 King's Road SW10
Tel: 0171 730 7088
Open: 10am–6.30pm seven days a week

One Nation is the first stop on the King's Road for many an aspiring model or actress. The clothes, from small independent English and French labels such as Sub Couture and Alexander Campbell, are dressy disco or slick day-wear. With only two or three of any garment ever in stock, you are almost guaranteed not to see anyone else in the same outfit at Hanover Grand. But it does mean that you have to go often to bag the best bits. Prices from £40, up to £250 for a winter coat.

The Common Market

121 King's Road SW3
Tel: 0171 351 9361
Open: Mon–Sat 9.30am–7pm and Sun 12pm–6pm

This is a series of shops within a shop, selling street-led fashion from Stussy, Hussy and Diesel. A huge range of Kangol hats and Daniel Poole T-shirts are also on display – enough choice to keep you occupied for hours.

City and East End

A Touch Too Wild

49 West Ham Lane E15
Tel: 0181 519 8237
Open: Mon–Sat 11.30am–6pm

Probably the best shop in Stratford (and well worth the trip), A Touch Too Wild combines extreme clubwear with retro and modern second-hand clothing. Around 11 designers' work is carried in the first half of the shop, and most of them are only a call away to provide a made-to-measure service on lacy shirts, rubber bodices and chintzy dresses. Through an archway is a cavern of second-hand bargains. The made-to-order platform boots are a third of the price elsewhere, starting at £38.

La La London

17 Lamb Street E1
Tel: 0171 247 3503
Open: Mon–Fri 11am–5pm and Sun 11am–6pm (closed Sat)

This boutique stocks glamorous, sometimes gimmicky, clubwear from designer Trusha Lakhani. To keep up with demand, styles are constantly changed and new ranges added, and the prices are kept convincingly low (from £10 to £60). Look out for silly but irresistible bags, vivid make-up (strictly for after dark) and other bits and pieces for wild nights out. The funky new menswear line is selling fast.

Pom

Unit 7a Embankment Place WC2
Tel: 0171 930 7828
Open: Mon–Fri 8.30am–7.30pm and Sat 10am–5pm

If you want something basic and smart but don't want to spend a small fortune, Pom is as good a place as any to start. Everything is either own brand or from small independents such as Pamplemousse.

Also at: 116 Cannon Street EC4, tel: 0171 929 2145, 80-82 Kingsway WC2, tel: 0171 831 7604 and 5 Station Arcade 137 Moorgate EC2.

Covent Garden

Alchemy

1 Shorts Gardens WC2
Tel: 0171 240 7600
Open: Mon–Sat 11am–7pm

Six years in the hot and happy Hyper Hyper have set Alchemy up as a leading club label. Along with the usual range of satin, stretch, lace and devoré, this spring sees the introduction of feminine, floaty tunics in sheer fabrics at £185 – all very neo-romantic.

Alphabet

39 Monmouth Street WC2
Tel: 0171 379 3850
Open: Mon–Sat 11am–7pm

Another Hyper Hyper success story, this time for male clubbers, Alphabet stocks searing shirts and Levi's 507 jeans in tweed and jumbo cord. Prices hover around the £40 mark, and new styles arrive every week – so you can wear a different look every time you step outside. Also available: shirts by Peter Werth, Retro ribbed tops and the incomparable Life and Legend sportswear.

American Classics

20 Endell Street WC2
Tel: 0171 831 1210
Open: Mon–Sat 11am–7pm

The store that was once loved by London for its stock of second-hand clothes is now concentrating on new lines such as Adidas, Levi's and Schott. The look is still strong, but the buzz has moved on. There are three shops called American Classics in the King's Road: number 398 is good for ultra-fashionable Stussy, Vans and Carhartt while number 400 stocks less-hyped American labels; number 404 still specialises in vintage denim and second-hand US clothes (see page 104).

Also at: 398 and 400 King's Road SW10, tel: 0171 352 3248.

Apple Tree

62 Neal Street WC2
Tel: 0171 379 5944
Open: Mon-Sat 10am–7pm

See page 212.

Biba

15 Shorts Gardens WC2
Tel: 0171 240 6694
Open: Mon–Sat 10.30am–6.30pm, late night Thurs till 7pm and Sun 12pm–6pm

Original Biba babes, who fought tooth and (burgundy) nail to get their hands on Biba baked beans and Biba lipsticks in the late Sixties, won't find the same boho extravagance from the modern label. Biba was brought back from beyond the fashion grave by Hong Kong businesswoman Ellen Shek last year, and makes every effort to look the part. Extensive use of velvet and dirge colours helps, but the Biba moment really died with Hendrix. That said, the second modern Biba collection, with its focus on opulent fabrics, rich colours and a hint of nostalgia, is in step with fashion's current mood – and who can argue with that? Buy your baked beans at Safeway, but come here for shimmy boots and floppy dresses.

Boxfresh

2 Shorts Gardens WC2
Tel: 0171 240 4742
Open: Mon–Sat 11am(ish)–6.30pm(ish)

Californ-I-A comes to Covent Garden with this surfie paradise, run by nice Neal, who claims to buy for himself in the hope that customers will agree with his choice. Seems that they do, since Boxfresh is wildly popular. Carhartt (also available by mail order) is a big seller, as are Penfield, DSL55 and the ubiquitous Tommy Hilfiger. Neal is also the exclusive British stockist of Belgian skater label G Star.

Burro

19a Floral Street WC2
Tel: 0171 240 5120
Open: Mon–Sat 10.30am–6.30pm, late night Thurs till 7pm and Sun 1pm–5pm

An individual menswear retailer that has gradually built up a reputation for innovative, affordable, streetwise design, Burro started in 1990 as a street label (immediately impressing the heavyweight buyers such as Joseph, Jones and Cruise), and last year won the *FHM* magazine Street Fashion Retailer of the Year Award. It is an energetic label for the guy who has everything – but wants that little bit more. Scour the rails for Sharp Eye (from former Duffer boy Barry K Sharp), the brilliant unisex 6876 by Kenneth McKenzie (the name refers to the "two greatest years in fashion history"), Klurk and Hedi Raikamo shoes. For spring 1997 the emphasis is on patched knitwear, hipster pants, cagoules and military-uniform influences.

Diesel

43 Earlham Street WC2
Tel: 0171 497 5543
Open: Mon–Sat 10.30am–7pm, late night Thurs till 8pm and Sun 12pm–6pm

Where else in London can you buy Wanker Pants? Where indeed but Diesel, the Italian jeans-company-turned-trend-machine. The past three years have been good to Diesel, and this newly opened space-age, metal-plated lifestyle boutique is proof of its success. Designed by Wieneke and Kylie (no, not that Kylie, although she is a Diesel fan) – who claim their inspiration came from a stay at the Betty Ford clinic – the flagship store sells everything you might need for a more successful life, from the 144 styles of (brilliant) jeans down to children's socks. Wanker Pants are hipsters, needless to say.

Dr Martens Dept Store

1–4 King Street WC2
Tel: 0171 497 1460
Open: Mon–Sat 10am–7pm, late night Thurs till 8pm and Sun 12pm–6pm

Five floors and 14,000 square feet form a showcase for the big-name boot and the spin-off clothing from DM. From 24-hole, ox-blood killer boots to the hair salon upstairs on the third floor (does a nice line in number-one crops, we hear), this is the Nineties exploitation of a mega-brand. Tourists love it –

but so should locals: the clothing is premium quality, hard-wearing and cool. In keeping with the workwear ethic, the Dept Store is constructed from steel, concrete, timber and exposed brickwork.

Duffer of St George

29 Shorts Gardens WC2
Tel: 0171 379 4660
Open: Mon–Fri 10.30am–7pm, Sat 10.30am–6.30pm and Sun 1pm–5pm

So hip it hurts – get ready to out-pose the staff, who have been doing this retro thing for years. This year, Duffer takes its message to the girls, with a brilliant collection of womenswear (much of it a down-sized version of the men's); there's a new Duffer Denim line on its way too. The main-line cuts are classic – skinny shirts in Jaffa-orange and sky-blue, flat-front hipsters and zip-up President's jackets. Girls get suedette biker jackets, epaulette shirts and hipsters in camel and canary yellow, with prices from £35 to £180. If you can get your hands on a Duffer fleece, buy it – they sell out fast, at a rate of 50 a week.

Errol Peak

29 Floral Street WC2
Tel: 0171 240 6224
Open: Mon–Sat 10.30am–6.30pm and late night Thurs till 7pm

Techno fabrics and a structured silhouette reflect Errol Peak's architectural background. His tiny Floral Street shop, which first opened in 1994 and is a partnership with Errol's mum, houses the collection and the occasional one-off piece. A small design studio is open to view "work in progress".

Hope and Glory

Thomas Neal's Centre, Earlham Street WC2
Tel: 0171 379 3283
Open: Mon–Sat 10.30am–6.30pm and Sun 12pm–5pm

The newly extended flagship store is home to H&G's entire collection – from jeans and shirts through to suits. The design philosophy incorporates Sixties and Seventies retro influences fused with a fashion-forward approach. The upshot is a line of hip young menswear for hip young men. The company does not believe in advertising, but instead relies on word of mouth to sell its product – it is selling like mad, so the gossip must be good.

Interstate

17 Endell Street WC2
Tel: 0171 836 0421
Open: Mon–Fri 11am–6.45pm, Sat 10.30am–6.30pm and Sun 12pm–6pm

Roberto Gaspali has owned this Aladdin's cave of American menswear labels since 1989. He buys with an eye for a classic style and stocks names such as Carhartt, Fred Perry, Everlast, Eastpak, Hanes and Ben Sherman, and a small range of vintage Levi's and Lee jeans. Just run your eye over the chock-full window displays (they feature one of everything in stock) to get an idea of what's going on inside.

John Crummay

43–45 Shorts Gardens WC2
Tel: 0171 240 3534
Open: Mon–Sat 10.30am–6.30pm

Crummay's obsession with aeronautics and space travel makes his own-label clothes stretchy, sculpted and high tech. Both the men's and women's ranges include T-shirts, jeans, knitwear and tailoring at their core, with prices from £25 for Tees and £99 for jackets.

Jungle

21 Earlham Street WC2
Tel: 0171 379 5379
Open: Mon–Sat 10am–6.30pm (occasionally on Sunday, depending on Saturday night)

See page 182.

Mambo

Thomas Neal's Centre, Earlham Street WC2
Tel: 0171 379 6066
Open: Mon–Sat 10am–7pm and Sun 12pm–6pm

"Not just another surf shop," according to owner Dare Jennings. So what is it, then? The Mambo label was started in 1985 and has evolved into a lifestyle store selling everything from watches, bags, posters, ceramics and socks to board shorts and surf shirts. A neon sign above the door of this spacious, hard-core Covent Garden store proclaims "Abbatoirs of taste"... Its catchphrase, "More a pair of shorts than a way of life", puts it all into perspective. Almost.

Name Workshop

44 Shelton Street WC2
Tel: 0171 240 8746
Open: Mon–Fri 10.30am–7pm, Sat 10.30am–6.30pm and Sun 1pm–5.30pm

In the next century, we will look back upon the fashion of this decade and dub it the Age of Moderation. We will think of shops such as Name Workshop and it will all come flooding back. This is a store of its time: a shop full of laid-back clothes for men and women, with walls featuring installations from new artists. The collections are split into Urban (combat-influenced techno sporstwear), Underwear (plain or with the Name logo), Denim (hipster and classic-cut jeans, together with biker, Harrington and safari jackets) and finally Mainline (long, lean lines in techno and natural fabrics). All of it desirable, all of it very *now*.

Nigel Cabourn

65 Long Acre WC2
Tel: 0171 240 8400
Open: Mon–Sat 10.30am–6.30pm and Sun 12pm–5pm

Cabourn Athletics, Cabourn Sport and Cabourn Jeans are the three elements in Nigel's slick shop. An eye for detail, innovation and humour makes for top-level, individual sportswear.

Oasis

13 James Street WC2
Tel: 0171 240 7445
Open: Mon–Sat 10am–7pm, late night Thurs till 8pm and Sun 12pm–8pm

Oasis – born six years ago – has expanded at a stellar rate, to reach a total of 102 stores throughout the UK. It currently holds the title of High Street Retailer of the Year from both *Marie Claire* magazine and the British Fashion Council. For anyone that shops there (who doesn't?), it's easy to see why: the aim to "provide a range of directional clothing with a sharp fashion edge, combining the essential elements of quality and value" is consistently met with ease by a perceptive design team aware of rapidly changing trends. They produce six collections annually, ensuring a constant turnover of stock, as well as "essential" items that run throughout the year. Another feature is the extended size range – often up to a size 16, which is a rare blessing on the high street. Watch out for "Oasis by Post" coming soon. If you're not buying Oasis by then, your fashion feelers need an overhaul.

For branches, call: 0171 452 1000.

Replay Country Store

52 Long Acre WC2
Tel: 0171 379 4631
Open: Mon–Sat 10am–6.30pm, late night Thurs till 7.30pm and Sun 12pm–6pm

Having started life as a shirt manufacturer, this Italian company now produces a full range of men's, women's and childrenswear in classic denim and seasonal fabrics. Spring is big on blue, while the women's swimwear and the kitsch shoe collection are new additions this season.

R Newbold

7–8 Langley Court WC2
Tel: 0171 240 5068
Open: Mon–Wed, Fri 10.30am–6.30pm, late night Thurs till 7pm and Sat 10am–6.30pm

Robert Brewster Newbold opened his factory and shop in Derby in 1885, producing workwear, suiting, military clothing and police uniforms. When Newbold was faced with bankruptcy a century later, Paul Smith stepped in and bought the business. The military uniform is the foundation of this year's look, based on garments produced for the British armed forces at the turn of the century. Cotton-drill fatigue pants, shirt-jackets and old-school sports kits come in bold red, lime and air-force blue, all stamped with the arrow symbol for authenticity.

Robot

37 Floral Street WC2
Tel: 0171 836 6156
Open: Mon–Sat 10am–6.30pm, late night Thurs till 7pm and Sun 12pm–5.30pm

This understated emporium, owned and run by Michael McManus since 1982, is crammed with up-to-the-minute menswear, including own-label shoes, Hudson, Berliners and Simple trainers. Clothing covers Diesel, Full Circle and Firetrap.

Ronen Chen

Thomas Neal's Centre, Earlham Street WC2
Tel: 0171 497 5433
Open: Mon 12.30pm–6.30pm, Tues–Sat 11am–7pm and Sun 1pm–5pm

Israeli-born Chen specialises in low-maintenance, soft Lycra dresses, T-shirts and fluid evening wear. Now an internationally recognised name, with two stores in London and stockists around the country, the business is growing apace. This season there are Seventies-influenced long dresses with plunging necklines and cut-out details in mint, lilac and white, with prices starting at £95.

Also at: Whiteleys Shopping Centre, Queensway W2, tel: 0171 792 5154.

Slam City Skates

16 Neal's Yard WC2
Tel: 0171 240 0928
Open: Mon–Sat 10am–6.30pm

You don't need a skateboard to shop here, but it helps. Slam City, nestled in Neal's Yard since 1988, is the first stop on the boarders' shopping map, for labels that will bring gasps of envy from their skate mates: Stussy, Pervert, Jive, Fuct, X-Large and, best of the lot, Holmes – a sportswear label that is fast becoming the favourite name on the street. There's a good selection of hard-to-find trainers too, from Etnies, DC and Duffs. Slam City is logo-crazy; it's not cheap, but it does have an international reputation built upon word of mouth.

Warehouse

24 Long Acre WC2
Tel: 0171 240 8242
Open: Mon–Sat 10am–7pm, late night Thurs till 8pm and Sun 12pm–5pm

Jeff Banks came up with a cunning and novel plan in 1976 – to produce well-designed and stylish clothes at an affordable price. At the time, it was an innovative approach, and Warehouse soon became a runaway success. The designers today have become adept at recreating catwalk trends at a fraction of the price (expect to pay around £29.99 for a shirt, £34.99 for boot-cut trousers and £60 for this season's floaty, floral-print dresses). The Definitives range (jersey tops, button-down shirts, flared trousers) is basic and good value, and in store all year round, while summer stock is right on the button, with Halston-style column dresses, Charlie's Angels pant suits and plenty of aquamarine and stripes. Don't expect ever-lasting clothes – as Jeff knew so well, fashion changes fast and a long life-expectancy is not necessarily at a premium.

For branches, call: 0171 287 3491.

Way Out West

53 Long Acre WC2
Tel: 0171 240 8717

Open: Mon–Sat 10am–7pm, late night Thurs till 8pm and Sun 12pm–6pm

The first Way Out West opened in The Lanes in Brighton, targeting the large student community with clubby separates at reasonable prices. Now there are three shops and the product range is growing – as is the customer base. The stretch-cord hipsters are wild (from £45).

Also at: 1 Crown Passage, Kingston-upon-Thames KT1, tel: 0181 974 5964.

Fulham

Fat Face

827 Fulham Road SW6
Tel: 0171 384 3115

Open: Mon–Sat 10am–6.30pm and Sun 12pm–5pm

Four years ago, Fat Face was started by a couple of avid skiers in the French Alps. Now it's available in the glorious but piste-free Fulham Road (unless you count the crowds outside Havanas on a Friday night). The clothes are designed for après-ski, après-surf or indeed après-any other winter sport you can imagine. Casual sweatshirts and fleeces are the best-sellers, in unisex small, medium, large and extra-large sizes, with prices from £30. For the teeny skiers there is the newly launched Brat Face – a range of kids' casuals along the same funky lines as the grown-up versions.

Also at: Thomas Neal's Centre, Earlham Street WC2, tel: 0171 497 6464.
For mail order, call: 01705 475555.

White Stuff

845 Fulham Road SW6
Tel: 0171 371 0174

Open: Mon–Wed and Fri 10.30am–6.30pm, Thurs 11am–7pm, Sat 10am–6pm and Sun 12pm–5pm

Wall-to-wall surf, ski, snow and skate-wear for armchair members of the Dangerous Sports Society. Everything in store – from the cool fleeces to the outdoor jackets and clubby headgear – is made under the White Stuff label. Fulham skiers wouldn't shop anywhere else.

Hampstead and Highgate

Leaver and Leaver

134 West End Lane NW6
Tel: 0171 328 3032
Open: Mon–Sat 8am–8pm

With the longest shop opening hours known to humankind (these people must be mad), Leaver and Leaver attempts to catch customers on their way to and from work. There is a mix of army and street gear from Peter Werth, Komodo, Free and Kangol, and second-hand Levi's and clubwear from Sub Couture. The staff also run a taxi service (they really are mad) from the back of the shop.

Yankee Doodle

82 Heath Street NW3
Tel: 0171 431 9242
Open: Mon–Sat 10am–6.30pm and Sun 11am–6pm

Whether you are a pseudo surfie or a street skate kid, Yankee Doodle is unmissable. All the essential street labels (Oxbow, Mambo, No Fear, Komodo, Quicksilver and Billabong) are here in force, as well as the gotta-have selection of "vintage" Levi's. The idea behind the store was to bring a more upmarket version of Camden Market to Hampstead – seems to be working a treat.

Also at: Lakeside Shopping Centre, West Thurrock, tel: 01708 8904666.

Highbury and Islington

Half Nelson

58 Islington Park Street N1
Tel: 0171 704 6646
Open: Mon–Sat 11am–6pm

Playing to the local media/music market, Half Nelson is extremely small and extremely orange. The interior can accommodate only a couple of rails, but they are more than enough to show that the two young designers here (Claire Nelson is one half of the partnership) know exactly what they are doing. Quirky women's suits in tweed and chalkstripe flannel, with intriguing detailing, hang alongside polonecks, pin-cord shirts, floral-print trousers and bright, sexy skirts. The range is split into two: Half Nelson is the tailoring line (from £40 to £200), while HN is the younger, funkier end of the spectrum (from £20 to £75). North Londoners should look no further for next summer's daring denim bikini.

Kensington

Daniel James

70 Kensington High Street W8
Tel: 0171 937 4207
Open: Mon–Sat 10am–7pm and Sun 11.30am–5pm

A dated concept (logo Tees), has recently been improved with the addition of jackets, shirts and trousers, while retaining "inventive" fabrics that give the designs a narrow edge. Prices start from £19.50 and go up to £120 for men's jackets.

Also at: 19a Jerdan Place SW6, tel: 0171 385 6144.

Hype DF

48–52 Kensington High Street W8
Tel: 0171 937 3100
Open: Mon–Sat 10am–6pm and late night Wed till 8pm

From the ashes of Hyper Hyper down the road – the streetwear bazaar beloved of Jerry Hall, Cher, Jean Paul Gaultier and the entire Goth population of London – rises the sleek phoenix of Hype DF. The quasi department store bills itself as "a junior Harvey Nichols", stocking lines from Biba (back on Kensington High Street for the first time in 21 years), Two Guys, W<, Sue Rowe, Sub Couture, and accessories from Janet Fitch and Mickey. In true Nineties style, the establishment includes a restaurant, two classy cosmetics counters, Calvin Klein knickers in the basement and a New-York-style nail boutique, complete with a men's department called Man-e-Cure. You won't find suburban Punks collapsed in the doorway – they are all over the road in the murky depths of Kensington Market – but you will discover a refreshing, clued-up store with an eye on the best new designers the capital has to offer. Spend an afternoon, spend a fortune, but don't miss it.

Restaurant open: Mon-Sat 10am-11pm.

Kookai

123d Kensington High Street W8
Tel: 0171 937 4411
Open: Mon–Sat 10am–7pm, late night Thurs till 8pm and Sun 12pm–6pm

Paris-based Kookai combines fun and formal merchandise for anyone who needn't adhere to a strict dress code at work or beyond. The clothes tend to follow trends in fashion in their colour, cut and style, although seduction and stretch are clearly constant themes from season to season. Every so often, a real winner arrives: last season's stretchy black trouser suit with boot-cut pants and double-breasted jacket was snapped up by the fashion press and passed off as a Gucci, darling. It's all fast, flimsy, flirty fashion with prices to match – from £59 for a summer shift dress, £99 for a tailored jacket and £49 for hipsters.

For branches, call: 0171 937 4411.

Morgan

6 Barkers Arcade, Kensington High Street W8
Tel: 0171 938 3424

Open: Mon–Wed, Fri 10.30am–7pm, late night Thurs till 7.30pm, Sat 10.30am–6.30pm and Sun 1pm–5pm

Morgan has got a thing about midriffs – it seems that almost everything the company makes reveals tummy buttons, ribs or expanses of flesh, so what you get is cropped tops, hipsters and itsy-bitsy Tees. Most of it finds its way on to the dancefloor at out-of-town discos. The French company bills its designs as "clothes with attitude", for the breed of teen who wants to look trend-conscious but also has a fair bit of money to spend. If you want to cling, step in.

For branches, call: 0171 636 5136.

Principles

9 Barkers Arcade, Kensington High Street W8
Tel: 0171 937 2233

Open: Mon–Sat 10am–6.30pm, late night Thurs till 7pm and Sun 11am–5pm

Don't yawn: Principles is exactly the type of shop that has gained the British high street its reputation overseas for good-value, high-quality, fashion-aware clothes. While the company is not out to send a shiver down your sartorial spine, it does the business when it comes to neat, nice fashion. The basic suits range is pepped up with skinny knits and pretty accessories; the Petites line has saved many a small woman from slitting her wrists (of the sleeves of badly proportioned jackets, you understand); and – since Principles' main customer has a family to buy for – there is a menswear range that is about as middle-of-the-road as the central reservation, and a cute range of kidswear for 0 to 8 year olds. And none of it will overstretch the family accounts, so mum can get herself a nice dress into the bargain.

For branches, call: 0171 927 1443.

River Island

124–126 Kensington High Street W8
Tel: 0171 937 0224

Open: Mon–Wed, Fri 10am–6.30pm, late night Thurs till 7.30pm, Sat 9.30am–6pm and Sun 12pm–6pm

Who shops here? Who knows. The models in the ad campaigns are 30-plus, but no customer looks old enough to buy a pint in a pub. The ranges aren't bad, with the occasional worthwhile buy – and River Island did win the Best Shoes prize at the High Street Design Awards, so it must be doing something right. The massive range of CAT clothes (outdoorsy, heavy-duty workwear to match the Caterpillar boots for adults, girls and boys) is another plus.

For branches, call: 0181 998 8822.

Notting Hill

The Dispensary

25 Pembridge Road W11
Tel: 0171 221 9290
Open: Mon–Sat 10.30am–6.30pm

It kicked off by selling second-hand clothes and young designer labels, but these days, The Dispensary is an indispensable stop for trend labels in logo-loopy W11. The own label is stronger by the month, with must-have funky dresses, Crombies and suits. The back-up comes courtesy of Sun and Sand, Hysteric Glamour, No Photos, John Smedley, Peter Werth and shoes by Patrick Cox. Watch out for The Dispensary's own-line version of the bootleg hipster, in a variety of fabrics, depending on the season (from £58).

Also at: 200 Kensington Park Road W11, tel: 0171 727 8797, and 9 and 15 Newburgh Street W1, tel: 0171 287 8145.

Kierra

31 All Saints Road W11
Tel: 0171 727 6139
Open: Mon–Sat 10.30am–6.30pm

Christine Atkinson, a graduate of St Martin's, opened her shop in 1994 and concentrates on cheerful, inexpensive, dip-dyed separates in blazing colours. Expect to pay £16 for a halterneck, £24 for flared jersey trousers and £70 for a winter jacket.

Low Pressure

186 Kensington Park Road W11
Tel: 0171 792 3134
Open: Mon–Sat 10am–6pm and Sun 11am–5pm

Ollie and Tim turned their hobby into a business, and now run the most relaxed surf-and-snow shop in London. Saturdays are packed with punters – most of them hanging out, although with the best selection of surf shorts and swimwear in town, they'd be mad not to buy before they leave. The list of labels includes Quicksilver, Ripcurl, Headworx, Gotcha, Mambo and Kana Beach as well as an own label designed by Marc Hare. Downstairs, there's a vast selection of wetsuits and second-hand snow- and surfboards; up the road is the Low Pressure Travel Company (124 Barlby Road W10). Watch this space – Low Pressure may soon be on the move.

Nothing

230 Portobello Road W11
Tel: 0171 221 2910
Open: Mon–Fri 11am–6.30pm and Sat 11am–6pm

Carla Portmans, the brains behind Nothing, has no formal fashion training, which explains the supreme lack of fuss in the clothes she produces. The ranges are intelligent enough to sell themselves, but head first for the stretch cotton hipsters (£59), which have evolved over the past couple of seasons into a best-seller. When Carla was asked to describe the clothes at Nothing, "directional pubwear" was the answer. No doubt you'll find plenty of Portmans's pieces in The Cow, Tom Conran's inn around the corner.

Sub Couture

204 Kensington Park Road W11
Tel: 0171 229 5434
Open: Mon–Sat 10.30am–6.30pm

Although the main label is Sub Couture (stretchy, sassy clubwear), the shop also runs Equipment shirts, Brown's Own Label collection, Azagury shoes, Cutler and Gross sunglasses and Dollargrand bags. Prices from £60.

Supra

253 Portobello Road, W11
Tel: 0171 221 6857
Open: Mon–Thurs 11am–6.30pm and Fri–Sat 10am–6.30pm

Just 15 yards off Portobello, and right in the thick of the Notting Hill experience, Supra is a skateboard and hip-hop shop specialising in street and urban sportswear. This translates as a uniquely hip combination of US-import labels with an East-coast vibe – including Stussy, Holmes, Fuct, Subware, Droors, Carhartt, Jethro Julius and Tommy Hilfiger.

Oxford Street and Regent Street

Astuces

44 South Molton Street W1
Tel: 0171 493 1428
Open: Mon–Sat 9.30am–6.30pm and late night Thurs till 7.30pm

See page 217.

Benetton

125 Oxford Street W1
Tel: 0171 439 1621
Open: Mon–Sat 10am–6.30pm and late night Thurs till 8pm

Oxford Circus is now home to a three-storey megastore of Italian fashion, housing the most comprehensive range of Benetton clothing and accessories worldwide. As Victoria Wood once said, there is a certain satisfaction to be had from walking into Benetton and unfolding all the jumpers, then leaving without buying anything. Lately, however, the stock has improved and the prices have become more realistic, so you almost find yourself walking out with a purchase before realising it. The design is simple, yet the colours are still strong enough to grab attention; these days, everything seems to be on hangers, though, which rather takes the fun out of it.

For branches, call: 0171 495 5482.

C&A

501–519 Oxford Street W1
Tel: 0171 629 7272

Open: Mon–Wed, Fri 9.30am–7pm, late night Thurs till 8pm, Sat 9am–7pm and Sun 12pm–6pm

The best thing about C&A is the ski gear, which is reasonably priced and durable.

For branches, call: 0171 629 1244.

Dorothy Perkins

379 Oxford Street W1
Tel: 0171 495 6181

Open: Mon–Sat 10am–7pm, late night Thurs till 8pm and Sun 12pm–6pm

It has Helena Christensen to model, Clements Ribeiro to perk up the design, and decent shops to sell it all in... so where does Dorothy Perkins go wrong? The name can't help – it sounds like the chairwoman of the local bridge club – and there are years of bad design and poor quality to contend with. But things are certainly looking up for the high-street old-timer. The spring collection is one of the best at this level, tuning into, but not ripping off, catwalk ideas. The capsule collection from Clements Ribeiro, winners of the 1996 New Generation Award, is perfect – but it is a pity that the company risks running it in only five of its many shops (call first to check if it is stocked at your local Dotty Ps). Then wear your mint-green chiffon dress with pride; just don't tell anyone where you bought it.

For branches, call: 0171 636 8040.

French Connection

249 Regent Street W1
Tel: 0171 493 3124

Open: Mon–Wed 10am–6.30pm, late night Thurs till 8pm, Fri–Sat 10am–7pm and Sun 10am–6pm

French Connection stocks key directional items for each season combined with essential basics such as stretch T-shirts, jeans, classic suits and the definitive denim jacket. Owner Stephen Marks is a stack-it-high, sell-it-low merchant – but the quality of the clothes puts FC a cut above the competition. If you are in Covent Garden, visit the most recently opened branch which is home to the French Connection Deli, a great place to grab a fashionably frilled brioche, a mini tart or a mango smoothie, with prices from just £1.

For branches, call: 0171 580 2507.

Hennes

261–271 Regent Street W1
Tel: 0171 493 4004
Open: Mon–Wed, Fri 10am–6.30pm, late night Thurs till 8pm and Sat 9am–6pm

Hennes is the Scandinavian import that is set for nationwide success if the planned expansion takes off. Not quite cheap enough to be a bargain hunters' heaven, yet not expensive either, Hennes occasionally comes up with the odd shirt or jacket that looks as though it's just dropped off the end of the catwalk. The underwear is good too. If you visit on Saturday, bring a book – the queues for the changing rooms can stretch round the block.

For branches, call: 0171 255 2031.

Hobbs

8 and 47 South Molton Street W1
Tel: 0171 629 0750 (shoes); 0171 495 1557 (clothes)
Open: Mon–Sat 10am–6.30pm, late night Thurs till 7pm and Sun 12pm–5pm

See page 215.

Jane Norman

388 Oxford Street W1
Tel: 0171 437 0132
Open: Mon–Wed, Fri 10am–7pm, late night Thurs till 8pm, Sat 9.30am–7pm and Sun 12pm–6pm

Cheap, cheap, cheap. Unfortunately, most of the stock looks it too. Jackets from £59.99, trousers from £29.99 and tops from £19.99.

Also at: 59 Brompton Road SW1, tel: 0171 225 3098.

Jeffrey Rogers

The Plaza, 120 Oxford Street W1
Tel: 0171 580 5545
Open: Mon–Sat 10am–7pm, late night Thurs till 8pm and Sun 12pm–5pm

Teenage girls want fast, fun fashion on the proceeds of their piggy banks – and that's where Jeffrey Rogers fits in. The clothes are cheerful, colourful and within reach if you are on a budget. There is now also a collection for girls in sizes 16–24 (see page 190) ensuring that the label caters for everyone.

For branches, call: 0171 208 4300.

Kate Jones

28 St Christopher's Place W1
Tel: 0171 935 4197
Open: Mon–Sat 10.30am–6pm and late night Thurs till 7pm

This is Kate Jones's first shop, although she had previously been retailing in the now-defunct Hyper Hyper since 1993. It is also the only stand-alone knitwear boutique in London. Jones's innovative knits have established her as one of the most talented and professional young designers around, with a celebrity following that includes Madonna, Elizabeth Hurley and Kylie Minogue. There's a vaguely vintage feel to much of it, with shaggy-collared cardigans and long cardi-coats. Prices range from £69 for a halter-neck top to £185 for a full-length dress.

Laura Ashley

256–258 Regent Street W1
Tel: 0171 437 9760
Open: Mon–Sat 10am–7pm and late night Thurs till 8pm

Did you know that there are 539 Laura Ashley stores worldwide, that 530,000 dresses are sold throughout the USA and Europe every year, and that the print designer used to be a shelf-stacker at the Co-op? No? Well, you probably didn't know that anxious shoppers used to queue outside the original store in Fulham Road to await the latest delivery, either. The power of the flower dress defies belief.

For branches, call: 01686 622116.

Levi's Flagship Store

174–176 Regent Street W1
Tel: 0171 439 2028
Open: Mon–Sat 10am–7pm, late night Thurs till 8pm and Sun 12pm–4pm

As if world domination of the jeans market were not enough, Levi's has also created its own complementary clothing line of T-Shirts, shirts and accessories. The store on Regent Street is designed to give you the ultimate Levi's shopping experience with a history of the label and two floors of fashion.

For branches, call: 01604 790436.

Marks and Spencer

458 Oxford Street W1
Tel: 0171 935 7954
Open: Mon–Wed, Sat 9am–7pm, late nights Thurs and Fri till 8pm, and Sun 12pm–6pm

Like moaning about the weather and drinking tea, Marks and Spencer is sewn into the fabric of British life. It is a weighty mantle – the company has to appeal to the blue-rinse brigade who want elasticated waists, and still attract the younger, slicker customer who wouldn't give an elasticated waist the time of day. At the Marble Arch flagship store, trial stock that is never likely to make it into the other stores is on offer – so it is possible to pick up well-made, sensibly priced one-offs (sometimes from consultant designer Betty Jackson) that do not carry the "everyone is wearing my clothes" warning. Marble Arch is also a tourist trap, so be prepared to wait to pay. Perhaps the most remarkable thing about Marks and Spencer is the underwear, which goes through the most rigorous testing to come out fitting perfectly; 35% of British women are wearing M&S knickers at this moment. If you're not, you should be.

For branches, call: 0171 935 4422.

Miss Selfridge

221–223 Oxford Street W1
Tel: 0171 434 3541

Open: Mon–Wed 10am–6.30pm, late night Thurs till 8pm, Fri–Sat 10am–7pm and Sun 12pm–6pm

Miss Selfridge began life (originally linked to the grand department store) in swinging 1966, and now boasts 129 stores and concessions across the country. The emphasis is on disposable fashion and fast turnover – from everyday separates to tiny, shiny clubwear, underwear, shoes and the Kiss and Make-up cosmetics range, which is remarkably good. To keep in step with the current "upmarketing" of the high-street chains, Miss Selfridge has recently introduced a bridge line, called The Collection, with higher prices, better quality fabrics and the aim of servicing twenty-somethings instead of teens.

For branches, call: 0171 910 1361.

Monsoon

264 Oxford Street W1
Tel: 0171 499 2578

Open: Mon–Sat 9.30am–6.30pm, late night Thurs till 8pm and Sun 12pm–6pm

Drippy hippy gear here is fast being nudged out by more directional styles. Investigate the basic jackets, dresses and well-priced evening wear – and cheap bags and scarves from Accessorize. Woodstock women can still find floppy dresses if they look hard enough.

For branches, call: 0171 313 3000.

New Look

309 Oxford Street W1
Tel: 0171 499 8497

Open: Mon–Sat 9.30am–7pm and Sun 12pm–6pm

New Look doesn't pretend to be anything other than what it is: affordable, disposable and young. Prices can be as low as £4.99. The jewellery, accessories and bags, often with special offers, make pocket money (remember that?) go a long way.

For branches, call: 0500 454094.

Next

(&)

327–329 Oxford Street W1
Tel: 0171 409 2746

Open: Mon–Sat 10am–6.30pm, late night Wed till 7.30pm and Sun 12pm–6pm

Next was a major player in the Eighties, engineering a high-street invasion with its mail-order catalogue that continues to this day. The design philosophy is to produce a basic range from season to season, with only slight alterations, and arrange the merchandise into carefully targeted, easy-access areas. But Next also comes up with some great fashion moments, such as last season's Gucci-esque velvet trouser suit and the shantung evening coat and trousers that were a dead ringer for Dolce and Gabbana. There is a brilliant, if chaotic, sale twice a year.

For branches, call: 0116 284 9424.

Richards

263–265 Oxford Street W1
Tel: 0171 499 5223

Open: Mon, Tues, Sat 10am–7pm, Wed, Fri 10am–8pm, late night Thurs till 9pm and Sun 12pm–6pm

Richards is known for womenswear offering value for money and versatility for anyone who favours function over high fashion. The main range caters for all sizes, while Richards Plus goes from sizes 16–26 and Richards Petite from sizes 6–16.

For branches, call: 0181 910 1028.

Top Shop/Top Man

(&)

214 Oxford Street W1
Tel: 0171 636 7700

Open: Mon–Sat 10am–7pm, late night Thurs till 8pm and Sun 12pm–6pm

Top Shop/Top Man proudly claims to be the biggest fashion store in the country – and it's also one of the cheapest and most cheerful. Who can gripe about the reproduction designer kit that is available here before you can say "sue me"? If you want clothes with life expectancy, head for Knightsbridge; if you want speedy, seedy fashion that gets the trends before they hit the end of the catwalk, and a radio station just for shoppers, you're in the right place. The stock (which is meanly sized) changes rapidly – you are almost guaranteed not to see the same thing twice – and the prices are some of the lowest around (from £70 for a suit).

For branches, call : 0171 291 2351.

Vicky Martin

15 St Christopher's Place W1
Tel: 0171 486 1102

Open: Mon–Sat 10am–6pm and late night Thurs till 7pm

Vicky Martin sells a range of sexy clubwear that takes a certain confidence (and a few exercise classes) to carry off. The dresses, in Lycra and lace, are affordable and provocative enough to get you noticed. Look out for tiny, tight and sparkly tops and trousers that your mother would not let you leave the house in.

Wallis

532–536 Oxford Street W1
Tel: 0171 408 0639

Open: Mon–Wed, Fri 10am–7pm, late night Thurs till 8pm, Sat 9.30am–7pm and Sun 11am–5pm

Wallis, part of the Sears group, is ageless, modest and kind to its customers. No trail-blazing fashion here, but plenty of easy-wear, easy-wash pieces with a cut to stand the test of time. Small women shouldn't miss the Petite Collection – great news for anyone used to having their trouser hems trailing the floor and their sleeves drooping around their ankles. W, the Wallis bridge brand, is made in more expensive fabrics and has a sharper fashion edge, enabling the company to trial new shapes and silhouettes. Prices from £45 for shirts and £80 for jackets, compared with £30 and £50 for the core collection.

Also at: 42–44 Kensington High Street W8, tel: 0171 938 1534, 272–274 Oxford Street W1, tel: 0171 499 1900, and West One Shopping Centre W1, tel: 0171 437 0076.

Soho and West Soho

Bond

10 Newburgh Street W1
Tel: 0171 437 0079
Open: Mon–Sat 10.30am–6pm

See page 214.

D'Uomo

8 Newburgh Street W1
Tel: 0171 437 0492
Open: Mon-Sat 11am–6pm

See page 214.

Home

39 Beak Street W1
Tel: 0171 287 3708
Open: Mon–Sat 10.30am–6.30pm and Thurs 11am–7pm

Home is split into two departments: upstairs is streetwear, downstairs – called Fluid and frenzied on a Saturday morning – is devoted to surf and skate gear. Essential names to look out for are Drawls, Dickies for American twill trousers, Prankster for girls and the own-label Passenger collection.

Kokon to Zai

57 Greek Street W1
Tel: 0171 434 1316
Open: Mon–Sat 11am–8.30pm

Roughly translated from the Japanese as "all sorts of things from around the world come West", Kokon to Zai is a concept fashion shop that brings together all that is hip in the international world of fashion design and puts it against a backdrop of hardcore house music. The stock changes about as rapidly as the bpm, but look out for funky glow-in-the-dark T-shirts, Japonica James dresses and a small selection from Jean Paul Gaultier. The future promises designers from Germany, Holland, France and Japan, marking KTZ out as an avant-garde store with a global perspective.

Kyng

29 Carnaby Street W1
Tel: 0171 287 2490
Open: Mon–Sat 11am–6.30pm

The atmosphere in Kyng, like most street and skate wear shops, is laid back and loud, with the bass from the record shop downstairs vibrating through the floor. In the small space, Nick Hughs offers a vast choice of labels such as Stussy, No Fear, Mambo, Daniel Poole and Fresh Jive, plus his deeply cool own-label collection.

Merc

17–19 Ganton Street W1
Tel: 0171 734 1469
Open: Mon–Sat 9.30am–6pm

For full-time mods and skinheads, or simply part-time Sixties devotees, Merc is one of the only places to find everything you need under one roof. From Harringtons and Sta-press to tonic suits and Crombies, the stock has the seal of approval from Oasis, Paul Weller and Blur. The own-label range covers all the basics, while Fred Perry and Ben Sherman provide trim-fit polo tops and button-down shirts, most of which are designed exclusively for the store. Prices start at £75 for a 3-button single-breasted suit, £24.95 for Sta-press, £3 for a pork-pie hat. Scooter boys and Yardbirds fans will feel equally at home here.

Also at: 1 Chalk Farm Road NW1, tel: 0171 267 6248 (also open Sun 10am–6.30pm).

Sherry's

24 Ganton Street W1
Tel: 0171 734 5868
Open: Mon–Sat 10am–6pm

Another boutique in the Carnaby Street Mod tradition, Sherry's has enjoyed a wider audience following the recent revival in Sixties music and fashion. Paul Weller, Cast and Menswear all shop here for original suits (a bargain at £80) or for button-down Ben Sherman shirts, Fred Perry T-shirts and John Smedley knits. Sherry's also has a fine selection of Crombies, Harringtons and original parkas that probably did the business down in Brighton in the tail end of the Sixties. For the girls, there are mod skirts and hipsters; for music lovers, there are CDs.

Shop

Basement, 4 Brewer Street W1
Tel: 0171 437 1259
Open: Mon–Sat 10am–6pm

Every so often, a shop comes along that pinpoints the mood of the moment, markets it with style and – hopefully – makes a mint in the process. Shop is just that – a frivolous, fun and funky stop ("Kind of East

Village", says owner Max Karie) for edgy sportswear and clubwear, girly dresses and all the accessories a babe could buy, dedicated to Courtney Love, Drew Barrymore and Traci Lords. Shop opened in 1994, after a spell operating from a laundry next door to Bar Italia in Frith Street. Don't expect any big names in the Bazooka-Joe pink environment, as the idea is to create a look that doesn't conform to the dictates of fashion – go instead for US style from Anna Sui, the entire Hysteric Glamour collection of wicked T-shirts and dresses, Stussy Sister, the brilliant Holmes collection and Fiorucci Tees-in-a-tin, £25. In the top price bracket, there's Tocca – one of the most covetable labels around – specialising in the pretty broderie anglaise dresses that the Supermodels wear when off-duty. Shop is one of London's best stores for street labels that are worth saving up for: it succeeds in capturing the spirit of Soho as it always should have been.

Sun Sun

17 Newburgh Street W1
Tel: 0171 287 0909
Open: Mon–Sat 10.30am–6.30pm

See page 214.

Vexed Generation

3 Berwick Street W1 (entrance through Blore Court)
Tel: 0171 729 5669
Open: Mon–Sat 12pm–6pm

Facts such as "Ten thousand people die prematurely each year from air pollution in Britain" (*New Scientist*) have inspired Vexed Generation's thought-provoking clothes with a conscience, which are useful, durable and kind to the environment into the bargain. The own-label collection of statement fashion is sold alongside labels such as House of Minky, Undercurrent and Boom Cortina. Expect the first release from Vexed Recordings this summer.

South-west

Yo

124b Putney High Street SW15
Tel: 0181 780 2622
Open: Mon–Sat 9.30am–6pm and Sun 11am–5pm

Another dodgy name (the South-west seems to be packed with them), but a good enough stop in Putney for high-street style from well-loved labels such as Morgan, French Connection, Planète Interdite and the ubiquitous Nougat.

All Over the Shop

Dubble Bubble

21 Turnham Green Terrace W4
Tel: 0181 995 5186
Open: Mon–Fri 10.30am–6pm and Sat 10am–6pm

As the name suggests, this energetic shop is full of fun, fashionable and inexpensive clothes that don't pretend to be anything more complicated. The emphasis is on a high stock turnover (new ranges arrive every fortnight) and service with a smile.

Omram

5 Sicilian Avenue WC1
Tel: 0171 405 4563
Open: Mon–Sat 9am–6.30pm

A compact menswear boutique in among Bloomsbury's second-hand book shops, selling Ben Sherman, Fred Perry, Seven, Farah, Levi's and Pepe.

Pulse

22 Castle Street, Kingston-upon-Thames KT1
Tel: 0181 546 1093
Open: Mon–Sat 9.30am–6pm and Sun 11am–5pm

Pulse is aimed at aspiring label-cravers, with Paul Smith, Gallagher, Henry Lloyd, Lacoste and shoes by Timberland and Patrick Cox. The owners would like to think they're on the pulse of men's street labels, although with the trend towards a leaner line they should (and will) be moving into suiting in the coming season.

Department Stores

Bond Street

Fenwick of Bond Street

63 New Bond Street W1
Tel: 0171 629 9161
Open: Mon–Sat 9.30am–6pm and late night Thurs till 7.30pm

Over its 100-year history, Fenwick's five floors have suffered a reputation for being a trifle dry and dreary on the fashion front. But in recent years, the store has set about updating its image and its merchandise to take advantage of the Bond Street renaissance going on outside. The family hired Michael Ellis-Jones – the man responsible for Harvey Nichols's transformation under Debenham's ownership – to massage the store into the modern age. The lower ground floor now boasts an extensive menswear section, while the ground, first, second and third floors are devoted to affordable womenswear from AO by Ally Capellino, Caroline Charles, English Eccentrics and Jasper Conran among others. Accessories are a strength, with some of the best hosiery, jewellery, bag and scarf selections in town (look out for Sally Gissing belts, Bill Amberg bags and Philip Treacy hats). According to one fashion commentator, "once anyone with pretensions to fashion cred would rather have been seen naked than in Fenwick". But no more; two hot stops are the unrivalled lingerie department (stocking Dolce and Gabbana, Valentino, Emporio Armani and a host of top labels), prescribed as a lunch-hour retreat to beat the blues – and the deeply cool Joe's Restaurant Bar on the second floor. From here, you can peer at Joseph jumpers over your grilled focaccia (£9.25). Fashion bliss.

Personality: she's hitting 30 but still wants to look up-to-date.
Fashion rating: 7/10
Best bit: the vast selection of accessories, lingerie and swimwear.

Also at: Brent Cross Shopping Centre, Hendon Way NW4, tel: 0181 202 8200.

Chelsea

Peter Jones

Sloane Square SW1
Tel: 0171 730 3434
Open: Mon–Sat 9.30am–6pm and late night Wed till 7pm

Not the hottest spot in the area for clothes, though far better for home wares. Delivery can be arranged to anywhere in the UK (it's free within 30 miles of the store). A well-used wedding list service keeps brides across London happy as they unwrap their Le Creuset and Dualit.

Personality: a prim and proper mother who is a dab hand at table decorations.
Fashion rating: 5/10
Best bit: the school uniform department, a favourite with fashion stylists – particularly for flat-front trousers and grey shirts.

Kensington

Barkers of Kensington

The Barkers Centre, 63 Kensington High Street W8
Tel: 0171 937 5432

Open: Mon–Wed, Fri 10am–6.30pm, late night Thurs till 7pm, Sat 9.30am–6.30pm and Sun 11am–5pm

Barkers is a mumsy department store with a mish-mash of stock: Joseph alongside Jacques Vert, candlesticks with Candlewicks, all of which suggests a lack of direction in the buying department. There is the usual array of make-up and accessories, with the occasional gem if you have the time to search (the shoe area on the first floor is a good place to start). In the store wars of the Nineties, Barkers has lost out to the sleek operations in Knightsbridge and West One. House of Fraser does it *so* much better at Dickins & Jones.

Personality: headless chicken.
Fashion rating: 4/10
Best bit: the hosiery department if your tights snag on the way to an interview in Kensington.

Knightsbridge

Harrods

87 Brompton Road SW1
Tel: 0171 730 1234

Open: Mon–Tues, Sat 10am–6pm and Wed–Fri 10am–7pm

A grand institution, known for its algae-green carrier bags, its liveried doormen and its tourist buses. The cable address used to be Everything London – and even today, Harrods remains an Aladdin's cave of ephemera both useful and utterly useless. Ronald Reagan once telephoned to request an elephant for a Republican Party Rally, to which the imperturbable reply was "Would that be African or Indian, sir?" As the ultimate London tourist attraction, the store is probably best avoided at busy times unless you know exactly what you are looking for; one shopper said, "you have to fight your way through the entire population of Idaho to get to the bakery department". So head straight for the International Designer Room for some of the best high fashion in the country, or visit the Jil Sander boutique for the most desirable coats and suits in the capital. Don't miss the increasingly strong Harrods own-label clothing and accessories collections – they are reasonably priced and wildly wantable. Another department worth a visit is Way In, home to young designers such as Antoni and Alison, Griffin and a comprehensive own-label shoe collection. Beware though – you will not allowed in with ripped jeans, shorts or vest tops and your Prada handbag must be carried, not slung over your shoulder.

Personality: well-to-do doyenne of the social world, crisp with hair-spray but wearing comfortable shoes.
Fashion rating: 7/10
Best bit: the food-hall, the new escalator.

Harvey Nichols

109–125 Knightsbridge SW1
Tel: 0171 235 5000
Open: Mon–Fri 10am–7pm, late night Wed till 8pm and Sat 10am–6pm

Joan Collins buys her make-up here (imagine the bill), Jamie Lee Curtis buys handbags, and the Princess of Wales – allegedly – flirts with millionaires in front of the security cameras in the basement. Harvey Nichols' reputation as the hottest fashion stop in the capital is well deserved: its windows stop traffic, its buyers are some of the best in the business and its Fifth Floor restaurant is the purveyor of chitlings to the Gucci-slingback classes. Thanks to some cleverly engineered marketing and a helping hand from Patsy and Eddy in *Ab Fab*, the store has earned a reputation for fash haggery – but all in the best possible taste, sweetie. Thus, the store manages to be sexier than Harrods (the Queen shops there, but Diana is a Harvey Nicks gal). Each floor is well-delineated to guide you in your search for the ultimate fashaholic purchase: the first floor is Contemporary Collections and International Designers such as Calvin Klein, Givenchy and Dolce and Gabbana; up to two and it's Personal Shopping (courtesy of the canny Deborah Shaw) and Designer Collections including Joan and David, Nicole Farhi, Whistles and Amaya Arzuaga; on the third floor, you'll find casual, beach and outerwear, a bustling lingerie department and Kate Spade handbags direct from New York. If you make it to the dizzy heights of the fifth floor, you can experience the ultimate fashion lunch, buy tuna loins and yellow chanterelles, gold candles in the shape of Venus de Milo, Nathalie Hambro's girl-who-has-everything gifts, and finish off your credit card with a trolley stop around the "art supermarket". Then buy a ticket to Leeds and do it all over again.

Personality: resting models with a propensity for shrieking "darling!" across crowded rooms
Fashion rating: 8/10
Best bit: carrying stuff-full Harvey Nichols bags out to a waiting taxi; cocktails from resident barman Chris Potts – try the Fifth Floor Smash (fresh strawberries, *fraises de bois* liqueur, Cointreau and champagne, £7.25)

Oxford Street and Regent Street

Debenhams

334-348 Oxford Street W1
Tel: 0171 580 3000
Open: Mon–Wed 9.30am–7pm, late nights Thurs and Fri till 8pm, Sat 9am–7pm and Sun 12pm–6pm

Make no mistake, Debenhams is well worth a visit if you happen to be in the West End with a lunch hour to spare. Recent collaboration with the UK's leading designers to produce fine-quality fashion at affordable prices has pushed the store forward, fast. Philip Treacy designs a range of hats, Bill Amberg and Lulu Guinness do bags and Sam de Teran provides a line of sumptuous swimwear. This is high design at a high-street price. The latest addition is Jasper Conran's "J" collection of affordable separates (tunic tops from £40, velvet evening dresses from £150 and a full-length, virgin-wool coat a mere £250).

Personality: happy, though slightly confused, girl-about-town.
Fashion rating: 7/10
Best bit: wearing a Philip Treacy hat to a wedding and knowing it cost less than the cake.

For further stores in the Debenhams group, call: 0171 408 3536.

D H Evans

318 Oxford Street W1
Tel: 0171 629 8800

Open: Mon–Fri 10am–7pm, late night Thurs till 8pm, Sat 9.30am–7pm and Sun 11am–5pm

Dan Harries Evans was – unsurprisingly enough – Welsh, a draper from Merthyr Tydfil who sold fancy goods in Oxford Street in the 1880s. He died penniless in 1928, after a series of disastrous property deals, but his name lives on in this marble-fronted department store on London's busiest, tackiest street. It is another House of Fraser store, again in dire need of an overhaul – in stock if not looks.

Personality: negligible
Fashion rating: 6/10
Best bit: having a make-over at the cosmetics counters.

Dickins and Jones

224–244 Regent Street W1
Tel: 0171 734 7070

Open: Mon–Tues, Fri 10am–6.30pm, Wed 10am–7pm, late night Thurs till 8pm, Sat 9.30am–6.30pm and Sun 11am–5pm

This flagship store of the House of Fraser group has been a shopping institution in Regent Street for the better part of two centuries. The Victorian customer wanted lace, furs, mantles and wedding *trousseaux*; a century down the line and things are a sight more relaxed – and, following an expensive overhaul, D&J has all the atmosphere and spick-and-span service of a New York department store. On the ground floor, the coffee shop is a good place to sit and watch the world go by, or to run your eye over the Hobbs concession across the aisle. Designer fashion, from Michael Kors, Giorgio Armani and Trussardi, is on the first floor, "co-ordinates" on the second (they sound dreadfully county, but look miles better), underwear and dresses on the third and (dull) eveningwear on the fourth. You can still get Wynciette nighties and tapestry thread here, but the modern store is better known for its fabulous Beauty Studio and unrivalled cosmetics hall. Meanwhile, the personal shopping service, inspired by Bergdorf Goodman in New York, is just a phone call away (0171 437 5658).

Personality: mid-life crisee who has come out of her shell after a fabulous new face lift.
Fashion rating: 8/10
Best bit: John Gustafson's Beauty Studio, where the make-overs and advice are free, but the products you are bound to buy aren't.

Fortnum and Mason

181 Piccadilly W1
Tel: 0171 734 8040
Open: Mon–Sat 9.30am–6pm

It all began with a grocery stall in a Piccadilly doorway in 1707 – the site of today's prestigious establishment. It soon grew to furnish Florence Nightingale with beef tea and Charles Dickens with hampers of lobster salad. When Piccadilly became a one-way street in 1962, Fortnum and Mason lost some of its customary panache, but marmalade was still sent to India, horse-radish sauce to Saudi Arabia and chocolate digestives continued to be packaged off to Zimbabwe. These days, the fashion is as piquant as the food, with tasty morsels from Christian Lacroix, Missoni and Jasper Conran, hats from Gabriela Ligenza and Bailey Tomlin, and heaps of delicious lingerie, jewellery and bags served up the old-fashioned way. A place to over-indulge.

Personality: a well-trained *maître d'* serving up a feast of fashion.
Fashion rating: 7/10
Best bit: afternoon tea, the apple-green carrier bags.

John Lewis

278–306 Oxford Street W1
Tel: 0171 629 7711
Open: Mon–Wed, Fri 9.30am–6pm, Thurs 10am–8pm and Sat 9am–6pm

The separates and knitwear are available elsewhere, and would hardly raise an eyelid at that (Fenn, Wright & Manson is about the best bet). But the lingerie is worthwhile, from La Perla, Calvin Klein, Warners et al.

Personality: an *old* friend.
Fashion rating: 6/10
Best bit: the fantastic haberdashery department on the ground floor.

Also at: Brent Cross Shopping Centre, Hendon Way NW4, tel: 0181 202 6535.

Liberty

210–221 Regent Street W1
Tel: 0171 734 1234
Open: Mon–Sat 10am–6.30pm, late night Thurs till 7.30pm and Sun 12pm–6pm

Liberty was founded in 1875 by noted dandy Sir Arthur Liberty, a Gilbert and Sullivan fan mightily impressed by the costumes in *The Mikado*. He trawled the world for exotica to bring back to London, and since then the store has sold goods with an Oriental bent to well-heeled customers from across the globe. Queen Mary rode in a carriage from Buckingham Palace to buy her jewellery here, and the Tudor-faced emporium soon made its name as a purveyor of furnishing fabrics, art nouveau furniture and prints to an eager British audience. Today, though the building itself feels much like a stately home stuck in an extravagant time warp, Liberty is best known as a key supporter of new and established names in contemporary and designer fashion, engineered by London's best fashion buyer Angela Quaintrell. The list is endless but includes Issey Miyake's Pleats Please, English Eccentrics, Yohji Yamamoto, Helmut Lang, Mui Mui, Lulu Guinness, Anya Hindmarch and Gilly

Forge. There are few better ways to cheer up a grey day than to trail through the five floors at Liberty. You may leave with an armful of hot new labels, or just with a pleasant glow. Either way, even with the imminent closure of 20 regional outlets, Liberty remains one of the most alluring department stores in the world.

Personality: the kind of person you've known for years, who suddenly announces she can speak Mandarin.
Fashion rating: 9/10
Best bit: the consistent, respected support for young British fashion designers.

Lillywhites

24-36 Regent Street SW1
Tel: 0171 915 4000
Open: Mon–Fri 9.30am–7pm, Sat 9.30am–6pm and Sun 11am–5pm

In 1863, cricketing professional James Lillywhite left the stumps and headed for retailing in Haymarket, London. He sold cricket bats and cigars, for what else could a gentleman possibly require? Since then, the company has introduced skiing to the UK (it was responsible for the first indoor dry ski slope in 1948), published the first football rules for the FA, designed the first tennis shorts for women and the aviation suit worn by Amy Johnson for her historic solo flight to Australia. Today, the only specialist sports department store in the country sells 50,000 tennis balls each year and 100 pairs of in-line skates every week. It stocks 70,000 different lines covering 35 different sports, many sold by professional tennis coaches, scratch golfers and world-class ski instructors. If it all leaves you out of breath, that, dear reader, is the point.

Personality: the chairman of the local golf club.
Fashion rating: 7/10
Best bit: initiating your fitness regime by using the stairs, rather than the lifts.

Selfridges

400 Oxford Street W1
Tel: 0171 629 1234
Open: Mon–Sat 9.30am–7pm and late night Thurs till 8pm

There's no place like it. So they say, yet Selfridges hit the doldrums several years ago, just as other London department stores caught on to the retail realities of the Nineties. Since then, a four-year, £70-million master plan has been put into action; today the layout is clearer (a central escalator atrium will be completed at the end of 1997), the stock vastly improved and Selfridges is now the star performer in the portfolio of retail giant Sears. Latest figures suggest that department stores are growing by 5% a year, helped by an ageing population who evidently prefer the security and variety of shopping under one roof – and Selfridges is all set to reap the benefit. The store now boasts the largest Polo Ralph Lauren menswear unit in Europe and one of the finest diffusion line-ups in London, including Bazar by Christian Lacroix, D&G and Future Ozbek. The "Spirit" department is a vast territory of club and street fashion names including Kookai, Calvin Klein, Red or Dead, Karen Millen, Diesel and The Design Collective. The list for the rest of the store reads like an A–Z of who's who in the fashion industry, from Amaya Arzuaga to the Zegna collection.

Personality: West-End girl with a taste for artichoke hearts and Belgian chocolates.
Fashion rating: 9/10
Best bit: relaxing at The Gallery Coffee Shop, surrounded by new purchases.

Simpson (Piccadilly)

203 Piccadilly W1
Tel: 0171 734 2002
Open: Mon–Fri 10am–7pm and Sat 9.30am–6pm

Having recently celebrated its diamond jubilee, Simpson is firmly established in the great traditions of British shopping – a sort of Queen Mum of department stores (the oak-lined board-room is, in fact, stacked high with "By Royal Appointment" certificates). The own-label, Daks Simpson, is well loved by the shires set, and the store offers a yawn-worthy range of designer labels such as Weekend by MaxMara, Pringle, Synonyme by Georges Rech, Paul Costelloe and Lacoste. Modernisation is on its way though, with a refit to the 60-year-old building on this year's schedule.

Personality: tweedy folk who are a whizz at bridge.
Fasion rating: 6/10
Best bit: window dressing to compete with Harvey Nichols.

Sogo

225-229 Piccadilly W1
Tel: 0171 333 9000
Open: Mon–Sat 10am–8pm and Sun 11am–5pm

The first stop on any Japanese tourist's essential London shopping trip, Sogo represents everything that is quintessentially English – at least, it does if you have just flown in from Tokyo. Dunhill, Mulberry, Austin Reed, Vivienne Westwood and Burberrys can be found on the lower ground floor, along with an authentic made-to-measure tailoring service. Sogo's eventual aim is to become the world's leading department store; this is the 34th outlet, so the title is within reach.

Personality: a tour guide carrying a bright-yellow umbrella to alert shoppers to Great British landmarks.
Fashion rating: 7/10
Best bit: California rolls in the Café Sogo sushi bar.

Second-hand & Vintage

Camden

Henry and Daughter

17–18 Camden Lock Place, Middle Yard, Chalk Farm Road NW1
Tel: 0171 284 3302
Open: Mon–Fri 10am–6pm and Sat–Sun 9.30am–6pm

See page 176.

Modern Age Vintage Clothing

65 Chalk Farm Road N1
Tel: 0171 482 3787
Open: 10.30am–6pm seven days a week

Garments in the front half of the shop can be bought or hired, while the stock in the back (the glamorous, glorious one-offs) is for hire only. The well-presented vintage and collectors' clothes from the Thirties to the Seventies are all in tip-top condition and reasonably priced. The back-room evening wear is hired on a flexible three-day basis, from £25 plus deposit.

Rokit

225 Camden High Street NW1
Tel: 0171 267 3046
Open: Mon–Fri 10am–6pm and Sat–Sun 10am–7pm

Rokit hardly qualifies as a bargain hunters' find, as it is neither tucked away nor is it cheap. It does, however, offer customers a better selection than most vintage outlets in Camden – the usual American Seventies retro, wacky shirts, flares and tops, culled from a huge import and wholesaling business. Vintage denim from Levi's, Lee and Wrangler starts at £20. The team also produces its own label from recycled fabrics, from £17. The stock spills out on to the pavement on Saturdays and Sundays, so be prepared to wade in.

Chelsea

American Classics Vintage

404 King's Road SW10
Tel: 0171 351 5229
Open: Mon–Sat 10am–6.30pm and Sun 12pm–5pm

Not to be confused with American Classics next door, this is a separate business concentrating on original core clothing from the Forties to the Seventies. Probably best known for its denim, the shop does a nice line in Forties tea dresses, Fifties bowling shirts, Sixties two-tone suits, Seventies Levi's, and civilian and WW2 flying jackets (they cost a bomb). Not for unexpected "finds", but popular with teens who've been told that vintage is very hot.

Bentleys

190 Walton Street SW3
Tel: 0171 584 7770
Open: Mon–Sat 10am–6pm

See page 220.

Bertie Wooster

(m)

284 Fulham Road SW10
Tel: 0171 352 5662
Open: Mon–Fri 10am–7pm and Sat 10am–5pm

Named after P G Wodehouse's quintessentially English character, this snug shop sells an eclectic selection of clothing – a clever combination of new and carefully worn tailoring that has its roots in the traditions of Savile Row. The second-hand suits are in faultless condition and range from single- and double-breasted two-pieces, to formal tails and evening coats that just beg for a monocle and a cheroot to set them off. Prices from £80, but should you desire a brand-new look, a made-to-measure suit starts from a mere £285.

Also at: 69 Moorgate EC2, tel: 0171 638 9550.

Hang Ups

(&)

366 Fulham Road SW10
Tel: 0171 351 0047
Open: Mon–Fri 11am–6.45pm, Sat 10.30am–6pm and Sun 12pm–4pm

Unlike many dress agencies that deal in either designer or high-street clothing, Hang Ups' rule of thumb is anything goes: anything fashionable, anything interesting, anything good quality – up to and including couture. There are always plenty of bargains, from Alaïa, Joseph, Nicole Farhi, Jigsaw or Ghost, and new samples from club label Sub Couture. Dig around to find kids' ethnic garments from Guatemala; downstairs is a childrens' boutique, with new clothes from Osh Kosh, Levi's and Oilily.

Steinberg & Tolkien

(&)

193 King's Road SW3
Tel: 0171 376 3660
Open: Mon–Sat 10.30am–7pm and Sun 12.30pm–6.30pm

As any fashion student or stylist worth their Prada purse knows, Steinberg and Tolkien is two floors of the very best vintage clothing from 1840 to 1980. Upstairs is given over to well-presented costume and period jewellery from 1900 to 1970; downstairs is a maze of men's and womenswear, and possibly the largest selection of couture in the world – all in immaculate condition. The rails are organised into ferret-friendly sections, either by era or designer (Schiaparelli, Chanel, Balenciaga and Lanvin, in all its faded, fabulous glory). If you're lucky, you'll bump into the grizzled Mr Steinberg, who imports the stock from his native America; get him to regale you with a tale or two of discovering a Dior in the most unexpected places. You might even find Narciso Rodriguez and John Galliano tussling over a couture frock. Not to be missed.

City and East End

The Cavern

154 Commercial Street E1
Tel: 0171 247 1889
Open: Tues–Fri 12pm–6pm and Sat 12pm–5pm

Virtually all of The Cavern's stock is unworn clothing from the Sixties and Seventies, so it's almost guaranteed to be in perfect condition. The shop began trading in 1990 and has expanded rapidly with this decade's ever-increasing fascination with anything retro. Embroidered flares cost £25; psychedelic Tees and denim hotpants are £16. A pair of original Pucci shoes, £50, were lurking in the shadows on our visit. Needless to say, they are not there any more...

Covent Garden

Blackout II

51 Endell Street WC2
Tel: 0171 240 5006
Open: Mon–Fri 11am–7pm and Sat 11.30am–6.30pm

If you are hung up on vintage clothing, WC2 is the postcode to head for – and Blackout II is the best starting point. It sells a bizarre mixture of old and very old kitsch and glam gear from the Twenties to the present day, including bags, shoes and fantastic accessories (snakeskin slingbacks, sequinned evening bags). Try to set aside a couple of days; that's how long it will take to hunt through the seemingly endless rails of flares, beady cardigans, acid-attack shirts and long draped evening dresses. Perseverance will reap rich rewards.

Cenci

31 Monmouth Street WC2
Tel: 0171 836 1400
Open: Mon–Fri 10.30am–7pm and Sat 10.30am–6.30pm

Cenci is expensive, but the stock is unique and in marvellous condition considering some of it can remember the Blitz. The ski and knitwear includes ancient Fair Isle jumpers, and the Italian labels from the *Dolce Vita* years are unmissable. Half-price stock is downstairs; take a packed lunch and stay the day.

The Loft

35 Monmouth Street WC2
Tel: 0171 240 3807
Open: Mon–Sat 11am–6.30pm

The Loft sells worn designer clothes from Giorgio Armani, Paul Smith, Moschino, Galliano, Westwood and Gaultier (menswear on the ground floor, womenswear downstairs). A dress agency service will take unwanted outfits off your hands; the staff will even collect from your home if you ask them nicely.

Oxfam

23 Drury Lane WC2
Tel: 0171 240 3769
Open: Mon–Sat 10.30am–6pm

One of the best branches in the capital for a selection of new clothing, together with well-sourced second-hand bargains.

For branches, call: 01703 704 411.

Sam Walker

41 Neal Street WC2
Tel: 0171 240 7800
Open: Mon–Sat 10am–7.30pm and Sun 12pm–7pm

See page 210.

Fulham

66 Fulham High Street

66 Fulham High Street SW6
Tel: 0171 736 5446
Open: Mon–Sat 11am–7.30pm and Sun 1pm–7pm

This shop sells second-hand menswear from Savile Row, Jermyn Street, Burberrys and Daks. There are original Crombies too, plus a mass of cufflinks, cravats and spatz for the old-school gent or dapper dandy.

Chiceria

93 Wandsworth Bridge Road SW6
Tel: 0171 371 0697
Open: Mon–Sat 11am–7pm

The name Chiceria is a combination of Chic and Galleria – an odd title for a dress agency, but infinitely preferable to the usual Second Time Around, Seconds Out puns that can put even a purposeful shopper off her stride. Designers such as Valentino, Rifat Ozbek, Escada, Chanel and Kenzo are all here, alongside high-street lines and decent accessories. Cast-offs are taken in on a 50/50 basis for two months, before being returned or donated to charity.

The Red Pepper

627 Fulham Road SW6
Tel: 0171 371 7440
Open: Mon–Sat 10am–6pm and Wed 11am–7pm

A no-frills dress agency that offers a good range of used clothes. Head for the designer rail, where you could pick up a more expensive but worthwhile little number, or check out the permanent sale rail parked outside the front door.

Greenwich

The Emporium

330–332 Creek Road SE10
Tel: 0181 305 1670
Open: Tues–Sun 10.30am–6pm

A cosy retro refuge for vintage clothing devotees, with stock from the Thirties to the present day. Leather jackets from £40–£200, sport shorts or skinny polonecks from £10. Make your way to the back of the shop for glitzy evening wear: mens' tails at around £75, suits at £25–£35, women's dresses from £25 and an alluring cabinet full of bags, gloves, cigarette cases and trinkets.

The Observatory

20 Greenwich Church Street SE10
Tel: 0181 305 1998
Open: 10am–6pm seven days a week

One of the best organised, and priced, purveyors of retro clothing in London, The Observatory is presumably named after Greenwich's biggest tourist attraction, and is equally worth a visit. Each garment has a ticket displaying not only the size but the condition – either "perfect" or "fair" – and is priced accordingly. We found original Farahs for a trifling £12.90, lace shifts for £16.90, a spotless Sixties mac for £19.90 and stretch polo tops for £5.90. Upstairs, a formal department features women's evening dresses and men's tuxedos at unmatched prices. Packed out at the weekends.

Hampstead and Highgate

Exclusivo

24 Hampstead High Street NW3
Tel: 0171 431 8618
Open: Mon–Sun 11.30am–6pm

The original "designer discount" store (now with a second branch in Covent Garden) is crammed full of, well, everything: not just designer bargains – including Nicole Farhi suits and a window full of Patrick Cox and Gucci shoes – but high-street and mid-range fashion, too. Don't be put off by the window, which resembles a jumble sale. It's simply a sign that every inch of space is being used to store the immense amount of stock. Roll up your sleeves and get stuck in.

Also at: The Designer Second Hand Store, 132 Long Acre WC2, tel: 0171 240 8765.

Labels

146 Fleet Road NW3
Tel: 0171 267 8521
Open: Tues–Sat 10.30am–6pm

You can find almost everything in this dress agency, from Marks and Spencer and Monsoon to Whistles and Nicole Farhi. Prices are reasonable, especially on reduced stock, which can be less than a quarter of the original price.

Penguin Society

(&)

144 West End Lane NW6
Tel: 0171 625 7778
Open: Mon–Sat 11am–6.30pm

"New and gently worn" is how Penguin Society describes its clothes, although from the outside the shop looks more like a second-hand store than anything else. Once inside, the stock speaks for itself – Armani, Versace, Boss and Nicole Farhi suits, shirts, skirts and accessories for men and women.

Highbury and Islington

162

(&)

162 Holloway Road N7
Tel: 0171 700 2354
Open: Mon–Sat 10am–6pm and Sun 11am–6pm

If you are on a budget but don't want everyone to know it, visit this shop for London's cheapest selection of retro fashion. Most of the Seventies Western and nylon shirts, Sixties day dresses and athletic tops cost between £3 and £10, while Levi's cost about as much as a packet of Marlboro. The only items over a tenner are the branded denim jackets and vintage leathers, which go up to £45 and are great value at that. The shop is located next door to the University of North London, so you may have to wrestle with the entire membership of the Students' Union to get to the bargains, depending on when you visit – you should be safe before noon.

Annie's Vintage Costume and Textiles

10 Camden Passage N1
Tel: 0171 359 0796
Open: Mon–Tues, Thurs–Fri and Sun 11am–6pm, Wed and Sat 10am–6pm

Annie's small but perfectly stocked shop is home to a beautiful selection of Twenties and Thirties evening dresses, all in mint condition. Fifties blouses, fitted Forties jackets and Edwardian coats are a speciality of the house. Upstairs is home to all things white – table- and bedlinen and a collection of original wedding dresses from the Edwardian era. Accessories include Panama hats, Twenties and Thirties dancing shoes and shawls. In winter, there is always a good stock of cashmere jumpers and Harris tweed. A busy, bustling gem of a shop, chock full with ideas.

Cloud Cuckoo Land

6 Charlton Place, Camden Passage N1
Tel: 0171 354 3141
Open: Mon–Sat 11am–5.30pm

Katharine Hamnett and the team behind Ghost are said to come here for inspiration, jostling with global customers with a taste for top-quality vintage clothing from 1910 to 1950. There is a particularly good stock of Twenties beaded flapper dresses (for around £100), Edwardian linen motoring coats and Fifties Perspex handbags from America. At the back of the shop, a converted yard with a stunning glass roof is home to the men's clothing, including Forties leather jackets and silk scarves.

Cobwebs

60 Islington Park Street N1
Tel: 0171 359 8090
Open: Tues–Sat 11am–6pm

Few outlets can beat Cobwebs for clothes from the Thirties to the Sixties. Floral cotton dresses à la Doris Day (from £18), dainty slips that Dorothy Parker would have killed for, and sweeping ballgowns are a must. At Christmas time, the menswear section stocks Harris tweed jackets, lounge suits and glam evening tails. There's also an abundance of antique leather briefcases in the window, and plenty more inside. Have a root around for the best bits.

Past Caring

76 Essex Road N1
No phone
Open: Mon–Sat 12pm–6pm

Clutter, clatter and some of the capital's best vintage buys make Past Caring a bargain hunters' playground. The owner gathers kitsch clothing – fake fur, garish hats – and household goods, mainly from the Sixties and Seventies, and sells them on at guaranteed low prices (dresses, jeans, shirts and blouses from £5; leather jackets from £35). Under the counter, there's a selection of sunglasses, evening bags and gloves, as well as bits and pieces of jewellery straight from the dressing-up box. Twice a year, the shop clears out its old stock to make room for the new, and everything is eventually reduced to £1.

To Be Continued

251 Holloway Road N7
Tel: 0171 609 4796
Open: Mon–Fri 10am–6pm and Sat 10.30am–6.30pm

An extension of an idea that started as a stall in Camden Market, selling "previously worn" Sixties and Seventies gear, including sportswear, Afghan coats, skinny-rib sweaters, flares, vests and leather jackets. Prices from £5 to £45, but it is worth haggling to get a fiver off.

Kensington

Designer Bargains

29 Kensington Church Street W8
Tel: 0171 795 6777
Open: Mon–Sat 10am–6.30pm

Designer Bargains deals only in top designer names – Chanel, Kenzo, Hermès, Moschino, Prada, Gianfranco Ferre and their ilk. Upstairs is the seasonal cache of labels while downstairs you'll find a constant supply of winter coats, leather, suede and extravagant evening wear. The shop also has a couple of unique features: a larger-sizes department (14 and above) and a promise to pay immediate cash for anything at all bearing a genuine Chanel label.

Knightsbridge

Pandora

16-22 Cheval Place SW7
Tel: 0171 589 5289
Open: Mon-Sat 10am-6pm

The friendly staff at this dress agency, just a stone's throw from Harrods, offer a service which is second to none. Customers can pick up Prada, Donna Karan, Moschino and Jil Sander for as little as a quarter of the original price, and quality is assured, since only clothes that are less than three years old are accepted. Call to make an appointment first, in true Knightsbridge tradition.

Salou

6 Cheval Place SW7
Tel: 0171 581 2380
Open: Mon–Sat 10am–5pm

Looking for a second-hand Chanel suit for a third of its original price? Come to Salou, where regular customers are telephoned should any suitable stock arrive. No rooting around, no wasted journeys. Is this a new dimension in home shopping?

The Exchange

30 Elizabeth Street SW1
Tel: 0171 730 3334
Open: Mon–Fri 10am–4.30pm

See page 202.

Notting Hill

295

295 Portobello Road W10
No phone
Open: Fri–Sat 8.30am–5pm

The cheapest second-hand clothes store on the Portobello Road, 295 sells anything (at all) from the Sixties or earlier that might be relevant to fashion now, at rock-bottom prices. Dresses from the Fifties and Sixties cost around £10, jumpers, tank tops and twinsets are between £6.50 and £8, and scarves are as little as £1. There is a wonderful selection of swimwear (£5), and if the prices aren't cheap enough there is always the bargain basket, where everything is 50p.

The Antique Clothing Shop

282 Portobello Road W10
Tel: 0181 964 4830
Open: Fri-Sat 9am-6pm or by appointment, tel: 0181 993 4162

Sandy Stagg aims to sell something for everyone from every era between 1860 and 1960, and with nearly 30 years' experience in the vintage business, she should know what to look for. There are intricate Victorian dresses, which will set you back anything up to £500, chiffon tea dresses at around £100 and Forties suits from £40. Anyone with a thirst for thrift should aim for the permanent sale rail, with reductions of up to 50%.

Crazy Clothes Connection

134 Lancaster Road W11
Tel: 0171 221 3989
Open: Mon 1pm–7.30pm, Tues–Wed and Fri–Sat 11am–7pm and Thurs 2pm–7pm

Under a mountain of vintage clothes are two of the most helpful and cherished figures in fashion retailing. Esther and her dad, Derrick, have been running their shop for four years and carry London's widest selection of vintage men's and women's clothes from the Twenties to the Seventies. Step inside and you won't be able to move for original Sixties suits, James Dean leather jackets, snakeskin platforms and strappy wedges – though Esther assures us that she knows exactly what she's got and where it is. A party hire service, from £50, makes Crazy's too good to miss.

The Designer Source

61d Lancaster Road W11
Tel: 0171 243 2396
Open: Mon–Sat 10am–6pm

The former Designer Sale and Exchange shop has been renamed The Designer Source, although the backbone of the business remains the same: second-hand and end-of-line samples from designers such as Alexander

McQueen, Ann Demeulemeester, Joseph, Whistles and Patrick Cox. Unlike many dress agencies, where the rails are so crammed that you can't see anything, The Designer Source is a little more discerning in its selection, singling out the most contemporary pieces and selling them at approximately a quarter of the original price.

JW Beeton

68 Ledbury Road W11
Tel: 0171 229 8874
Open: Mon–Fri 11am–7pm and Sat 10.30am–6.30pm

See page 208.

Merchant of Europe

232 Portobello Road W11
Tel: 0171 221 4203
Open: Mon-Sat 11am(ish)-6pm

Visit this shop for a crazy, covetable collection of couture, period clothing and wacky accessories from the Twenties to the Seventies. Items can be hired at one-third of the retail cost per night. A new project for 1997 is the Merchant of Europe own-label contemporary clothing collection, designed by the shop's owners Malou and Nev to reflect some of the ideas that pass through the shop; expect an wild mix of cultures and fabrics at prices from £10.

Oguri

64 Ledbury Road W11
Tel: 0171 792 3847
Open: Mon–Sat 10am–5.30pm

See page 208.

Orsini Gallery

284 Portobello Road W10
Tel: 0181 968 1220
Open: Mon–Thurs 1.30pm–5.30pm, Fri 8.30am–5.30pm and Sat 9am–6pm

Every garment here – from the 1850s to the present day – is washed and restored to as near its original condition as possible, making the shop a favourite with film and television companies. Prices vary depending on age and condition: a Fifties summer dress is around £25, Thirties evening dresses are £75–£85 and an authentic wedding outfit averages at £150 for the dress and £65–£95 for a headdress. You can even buy a Bakelite wireless on your way out.

Vent

178a Westbourne Grove W11
No phone
Open: Fri–Sat 11am–6pm

See page 209.

Oxford Street and Regent Street

Catwalk

42 Chiltern Street W1
Tel: 0171 935 1052
Open: Mon–Fri 11.15am–6pm, Sat 11.15am–5pm and late night Thurs till 7pm

Ever bought one of those garment glitches – you know, the acid-yellow jacket and matching jodhpurs? The skirt you bought to encourage you to lose that half-stone? Take it all to Catwalk and trade it in for something you will really wear from the rails of second-hand designer clothes. Just don't fall for another fashion *faux pas*.

Charon

74 Marylebone Lane W1
Tel: 0171 486 2901
Open: Mon–Fri 10.30am–5pm and Sat 10am–4pm

The joy of a shop such as Charon is truffling through the immense amount of stock, never knowing quite what you'll find. The clothes are part second-hand, part the unwanted, unworn wardrobes of shopaholics – although there are a few genuine antiques in the mix. Labels are mainly designer, and prices can be anything from £5 to £500. On one visit, we clocked up a selection of Hermès scarves at £70 to £80, a Caroline Charles suit at £75, a Joseph skirt for £25 and a wonderful pair of "early" Patrick Cox shoes for £20.

L'Homme Designer Exchange

50 Blandford Street W1
Tel: 0171 224 3266
Open: Mon and Fri 11am–6pm, Tues–Thurs 11am–7pm and Sat 11am–5pm

It is hard to imagine the average British male clearing out his wardrobe, never mind having the forethought to take it to be re-sold – so it's rare to find a men's dress agency (for want of a better expression). And it is rarer still to find one with such a huge, if at times outrageous, selection of clothing. Film, TV and music stars have been known to bring things in to be sold – although not in person. If you are on the buying side prices vary, but they tend to work out at around one-third of the original: an Armani suit for about £200 and jeans, shirts and jackets from as little as £15. Elton John's jacket, anyone?

The Salvation Army/Cloud Nine

9 Princes Street W1
Tel: 0171 495 3958
Open: Mon–Fri 10.30am–5.30pm and Sat 11.30am–5.30pm

Although downstairs is the usual charity shop outlet, upstairs is home to Cloud Nine, a rummage revelation of the best second-hand bargains from the Salvation Army HQ. Expect to find unusual period garments from the Fifties, Sixties and Seventies at no extra premium. There is also a hire service at a fifth of the retail cost per day and a student discount (12%) for anyone for whom the £4.95 average price is out of reach.

Soho and West Soho

Oxfam No Logo

(&)

26 Ganton Street W1
Tel: 0171 437 7338
Open: Mon–Sat 11am–6pm

Those thoughtful people at Oxfam have set up this store to save us the hassle of wandering around the shires in search of great Seventies flares and Sixties slingbacks; instead they gather it all up and put it into one unusual shop. As well as second-hand stock, the shop receives donations of clothing from film production companies and high-street stores, and there's a team of seamstresses on hand to restyle the clothes. Shirts from £8.99, flares from £14.99 and sports tops from £9.99. In the winter, a great selection of leather and fake fur arrives, from £24. All the staff, including the manager, are volunteers, so if you have any spare time, you know what to do with it.

Yesterday's Bread

29 Foubert's Place W1
Tel: 0171 287 1929
Open: Mon–Fri 11.30am–6.30pm and Sat 11am–6pm

A unique idea: this shop sells purely retro Sixties and Seventies gear. If that sounds familiar, the unique bit is that all the stock is unworn and in immaculate condition. The owners collected clothes throughout the Eighties, and as a result, many of the items are one-offs and collectors' pieces. Despite the flawless condition, the prices are surprisingly low, with mini dresses and shirts from £20. Accessories are both practical – watches and bags – and quirky: dinky plastic umbrellas and "pop wheels" (the Seventies solution to traffic problems). For retro parties, staff will kit you out in kipper ties, Afro wigs, glitter eyelashes and an Abba-style stick-on moustache.

South-west

Butterfly Dress Agency

3 Lower Richmond Road SW15
Tel: 0181 788 8304
Open: Mon–Fri 10.30am–6.30pm and Sat 10am–5pm

On the edge of Putney Bridge, Butterfly has a superb range of barely worn clothing that might boast a label from Whistles, Alberta Ferretti or Gucci, depending on when you visit and how lucky you are. Although it's a little more expensive than most agencies, there are still bargains to be had – and it's a good place to take your discarded clothing if you want a fair price.

Second Time

6 King Street, Richmond TW9
Tel: 0181 940 8649
Open: Mon–Sat 10am–5.30pm

This is a well-stocked boutique aimed at the local ladies who like Jasper Conran and Betty Jackson suits. When they don't like their own any more, they come here and swap them for someone else's.

Victoria

Cornucopia

12 Upper Tachbrook Street SW1
Tel: 0171 828 5752
Open: Mon–Sat 11am–6pm

Cornucopia is a very apt name for what has become a renowned hang-out for fashion stylists, costume designers and vintage-clothing bounty hunters alike. Hanging from the ceiling and crammed on to rails are dusty day dresses, coats and suits from the late nineteenth century through to the Fifties, with some modern items thrown in for good measure. If you get confused, the shop is arranged by era, with separate sections for ancient shoes, silk scarves and squares, belts and exquisite costume jewellery, housed in a display case that stretches from one side of the shop to the other – although a bit of a spring clean wouldn't go amiss. Beware the hooked pole that allows access to the upper rails: it rips through ancient silk like a knife through butter.

Ted's Corner

34 Gillingham Street SW1
Tel: 0171 630 1177
Open: Mon–Sat 10am–6pm and Sun 11am–5pm

Husband-and-wife team Dave and Bernadette have been behind the counter at Ted's for three years, although you may have come across them before that in their down-at-heel quarters in Wilton Road Market. The shop's theme is the Fifties, with reproduction circle skirts, leopard-print drape jackets and drainpipes made from original patterns in modern fabrics. The pair also provide a made-to-measure service, and the results of their work can be seen in the many photos that adorn the walls. There are winklepickers and brothel creepers to choose from, too. Look upon it as a Teddy Boys' picnic.

All Over the Shop

146 King Street

King Street W6
Tel: 0181 741 4625
Open: Thurs–Sat 11am–6pm

This unnamed shop is a real find for anyone who wants to own a few designer labels without spending a fortune. Debbie Potts, who came up with the idea for the business after noticing the surplus clothing in friends' wardrobes, runs the shop in two ways. First, she will sell your unwanted, good-quality clothes on a 50/50 basis. Second, she takes in suppliers' samples and overruns and sells them to the public at a knock-down price. Much of the stock is as good as new... we won't tell if you don't.

Anything Goes

16 Webb's Road SW11
Tel: 0171 924 6220
Open: Mon–Fri 10.30am–5pm and Sat 10.30am–4.30pm

This is an agency for men's, women's and children's clothes, taken in on a 50/50 basis and kept for six weeks before being returned to the owner if unsold.

Delta of Venus

151 Drummond Street NW1
Tel: 0171 387 3037
Open: Mon–Sat 11am–6pm

Delta of Venus stocks a concoction of the best vintage clothing, records (remember LPs?) and pop paraphernalia, much like the bits and bobs you'd find at a carboot sale – thus saving you the bother of getting up at the crack of dawn on a Sunday and tramping around a muddy field. A sharp eye for timeless design has helped owners Chris and Leigh to amass their bohemian collection, which includes Seventies shirts, Sixties dresses and accessories. For the culturally inclined, there are essential unnecessaries such as original Joe 90 and Thunderbirds annuals, Ericsson phones and Seventies mushroom lighting.

Dynasty

12a Turnham Green Terrace W4
Tel: 0181 995 3846
Open: Mon–Sat 10.30am–5pm

Maha Roustom runs the women's side, while Paul Sheldon looks after the men in this dress agency. Women seem to be more keen on recycling, as their part of the shop is packed full of bargains while the men's area is more sparsely populated. Apparently some men who visit don't even realise they've walked into a second-hand shop: wake up boys – since when have you been able to get your hands on a Giorgio Armani suit for £175 or an Hermès tie for £6?

Also at: 63 Kensington Church Street W8, tel: 0171 376 0291.

Humana

128 Uxbridge Road W12
Tel: 0181 749 1437
Open: Mon–Sat 10am–6pm and Sun 11am–5pm

This is a worthy dumping ground for unwanted clothes. Money raised is guaranteed to go to health-care, education and drought-prevention programmes in less-developed countries such as Zambia, Zimbabwe and Malawi. Some of the stock is a good buy too, particularly the retro shirts, vintage Levi's and sports tops at a bargain-bucket price.

For branches or collection of unwanted garments, call: 0181 896 2700.

Laurence Corner

62–64 Hampstead Road NW1
Tel: 0171 813 1010
Open: Mon–Sat 9.30am–6pm

A must for any army-surplus junkie, Laurence Corner has been in its weird little location for over 40 years and is the only shop of its kind in London. The bizarre prices start with hats for £1.23. Among the wonderful stock, you can find government boiler suits (£15.39), bus conductors' shirts (£6.79), Worcester Constabulary police capes (£35) and gas-mask bags. The fatigues, army shirts, commando sweaters and donkey jackets are very Prada, if you squint. The store also has a costume department where you can borrow almost any conceivable outfit - from a suit of armour to the back end of a pantomime cow – with prices from £38 for a week's hire.

Q Shop

430 Coldharbour Lane SW9
Tel: 0171 326 0500
Open: Mon–Sat 10am–8pm and Sun 12pm–6pm

The best thing to happen to Brixton since the revamped Ritzy opened its doors, Q is situated on the site that was once Ed's Supermarket. The 10,000 square feet of recycled American clothing is organised just like Asda, in aisles of jeans, combats, shirts, jackets and suits from the Fifties to the present day. The shop is loud and proud, and you'll have to scratch around for the best buys; if you are in a hurry, head straight for the leather jackets and coats towards the back wall. Prices are very low, between 50p and £30, and with 1,000 new items arriving daily, Q is well worth visiting regularly.

Markets & Malls

Camden

Camden Council is proud to announce that its Market is currently London's fourth-largest tourist attraction, pulling in five million visitors a year. Great news, doubtlessly, for the Council and the stall-holders, but for London shoppers, this means just two things: higher-than-average prices and truck-loads of people, most of them wandering aimlessly around with CamCorders. I have encountered French tour parties who come to London just for the Camden experience. They don't, of course, find it – it left long ago for less accessible territory. After 23 years, the Market today divides into different speciality areas, so plot your course wisely to avoid being carried along in the fray. Police are currently threatening to outlaw the street stalls, which may come as a relief to pedestrians but could kill the capital's most successful market.

Camden Lock

Chalk Farm Road NW1

Open: Mon–Sun 10am–6pm

The Lock is the site of Camden's roots from the Seventies, where the whole vibe began. Nowadays, it is home to an indoor and outdoor ethnic maze of individual stalls and shops (some worth visiting, others well worth ignoring) offering jewellery, clothing – new and used – and accessories. The units to look out for are the established stall holders who offer the best quality at good-value prices; for street and club fashion, come to the Lock first, then scoot along to the old club venue at the Electric Ballroom on the High Street.

Camden Market

Camden High Street NW1

Open: Thurs–Sun 9am–5pm

Camden ain't what it used to be, or so says anyone in the area in the know. One thing that hasn't changed, however, is the Market and its sprawl of 120 predictable second-hand and new stalls, selling everything from retro club kit and suede and leather from decades ago, to the work of up-and-coming young designers. The best days to visit are Thursdays and Fridays, when the stalls are marginally quieter; the weekend is a bore – unless you enjoy elbowing your way past the Eurostar crowds to get at "bargains" that you can buy more cheaply elsewhere.

The Stables

Chalk Farm Road NW1

Open: Sat–Sun 9am–6pm

The Stables (first built for the horses that hauled barges on Regents Canal in the nineteenth century) is easily the best of Camden's markets – if you can stand the infernal smell of joysticks battling with chicken curry. The site is a mass of outdoor stalls and indoor units offering a wide selection of new and used clothing from designer and high street to retro vintage and the odd antique collectable. Some of the stalls are so full of stock that the thought of rooting through is a daunting one, but persevere and you will chalk up some great bargains. Names to spot on your way round include: Cyberdog for fluorescent clubby T-shirts and dresses sold in an Ultraviolet environment; Clip's vintage jackets; Gary Holder for bleached velvet jackets and trousers; Mothball's recent and ancient second-hand items, sourced with a modern direction in mind; Retropolis, as the name suggests; Threads for serious and wacky, new and used bargains; and the Hat Stop for old-fashioned bowler hats.

Chelsea

King's Walk Shopping Mall

122 King's Road SW3
Tel: 0171 823 8448
Open: Mon–Fri 9.30am–7pm, Sat 9am–7pm and Sun 12pm–6pm

The Mall opened nine years ago, offering an unstartling selection of well-known shops over three floors. Top spots include the magnificent What a Circus (see page 226) and Octopus (see page 210).

City and East End

If you fancy your chances as a bit of a Pete Beale down the East End markets, you first need to obtain a licence from The Tower Hamlets Central Markets Office (0171 377 8963).

Brick Lane Market

Bethnal Green Road, Cheshire Street and Brick Lane E1
Open: Sun 6am–1pm

A vast carboot sale, Brick Lane is bustling, brazen and brilliant. Once the place to pick up anything from a pair of Seventies platforms to opulent sari fabrics, today – sadly and inevitably – the Lane has been invaded by a host of new stalls selling cheap market stuff. There are still some fantastic finds if you trawl through the disorganised debris of broken watches, decades-old prams and spanner-and-socket sets, but get up early as the market is packed out by 7am, and is packed up by 1pm. Don't forget to stop off for breakfast beigels from Beigel Bake – and don't buy the bicycles (most of them are hot).

Clerkenwell Green Association

The Clerkenwell Green Association – covering Cornwell House and Pennybank Chambers – provides much-needed work space and financial support for a band of talented young designers and craftspeople. Since 1979, more than 40 businesses and individuals have been helped by the Clerkenwell

Award Scheme – a charity that supplies workshops at reduced rents and free advice on managing a business. Names to have prospered through the Scheme include Edwina Ibbotson (milliner), Emily Jo Gibbs (accessories) and Copperwheat Blundell (fashion designers). Below are a selection of businesses that welcome individual commissions and enquiries.

Cornwell House

21 Clerkenwell Green EC1
Tel: 0171 251 0276

Asta Barrington *Unit 17*

Tel: 0171 251 1763

A recent graduate of the Royal College of Art, where she took an MA in embroidery, Asta Barrington creates a range of gorgeous blankets and scarves that use the shrinkage of wool in their design. The resulting fabric is washed, dyed and stitched. Available at The Cross in Holland Park (see pages 165–6).

Baggy Bottom Designs *Unit 38*

Tel: 0171 336 6837

Not hip-hop pants, but novel jewellery from Rebecca Skeels. Pendants, cufflinks, rings and earrings in asymmetrical patterns and geometric shapes.

Catherine Mannheim and Mark Nuell *Units 23–24*

Tel: 0171 253 0647

Catherine Mannheim has run her own jewellery workshop in London since 1967 and works in silver and coloured gold. Mark Nuell came to London from Australia to make gold and silver jewellery set with semi-precious stones.

Emily Jo Gibbs *Unit 15*

Tel: 0171 490 8834

Emily makes tiny evening bags that incorporate delicate filigree roses, bumble bees and butterflies on coloured taffeta and satin. As well as commissions, Gibbs' work is available at Liberty, Caroline Charles, Browns and Harvey Nichols.

Gilian Little *Unit 39*

Tel: 0181 673 6845

Textile designer Little works with natural fibres using weave and knit techniques and devoré to produce limited-edition scarves.

Pennybank Chambers

33–35 St John's Square EC1
Tel: 0171 251 0276

Alexandra Eton *Unit 54*

Tel: 0171 251 6594

Alexandra Eton studied at Chelsea and St Martin's before gaining a place on the Clerkenwell Green Scheme. Her textiles have been used by designers Fabio Piras, Antonio Berardi and Paul Smith; she also creates her own range of ethereal, feminine scarves.

Barber Green *Unit 17*
Tel: 0171 608 0362

Made-to-measure collections for working women, from office suits to evening wear in silk, fine worsted and cotton.

Dominic Walmsley *Unit 22–23*
Tel: 0171 250 0125

In a few short years, Walmsley has earned an enviable reputation as an innovative and original jewellery designer. He works mainly in gold and silver set with garnets, rubies, blue topaz, sapphires and emeralds.

For private commissions, call: 0171 377 2800.

Doreen Gittins *Unit 38*
Tel: 0171 336 0676

There's not a great deal of room for Doreen in her tiny unit, as her loom takes up most of the space. Even so, she manages to create beautiful silk, cashmere and wool scarves that she then hand-dyes in wild technicolour.

Heather Stowell and Sarah Pulvertaft *Unit 26*
Tel: 0171 253 0646

Sarah's jewellery is mainly silver, with tiny moving parts or enamel work; Heather uses melted and hand-coiled silver to create delicate torques, earrings and chains.

Karen Shannon *Unit 27*
Tel: 0171 250 1177

Visit this unit for millinery with a theatrical bent; Karen designs hats for the Scottish National Ballet, so her creations are stagey and bold. She exhibited at London Fashion Week for the first time in 1996.

Quinton and Chadwick *Unit 11*
Tel: 0171 336 8434

A pair who design in Tactel to produce a hand-framed collection of knitwear, sold at Diverse in Islington and Moda in Blackheath.

Leather Lane Market

Leather Lane EC1
Open: Mon–Fri 10.30am–2pm

Sandwiched between the City and the East End, and only open during the week, Leather Lane Market is best visited at lunchtime, when all the stalls are up and running and all the stall holders are singing out about their wares. If you are after end-of-run high-street bargains, rip-off perfumes and cheap lingerie, Leather Lane is your kind of place. The magazine stall at the Clerkenwell Road end sells second-hand mags on almost every subject under the sun.

Petticoat Lane

Middlesex and Wentworth Streets E1

Open: Wentworth Street, Mon–Fri 10.30am–2.30pm, and all streets Sun 9am–2pm

It smacks of a knees-up down the local, cockles and whelks, apples and pears, but Petticoat Lane is a disappointment if you are in the market for a genuine East-End outing. Yet it holds on to its title as the most famous of London's markets, and is packed every Sunday, whatever the weather. With over 1,000 stalls in narrow shop-lined streets, it is easy to get waylaid – so get a map. There are new and second-hand clothes, shoes and trainers and stalls selling high-street seconds at half-price. And yes, if you look hard enough, you can buy a bag of whelks.

Roman Road Market

Roman Road E3

Open: Tues, Thurs and Sat 8.30am–3pm

One of the largest and longest-established of the East End markets, Roman Road has a vast selection of clothing stalls ranging from the cheerfully cheap to the woefully mass-produced. The best stalls offer high-street stock at knock-down prices or market copies of catwalk styles. Also worth a look are many of the bargain-bucket shops that line Roman Road.

Whitechapel Market

Whitechapel Road E1

Open: Mon–Sat 8.30am–5.30pm and Thurs 8.30am–1pm

A glorious combination of colours, aromas and cultures, Whitechapel Market has been around for centuries. It's a good place for fruit, flowers and unusual groceries, but the clothes are nothing to go out of your way for. Most are reduced to clear or end-of-line; suits (spelled "suites") go for the bargain price of £12.99, with an unwritten guarantee to fall apart after their first outing.

Covent Garden

Covent Garden Market

Covent Garden WC2

Tel: 0171 836 9136

Open: 10am–7pm seven days a week (this varies according to time of year)

Don't be fooled by the endless stream of tourists heading religiously from Covent Garden Tube in the direction of the market, as all is not as it seems. Most of the stores to be found (Kookai, Whistles, Hobbs, Cable and Co and Monsoon) are probably in your local high street, which, let's face it, is a lot less bother. The stallholders that peddle their wares from the Apple Market in the North Hall tend to stick limpet-like to their sites from year to year with a very average selection of velvet berets, hand-knits and "sterling silver" jewellery.

Gabriel's Wharf

Callan White

Unit 13 Gabriel's Wharf, 59 Upper Ground SE1
Tel: 0171 928 6090
Open: Mon–Fri 11am–6pm and Sat–Sun 12pm–6pm

The partnership between Alison White and Nancy Callan began just a year ago, but they have already made their mark. You can buy clothes off-the-peg or opt for made-to-measure in a sample design or have one of your own ideas made up; the final result will be ready in under three weeks. The prices are amazingly accessible, with tops from £20, dresses from £90 and jackets from £140. If you want to make the look complete with matching accessories, there are also a variety of hats, gloves, shoes and bags from which to choose.

David Ashton

Unit 6 Gabriel's Wharf, 56 Upper Ground SE1
Tel: 0171 401 2405
Open: Mon–Fri 11am–5.30pm

Much of David Ashton's work is done on a commission basis, where customers combine elements of various different pieces of jewellery to create a truly personal item. The designs are pretty and delicate, with simple lines, precious stones and geometric accuracy to reflect David's interest in precision engineering and his past experience of constructing scientific medical instruments.

Lauren Stanley

Unit 4 Gabriel's Wharf, 56 Upper Ground SE1
Tel: 0171 928 5782
Open: Tues–Sat 11am–6pm or by appointment

Lauren Stanley's designs use contemporary textiles which are stitched, collaged, appliquéd and embroidered to create eclectic garments for men or women. You can even have a wedding dress made up from old lace handkerchiefs, or a suit panelled from strips of recycled fabric. Recycled accessories by Rachel Hemmingway, Julie Arkell and Jo Watson are also available.

Mantie Maker

Unit 5 Gabriel's Wharf, 56 Upper Ground SE1
Tel: 0171 633 0448
Open: Tues–Fri 11am–6.30pm, Sat and Sun 12pm–6pm

Mantie Maker is an archaic Scottish term meaning dressmaker; here, an ever-changing ready-to-wear collection of accessible fashion is available with prices from £30, or you can bring in your own design and see it made up in your choice of fabric.

Oxo Tower

Bargehouse Street, Southbank SE1

Open: Tues–Sun 11am–6pm

Following a three-year, £20-million refurbishment plan by Coin Street Community Builders, Oxo Tower (formerly a cold store and processing plant for the Oxo Company) opened its doors to the public last year as a centre for contemporary designers. Jewellers, textile designers and enamellists provide individual, hand-crafted artefacts, while Harvey Nichols' Rooftop Restaurant Bar and Brasserie does a nice line in modern food and great views – if you can get a booking (try on: 0171 803 3888).

Greenwich

Greenwich Market

If you have a lazy Sunday afternoon to while away, nothing on your mind and a few quid in your pocket, try Greenwich Market. Spread across most of Greenwich at the weekend, the market includes scores of stalls selling battered second-hand and brand new clothing in every price range.

The Antiques Market

Greenwich High Road SE10
Tel: 0171 240 7405

Open: Sat–Sun 9am–5pm

Despite the name, the antiques market also sells second-hand clothes, marvellous old jewellery and crafts.

Bosun's Yard

59 Greenwich Church Street SE10
Tel: 0181 293 4804

Open: Sat–Sun 9am–5pm

An indoor craftmarket, too touristy for Londoners' tastes, with home-made hats, waistcoats and scarves.

The Central Market

Near Stockwell Street SE10

Open: Sat–Sun 9am–5pm

This outdoor market combines second-hand and retro clothing with vintage denim. There's also a brilliant Thai food stall for a bargain lunch.

The Craft Market

College Approach SE10
Tel: 0181 293 4224

Open: Sat–Sun 9am–5pm

The biggest of the bunch on the site of the original nineteenth-century market, with individual stallholders selling men's shirts, hand-painted ties, dresses and cute childrens' clothes.

The Flea Market
Thames Street SE10
Tel: 0181 305 2167
Open: Sat–Sun 9am–5pm

The smallest of Greenwich's markets, a carboot-style outdoor area where traders haggle over old clothes and junk.

Highbury and Islington

Chapel Market

Chapel Street N1
Open: Tues–Wed, Fri–Sat 9am–5pm, Thurs and Sun 9am–12.30pm

The cheery expanse of Chapel Market has been part of Islington life for more than a century, and on Saturdays and Sundays it covers the entire length of the street. The fashion is faddy and cheap, but you can pick up the odd half-decent "disposable" outfit if value rather than quality is your motive. Look out for the "Under a Fiver" stall, which is routinely surrounded by bargain hunters. Lining the street, a series of cheap shops are worth investigating while you queue for your satsumas and spuds.

Kensington

Kensington Market

49–53 Kensington High Street W8
Tel: 0171 938 4343
Open: Mon–Sat 10am–6pm

The most claustrophobic indoor market in London has been absurdly popular since the early days of Punk in 1976. Grungy units selling T-shirts, caps and black leather stand out among Seventies retro stands, tattoo parlours and tarot-reading stalls. The list of participants is endless, but currently includes Children of Vision, Ad Hoc, LSD (for leather, suede and denim), Ermm... for cute T-shirts, and Strip.

Notting Hill

Portobello Green Arcade

281 Portobello Road W10

Hidden away at the bottom end of Portobello Road is Portobello Green, a tiny shopping arcade full of individual designers each with their own unit. The Arcade was built in 1981, yet it remains a secret from all but the most determined shoppers.

Ann Baynham *Unit 9*

Tel: 0181 964 5557

Open: Mon–Sat 10am–6pm

One of many young designers for whom Hyper Hyper was a starting point. Behind the minuscule shop front lies the work room, where the production is carried out. The clothes, meanwhile, are textiles-based and guaranteed not to break the bank.

Lucy Barlow *Unit 14*

Tel: 0181 968 5333

Open: by appointment

Following an apprenticeship with Philip Somerville, training with Jean Barthet and a career with John Boyd, Lucy Barlow is surprisingly unaffected by her grand beginnings. Her millinery is influenced by Audrey Hepburn – elegant, traditional and flattering, with the ostrich-feather straw hat the signature piece.

Morgana Jewellery *Unit 24*

Tel: 0181 960 2178

Open: Tues–Fri 11am–6pm and Sat 10am–6pm

Melanie Dostal and Silvia Edin are the names behind the Morgana jewellery range, a unisex silver collection (from £8 for a pendant to £65 for a more intricate piece). They will, however, happily make to order. Alongside the jewellery is the work of Anna Scholz, whose "non-sizeist" designs run from sizes 10 to 28. Unlike most labels that cater for the larger figure, Anna's collections are not a range of "tents"; she combines structural fabrics with basic shapes to flatter the fuller figure without patronising it.

Preen *Unit 5*

Tel: 0181 968 1542

Open: Mon–Sat 10am–6pm

The energy of Thea Bregazzi and Justin Thornton's partnership is reflected in their intoxicating womenswear, which is sold as far afield as Australia, Japan and New York. Closer to home, the showroom-workroom-shop acts as a showcase for one-off pieces: expect a predominance of evening wear in crêpe and chiffon, feather bodices and showy trouser suits.

Saffron *Unit 21*

Tel: 0181 964 2909

Open: Mon–Sat 10.30am–6pm

Most of Saffron's products originate from India. The "Manjitha" jacket is made from old and new fabrics from northern India, which means each one is unique (from £65). There is also a wide and wonderful selection of printed and velvet scarves from £29.50.

Souled Out *Unit 25*

Tel: 0181 964 1121

Open: Mon 10am–6pm, Tues–Thurs 12pm–6pm and Fri–Sat 9am–6pm

"Frank", the man behind Souled Out, has a reputation for customising second-hand clothes and making them look it. This format is changing slightly, and the stock here is currently made up of the work of young designers alongside Souled Out's own curious creations. The emphasis is on club and streetwear with tie-dye Tees, quilted skirts, knitwear and combat gear.

Suite 20 *Unit 20*
Tel: 0181 969 1399
Open: Mon–Thurs 11am–6pm and Fri–Sat 9am–6pm

Olivier van de Velde began his career selling clothes on holiday in Ibiza (nice work if you can get it) before opening his own retail outlet. The fashion is a mix of recycled Seventies fabrics and clubby designs, tailor-made for the Ibiza club scene experience.

Portobello Market

Portobello Road W11
Open: Mon–Sun 9am–5pm

It's a day out, it's pure entertainment, and it's now so popular that Saturdays are virtually off-limits unless you enjoy pack-hunting. The best time to visit for fashion is early on a Friday morning, when the stylists and fashion designers roll out of their nearby flats to scour the stalls for vintage inspiration. Thousands of antique stalls and shops line Portobello Road proper, while the clothes are piled high under the Westway at the northern end. There are plenty of traders selling new, second-hand, retro clothing, hippy kit, joysticks and Victorian nighties. Leather jackets, retro sportswear and vintage Levi's stalls are here by the score, and the atmosphere alone is worth the trip. Two absolute musts are the vintage shoe stall under the Westway, where you can ferret out a pair of Fifties dancing shoes from the jumbled heaps, and the second-hand cashmere stalls, where original Pringles and olden-day skinny-fit sweaters are a brilliant bargain.

To get a stall, call: 0171 727 7684.

Whiteleys

Queensway W2
Tel: 0171 229 8844
Open: 10am–10pm seven days a week (varies from shop to shop)

To my mind, the chief pleasure at Whiteleys is to see how fast I can get from the entrance to my seat in the multi-screen cinema, salty popcorn at my side. For others, though – particularly those with rain allergies and a penchant for shopping *en masse* (should this be renamed "sheeping"?) – the grand old building is shrine to purchasing in style, a temple of retail opportunity all set against the bingy-bongy Musak that makes it all feel so tranquil and beautiful. While you wile away the hours, here are a few facts with which to wow your friends: Whiteleys was the first department store in the country; Eliza Doolittle was sent there to be "attired" in *My Fair Lady*, and Carlton uses Whiteleys to shoot *Capital Woman* with Julia Carling; more people visit here in a year than visit St Paul's Cathedral and the M&S sells more cartons of milk at the Whiteleys outlet than at any other branch... is it desperate shoppers trying to drown themselves before they face another Mondi/Oasis/Rodier/jacket potato in the upstairs restaurant gallery? Who knows. All we can tell you is that Accessorize, Benetton, Cecil Gee, Esprit and the rest do amazing business here.

Oxford Street and Regent Street

The Plaza

Oxford Street W1
Tel: 0171 637 8811
Open: Mon–Sat 10am–7pm and late night Thurs till 8pm

Another nine-year-old mall, born at the tail end of the Eighties, when mall shopping was deemed to be the epitome of a modern retail nirvana. A recent refurbishment has spruced up The Plaza, but the usual culprits (The Gap, Oasis, Jeffrey Rogers, Morgan, Warehouse, Knickerbox) are all in attendance. Head for the food court on the first floor.

All Over the Shop

Brent Cross Shopping Centre

Hendon Way NW4
Tel: 0181 202 8095
Open: Mon–Fri 10am–8pm, Sat 9am–6pm and Sun 11am–5pm

For the ultimate all-American Mall experience you can't beat Brent Cross for authenticity. If you're after personalised shopping with a smile however, then this is not for you. Hoards of hypnotized shoppers trail robotically round the maze of retailers in search of something, *anything*. A good time to visit is this spring when the Centre is celebrating its twenty-first birthday – watch out for offers and parties galore at shops such as Fenwick, John Lewis, Marks and Spencer, Austin Reed, The Gap/Gap Kids, Miss Selfridge, Monsoon, Mother-care and Wallis.

Shoes

Bond Street

Armando Pollini

35 Brook Street W1
Tel: 0171 629 7606
Open: Mon–Sat 10am–6pm and late night Thurs till 7pm

See page 10.

Bally

116 New Bond Street W1
Tel: 0171 491 7062
Open: Mon–Sat 10am–6pm and late night Thurs till 7pm

Carl Franz Bally set up business in 1851 in Switzerland and first opened in New Bond Street in 1892. Today, the shoes are as elegant as ever, with an unerring ability to make feet seem slim and dainty. The importance of good-quality leather and fine design is stressed in all the products, and this is reflected in the recent redesigning of many of Bally's 500 stores, which has given them a more modern, streamlined look. Even so, this shoe shop is for mature tastes.

For branches, call: 0171 287 2266.

Bruno Magli

49 New Bond Street W1
Tel: 0171 491 8562
Open: Mon–Sat 9.30am–6pm and late night Thurs till 7pm

The Bruno Magli story started in the early Thirties with a craftsmanship and commitment to quality continued by Morris Magli and his wife Rita today. From suede court shoes to monogrammed slippers, couture diamanté evening shoes to over-the-knee leather boots, the label is as stylish as the Mario Testino advertising campaign that promotes the range. There is also a distinctive array of upmarket loafers and brogues for men (was OJ Simpson wearing them on that fateful night?), and an accessories line of smart leather bags to match the shoes, should you require a top-to-toe Magli look.

Also at: 207 Sloane Street SW1, tel: 0171 235 7939.

Carvela

96 New Bond Street W1
Tel: 0171 629 8673
Open: Mon–Sat 9.30am–6pm and late night Thurs till 7.30pm

Carvela, part of the Kurt Geiger group, reflects the latter's grace and charm of design at around half the price (from £44.99 to £59.99). This summer's collection of wearable classics in leather and suede is sure to be a winner.

Cesare Paciotti

11 Old Bond Street W1
Tel: 0171 493 3766
Open: Mon–Sat 10am–6pm

Established as an Italian family business in 1948 by Guiseppe Paciotti, Cesare Paciotti was initially a name associated with fine men's shoes, sewn and finished by hand. Today the company adheres to traditional processes, but combines them with the latest production methods and innovation in fabrics. Influenced by cultures from around the world, Cesare (son of Guiseppe) produces sleek styles and shapes in sometimes startling colours.

Florsheim

103 New Bond Street W1
Tel: 0171 495 3661
Open: Mon–Sat 9am–7pm

With over 6,000 stores across the United States and more opening in Australia, Mexico, the Middle East and Europe, Florsheim looks set to become a name to watch in footwear. Jack Nicholson wore them in *Chinatown*, Tom Cruise wore them in *The Firm*, Snoop Doggy Dogg, Darryl Hall and Placido Domingo wear them in real life. Don't expect high fashion, as the criterion here is supreme comfort – based on a patented system of millions of little air bubbles, so you are literally "walking on air". Phone for a personal visit from a Florsheim shoe specialist if you can't make it to Bond Street: your shoes will be delivered free the next day, with a 15% discount on a second pair.

Fratelli Rossetti

177 New Bond Street W1
Tel: 0171 491 7066
Open: Mon–Fri 10am–6pm and Sat 10am–5.30pm

This newly refurbished flagship store is designed as a luxurious yet unobtrusive shopping environment, with chocolate leather seats and an extended space to house bags and leather garments. The masculine–influenced collection has softened up to make way for a more feminine look: open-toe mules in camel, cream and gold, and mod-influenced suede loafers and desert boots. Fans include Catherine Deneuve, Melanie Griffith and Gary Oldman.

Also at: 196 Sloane Street SW1, tel: 0171 259 6397.

George Cleverley

12 The Royal Arcade, 28 Old Bond Street W1
Tel: 0171 493 0443
Open: Mon–Fri 9am–5.30pm and Sat 10am–2pm

An old-school shoemaker, George Cleverley worked here from the age of 15 until his death at the age of 93. It is not surprising, therefore, that the shoes are exquisitely made and expertly crafted. Prices are steep – £990 for a basic leather pair and up to £1,700 for crocodile and exotic skins – and take up to six months to make. The house style is the elegant and light-weight chisel-toe brogue, as worn by Laurence Olivier, Humphrey Bogart and Terence Stamp.

Joan and David

150 New Bond Street W1
Tel: 0171 499 7506
Open: Mon–Sat 10am–6pm and late night Thurs till 7pm

See page 14.

Kurt Geiger

96 New Bond Street W1
Tel: 0171 499 2707
Open: Mon–Sat 9.30am–6pm and late night Thurs till 7pm

This season, square-toe shoes, luxurious loafers and platform sandals in neutral colours are the Geiger specialities. Prices start at an unstartling £80.

Pied à Terre Rouge

31 Old Bond Street W1
Tel: 0171 629 0686
Open: Mon–Sat 10am–7pm

Pied à Terre is currently streamlining operations into two types of store – Rouge and Lifestyle. Rouge sells hand-made shoes from northern Italy at the upper end of the price bracket (£110–£200) as well as designer ranges from Phillippe Model, Todd Oldham and Michel Perry. Lifestyle, available in Kensington High Street (see page 141) and across London, is the lower-priced line.

For branches, call: 0171 491 3857.

Russell and Bromley

24–25 New Bond Street W1
Tel: 0171 629 6903
Open: Mon–Sat 10am–6.30pm and late night Thurs till 7pm

After a canny bit of repositioning, Russell and Bromley has discarded its frumpy image and set about providing reasonably priced versions of the season's staples. The catwalk influence is clear – summer's designs include chunky-heeled strappy sandals and pancake-flat flip-flops – making Russell and Bromley a firm favourite among fashion aficionados. The shop also carries ranges from Donna Karan, Bruno Magli and Luc Bergere. Russell and Bromley bags are some of the best in the business; watch out for the camel shoulder bag accompanying London's best-dressed around town this summer.

For branches, call: 0181 460 1122.

Salvatore Ferragamo

24 Old Bond Street W1
Tel: 0171 629 4142
Open: Mon–Fri 9.30am–5.30pm and Sat 9.30am–5pm

Ferragamo invented the cork platform (as a solution to wartime shortages of traditional shoemaking materials), and has been a leading shoe manufacturer for decades. Today, though, the range is in need of an overhaul. The quality, however, is never in doubt – try the buckled courts or high-heeled sandals with embroidered details. Or the Evita shoe, made for Madonna in her latest role. Prices range from £110 to £539.

Timberland

72 New Bond Street W1
Tel: 0171 495 2133
Open: Mon–Sat 10am–6pm and late night Thurs till 7pm

See page 44.

Camden

Holts Footwear

5 Kentish Town Road NW1
Tel: 0171 485 8505
Open: Mon 9.30am–5pm, Tues and Thurs–Sat 9.30am–5.30pm and Sun 11.30am–4.30pm

With more authenticity than the rest of the Camden bootstores put together, Holts is the third-oldest shoe shop in London. The huge stock of Dr Martens attracts Julian Clary, Liam Gallagher and Rory Bremner – a better bet, however, is the own-label Gladiator range with prices from £35.

Chelsea

Deliss

41 Beauchamp Place SW3
Tel: 0171 584 3321
Open: Tues–Fri 9.30am–5.30pm and Sat 12pm–5pm

See page 185.

Johnny Moke

396 King's Road SW10
Tel: 0171 351 2232
Open: Mon–Sat 10.30am–6.30pm

Johnny Moke's international clientele, which includes Tom Cruise, Cher, Neneh Cherry and Jack Nicholson, is a testament to his talent for designing highly fashionable but ferociously spirited shoes (like Moke himself). Originally only made-to-order, the shop now has a ready-to-wear line for those of us who are not prepared to wait. Moke also promotes the work of young accessories designers, who give the shop an added edge with their fresh ideas and creations. A second store in opens Bond Street this summer.

Lello Bacio

311 King's Road SW3
Tel: 0171 352 2276
Open: Mon–Sat 10.30am–6.30pm and Sun 12.30pm–5.30pm

Italian Antonio Scuotto brought the Lello Bacio name to England in 1978 and opened the first shop in 1992. With 50 years of shoemaking experience to its credit, the family business is now firmly established in its home town of Naples and is set to do something similar in London. The shoes range from feminine loafers to knee-high boots in first-rate Italian leathers. Prices from £66 to £150.

Manolo Blahnik

49–51 Old Church Street SW3
Tel: 0171 352 8622
Open: Mon–Fri 10am–6pm and Sat 10.30am–5pm

If shopping is part practicality, part dream, then Blahnik is the biggest dream-maker of them all. His leather-soled high heels grace the twinkle toes of *Vogue* editors across the world (so delicately crafted and pliable that you can never hear them coming). Top fashion designers will not have their catwalk shoes made by anyone less, and now Cinderellas everywhere are discovering the transforming powers of a Manolo Blahnik heel – and are happy to pay between £270 (day) and £290 (evening) for the privilege. Customers of this store have even been known to convert whole rooms in their house to accommodate their addiction, with Polaroids stuck to the original boxes for easy reference. The reason for this kind of allegiance is that Manolo gives women legs – shapely, sexy legs that end in a wisp of a shoe.

Patrick Cox

8 Symons Street SW3
Tel: 0171 730 6504
Open: Mon–Sat 10am–6pm and late night Wed till 7pm

"Shoes and Antiques" announces the sign on the door – and inside the living-room interior of the original Patrick Cox shop, both are in high demand. The Canadian designer, who made the shoes for John Galliano's first collection in 1985 and has loafer-ed London for the past four years, is as hip as ever, accorded the kind of hype more usually reserved for film stars. This shop only stocks the (less copied) main-line collection. This season, high heels and strappy sandals come in bronze, cream and banana leather, snakeskin and satin; you will find the more reasonable Wannabe range down the road.

Wannabe at: 129 Sloane Street SW1, tel: 0171 730 8886.

R Soles

109a King's Road SW3
Tel: 0171 351 5520
Open: Mon–Sat 9.30am–7pm and Sun 12.30pm–6pm

Footwear for people who are every inch what the name suggests: think Jimmy Nail and you'll have an idea. Every style of cowboy boot, shoe and Western accessory that you could wish for, yee ha!

City and East End

Emma Hope

33 Amwell Street EC1
Tel: 0171 833 2367
Open: Mon–Sat 10am–6pm and late night Thurs till 7pm

Hope is one of the capital's great craftswomen, making pretty, practical shoes that always feature her design signatures – curvy heels, high tongues and luscious fabrics. The baroque elegance of her footwear has found favour with designers as diverse as Anna Sui, Paul Smith, Nicole Farhi and Betty Jackson. This summer, silk velvet, suede and nappa leathers are the foundation of the collection, starting at £160 and now available from Hope's new boutique, two doors up from Patrick Cox. The wedding collection of precious mules can be made to order to match The Dress.

Also at: 12 Symons Street SW3, tel: 0171 259 9566.

Gordon Scott

84 Old Broad Street EC2
Tel: 0171 374 2002
Open: Mon–Fri 8.30am–6pm

Specialists in wide fittings and large sizes since 1959, Gordon Scott stocks sturdy City shoes from Crockett and Jones, Church's, Bally and Van Dal, as well as a fine own label. Sizes from 5–15 for men and 2–9 for women.

J Amesbury and Co

32 Elder Street E1
Tel: 0171 377 2006
Open: by appointment

See page 180.

Covent Garden

Bertie

25 Long Acre WC2
Tel: 0171 836 7223
Open Mon–Sat 10am–7pm, late night Thurs till 8pm and Sun 12pm–6pm

Shoe shops are ten-a-penny in the capital, but if you want to cut out the leg work, head straight for Bertie, a high-street name that has improved in leaps and bounds over the past two years. The shoes are distinctive, sometimes daring and always superbly made. For a little more than high-street prices and a good deal less than designer, you can pick up anything from high strappy platform sandals to moccasins, mules and chunky clogs. Spring's own-label collection comes in earthy, natural shades and a gentle blue too. Cool designer ranges from Freelance (a favourite with fash-mag stylists), Costume National and Biba make Bertie the best shoe stop in town.

For branches, call: 0171 935 2002.

Birkenstock

37 Neal Street WC2
Tel: 0171 240 2783
Open: Mon–Tues 10am–6pm, Wed–Fri 10am–7pm and Sat 10am–6.30pm

See page 209.

Camper

39 Floral Street WC2
Tel: 0171 379 8678
Open: Mon–Sat 10am–6.30pm, late night Thurs till 7pm and Sun 10am–6pm

Lorenzo Fluxa's Spanish label is hot on traditional craftsmanship and innovative fabrics. This, his sole British shop, opened in October 1995, and aims to attract customers with its simple sales technique: shoes are laid out on a "banqueting table", so shoe shoppers get to see the entire range of boots and shoes in soft kid leather in one go. They also come in colour-coded boxes, to enable Imelda Marcos types to keep tabs on their collection of Campers.

Freelance

55 Neal Street WC2
Tel: 0171 379 7856
Open: Mon–Tues 10am–6pm, Wed–Fri 10am–7pm and Sat 10am–6.30pm

See page 211.

Logo Shoes

Thomas Neal's Centre, Earlham Street WC2
Tel: 0171 379 0331
Open: Mon–Sat 10.30am–7pm and Sun 12.30pm–6pm

If you want something with a high-street price, but without a mass-produced look, then this store, on the lower ground floor of Thomas Neal's chill-out zone in Covent Garden, is worth a look. The shop stocks Italian men's and women's shoes, boots and sandals, all for under £100.

Office

57 Neal Street WC2
Tel: 0171 379 1896
Open: Mon–Sat 10am–7pm and Sun 10am–6pm

See page 211.

Offspring

(&)

60 Neal Street WC2
Tel: 0171 497 2463
Open: Mon–Sat 10am–7pm and Sun 12pm–6pm

See page 211.

The Natural Shoe Store

(&)

21 Neal Street WC2
Tel: 0171 836 5254
Open: Mon–Tues 10am–6pm, Wed–Fri 10am–7pm, Sat 10am–6.30pm and Sun 12pm–5.30pm

See page 209.

The Old Curiosity Shop

(&)

13–14 Portsmouth Street WC2
Tel: 0171 405 9891
Open: Mon–Sat 11am–7pm

Billed as the oldest shop in London and – according to local legend – the inspiration behind Charles Dickens's novel, The Old Curiosity Shop is a higgledy piggledy, crooked box of a place. It is worth visiting – as many tourists do – for the atmosphere alone. Ten different designers' work is on sale from the wonky shelves, including rustic knitwear and hand-made shoes which are very obviously one-offs, from £200. Hand-made accessories from S Tek and Effra are as unusual and eclectic as the shop itself. You might not want to wear the shoes, but they make rather appealing ornaments.

Greenwich

Treads

(&)

12 Greenwich Market SE10
Tel: 0181 305 0280
Open: various (phone to check)

Contemporary bespoke shoemakers Treads have been around in Greenwich market for the past ten years and, despite somewhat erratic opening hours (for which they make no apologies), the shop is a shoe heaven. "Off-the-shelf" styles include Dr Martens boots and shoes, cosy clogs and retro Sixties and Seventies footwear, with prices from at £35. The made-to-measure shoes are inventive and worth the wait.

Hampstead and Highgate

Spice

50 Highgate High Street N6
Tel: 0181 340 5230
Open: Mon–Sat 10am–6pm and Sun 12pm–5pm

Italian shoes are held to be among the best and most expertly made in the world, and the stock at Spice certainly confirms this. The classic styles to be found here combine understated elegance with an element of high fashion, resulting in a range of stylish footwear that won't break the bank. Prices start at around £65 for women and £75 for men. Hot foot it here fast.

Also at: 162 Regent's Park Road NW1, tel: 0171 722 2478.

Highbury and Islington

Gill Wing Shoes

192 Upper Street N1
Tel: 0171 226 8012
Open: Mon–Sat 9.30am–6pm and Sun 10am–6pm

Gill Wing seems to have the monopoly on this patch of Islington, with a gift shop, a coffee shop and a jewellery store to her name. The shoe shop, however, is the best of the lot. Trendy feet are in the wrong place, but feet in the market for comfort and support are very much at home here. Birkenstock (the Glastonbury favourite), Rockport, Camper and childrens' shoes from Ricosta and Elephanten are all well worth a look. Prices start at £35.

The Little Shoe Box

89 Holloway Road N7
Tel: 0171 607 1247
Open: Mon–Fri 8.30am–5.30pm and Sat 9am–3pm (closed in August)

One of a kind – more's the pity – The Little Shoe Box provides fantasy fetish footwear in sizes 4–13, for uninhibited souls residing north of the river. The Spyrou family (three generations of sons) have run the business for around 30 years, and in that time have booted Gary Glitter, Jimmy Savile, Benny Hill and Rod Stewart. The weird, wild and wacky stock includes thigh-high patent boots with a nail-head heel – but there are more modest strappy slingbacks too, all with the obligatory stiletto heel (ankle padlocks optional).

Kensington

Atticus

14 Kensington Church Street W8
Tel: 0171 376 0059
Open: Mon–Sat 10am–7pm, late night Thurs till 8pm and Sun 12pm–6pm

A mellow and marvellous independent shoe retailer, Atticus has been increasing its ranges and developing an individual style since opening four years ago. There are now two levels of merchandise – the main-line collection (sandals, loafers and brilliant leather and suede boots, with prices from £25 to £100) and the designer collection of more directional styles, priced slightly higher. Unlike many shoe shops, there is a high turnover of stock ensuring that you don't see the same styles all season. So go in often.

Dune

66–68 Kensington High Street W8
Tel: 0171 795 6336
Open: Mon–Sat 10am–7pm, late night Thurs till 8pm and Sun 12pm–6pm

Judging by the visual merchandising, or lack of it, Dune is concentrating on the design aspect of its weighty shoes rather than on its stores. Either way, it's not quite there, but it does have the occasional half-decent pair of reasonably priced shoes if you are lost for ideas and haven't discovered Atticus or Office up the road.

Also at: 33 King's Road SW3, tel: 0171 824 8440.

Pied à Terre Lifestyle

102 Kensington High Street W8
Tel: 0171 376 0296
Open: Mon–Sat 10am–8pm and Sun 12pm–6pm

This is an impressive shoe store that is doing its utmost to simplify proceedings before its customers wander off in search of a less confused retail range. Today, the Pied à Terre banner covers "Lifestyle" and "Rouge" (see page 134) – so here, you will find the marginally cheaper main line, which encompasses clothes and shoes in one store. A step up from the high street in ideas, but a world away from designer level in price, the label subtly manages to meet the needs of the season with wardrobe staples and a few off-the-catwalk models for trend-hunters. Prices start from £50 for well-made leather shoes, and from £100 for ankle- and knee-high boots. The fashion line concentrates on simple suiting in clean silhouettes for work rather than play.

For branches, call: 0171 491 3857.

Knightsbridge

Joseph Azagury

73 Knightsbridge SW1
Tel: 0171 259 5075
Open: Mon–Sat 10am–6pm and late night Wed till 7pm

While brother Jacques makes nice clothes across the road (at number 50), Joseph is over this side with some of the most delicate, slender and modestly fashionable shoes in London. The designs are really worth scouting out, particularly if you have never been in the market for clumpy, clumsy footwear from other quarters. Joseph takes a trend – for strappy sandals, say, or skinny platforms – and turns it into something delightful. The prices are surprisingly modest too, from £100.

Also at: 117a–119 Walton Street SW3, tel: 0171 589 2155.

Comoedia

(&)

25 Beauchamp Place SW3
Tel: 0171 225 3014
Open: Mon–Sat 10am–6pm and late night Wed till 7pm

As any fashion fiend worth her stripes will tell you, you get what you pay for. The shoes here are very high quality – an Everest to the foothills elsewhere. The designer is Italian Claudio Rebaudo, a former architect whose structural shoes, bags and belts are a pleasure to wear. The price seems irrelevant, but shoes start at £79 and go up to £300 for made-to-measure.

Gina

189 Sloane Street SW1
Tel: 0171 235 2932
Open: Mon–Sat 10am–6pm and late night Wed till 7pm

Idin and Attila Kurdash, the brothers behind Gina, learnt quickly that in order to entice their century-old family business into the Nineties, they would have to play the press. That's why the company produces several key "trend" designs each season, destined to appear in the pages of the glossies, while the core business is in simple, seasonless shoes, each pair meticulously crafted (with up to 20 tiny stitches per inch). As a result, Gina is one of the most respected names in British shoe design. Summer's offerings include wedges, slingbacks and thongs in kid leather, velvet and silk – plus an exotic Gypsy range for all those ruffle-and-frill fashion shoots of the season.

Jimmy Choo

20 Motcomb Street SW1
Tel: 0171 235 6008
Open: Mon–Sat 10am–6pm

The Choo shoe – high-heeled and T-barred – goes to more fashionable parties than Tamara Beckwith. Look down at any well-heeled, stylish event and plenty of the delicate little feet will be sporting Choo's confections in satin and crepe. Until last year, the Malaysian designer produced only custom-made shoes for his loyal following, who would venture far from their Knightsbridge stamping ground to his north London workshop to get their hands on a pair. Now, ready-to-wear shoes (with dainty glass detailing) are available at his new Belgravia boutique, just a stone's throw from Sloane Street. Prices from £120.

Senso

23 Brompton Arcade SW3
Tel: 0171 584 3484
Open: Mon–Sat 10am–6.30pm and late night Wed till 7.30pm

Senso shoes are made in Italy and Spain and have become a firm favourite among fashion folk. The own label combines a feel for trends with a commitment to quality, while the groovy shop also carries some of the best footwear imports: Costume National, Accessoire and Rudolphe Menudier, alongside bags by Sequoia and scarves by English Eccentrics. If the price, which starts at £69, is out of reach, try the sale shop a few doors along at number 15.

Also at: 6 South Molton Street W1, tel: 0171 499 9998.

Sergio Rossi

12 Beauchamp Place SW3
Tel: 0171 225 0663
Open: Mon–Sat 10.30am–6.30pm and late night Wed till 7pm

Rossi makes shoes for Versace, Alaïa and Dolce and Gabbana – who all know a very good thing when they see it. The shoes look and feel fantastic; best sellers include seductive high heels and sexy loafers. Prices from £110.

Stephane Kélian

48 Sloane Street SW1
Tel: 0171 235 9459
Open: Mon–Sat 10am–6pm and late night Wed till 7pm

Stephane Kélian not only makes his own range of superbly crafted, covetable shoes, but also manufactures for Claude Montana, Jean Paul Gaultier, Issey Miyake, Kenzo and Martine Sitbon. The styling doesn't change enormously from season to season, since the emphasis here is on modifying the subtle details. If it ain't broke... Should you wish to invest in a classic Kélian, opt for the seamless style worn daily by the magazine editors of the glossy world. This shop also stocks the more grown-up, more sparkly Maud Frizon range.

Also at: 11 Grosvenor Street W1, tel: 0171 355 3201.

Wannabe

129 Sloane Street SW1
Tel: 0171 730 8886
Open: Mon–Sat 10am–6pm and late night Wed till 7pm

No fashion victim can lay claim to the title without the requisite pair of Wannabes in the closet. Patrick Cox's canny reworking of the classic loafer –

a bit of height here, a new fabric there – has been the success story of shoe retailing in the Nineties. Now Wannabes have their own shop, on Sloane Street, no less. Every Saturday, the space-age interior is packed to the rafters with loafer-loving kids, who go a bundle on Cox's sportswear clothing too.

Main-line at: 8 Symons Street SW3, tel: 0171 730 6504.

Oxford Street and Regent Street

Baldinini Trend

23 James Street W1
Tel: 0171 224 4818

Open: Mon–Sat 10am–7pm, late night Thurs till 8pm and Sun 11am–3pm

Hand-made shoes are a luxury out of reach of most – but Baldinini, a family business now in its fourth generation, manages to make 85% of its work by hand with prices that are accessible to all (from £80). There are already 14 shops in Europe, the USA and the Far East, so it seems that Britain is the last to catch on to the company's refined method of shoemaking.

Cable and Co

48 South Molton Street W1
Tel: 0171 629 9969

Open: Mon–Sat 10am–6.30pm and late night Thurs till 7.30pm

See page 217.

Church's

201 Regent Street W1
Tel: 0171 734 2438

Open: Mon–Sat 9am–6.30pm and late night Thurs till 7.30pm

Perhaps the most famous shoe manufacturer in Britain, Church's is popular with tourists and true Brits alike for its classic courts, brogues and loafers for men and women. The Northamptonshire family business, together with its sister group Jones the Bootmakers, now has 103 branches across the country banking on the trad not fads.

For branches or mail order, call: 01323 649408.

Clarks

260 Oxford Street W1
Tel: 0171 499 0305

Open: Mon–Sat 9.30am–6.30pm, late night Thurs till 8pm and Sun 11.30am–5.30pm

The introduction of Clarks desert boots was a high point in its 170-year history. Hand-assembled from top hides and plantation-rubber crepe, over

275,000 pairs are sold every year, some to Paul Weller and Liam Gallagher, and even to Calvin Klein, Workers for Freedom and Margaret Howell for their catwalk shows. The low point was the scuffed school shoes that most of us had to wear in the playground. Over the years Clarks has stuck with its reputation for comfort over fashion, but this is about to change with the addition of more directional ranges aimed at the younger customer. Look out for simple loafers, boots and pumps in a wide range of sizes and width fittings, with prices starting from £20, plus a genuinely cool range of pastel Desert boots (known as Le Clarks in Europe) for this summer.

For branches, call: 01458 443131.

Crispins

28–30 Chiltern Street W1
Tel: 0171 486 8924
Open: Mon–Fri 10am–6pm, late night Thurs till 7pm and Sat 9.30am–4.30pm

Are your feet out of step with the norm? Crispins will have the shoes for you. Sizes range from 4 to10 in A and AA fittings and from 8½ to 12 in standard B and C fittings. Most are traditional, but there are high-fashion shoes too.

Dolcis

333 Oxford Street W1
Tel: 0171 493 9626
Open: Mon–Fri 10am–6.30pm, late night Thurs till 8pm, Sat 9.30am–6.30pm and Sun 12pm–6pm

Fashion fads and trendy teenage needs are catered for by Dolcis, part of the British Shoe Corporation (along with Cable and Co, Roland Cartier and Lilley and Skinner), which has claimed high-street domination for feet. The price is cheap but you get what you pay for, so don't expect shoes that last a lifetime. The atmosphere, however, has improved after a nationwide refurb.

For branches, call: 0171 495 8135.

Due Passi

27 James Street W1
Tel: 0171 224 1921
Open: Mon–Sat 10am–7pm, late night Thurs till 8pm and Sun 12pm–5pm

A combination of living in Italy and studying footwear design made designing for Due Passi a natural progression in Keith Buchanan's career. The stock is a mix of own-label and Unisa classics in beautiful leather, with prices starting at £45. Many are crepe-soled, making them comfortable as well as fashionable.

Faith

192–194 Oxford Street W1
Tel: 0171 580 9561
Open: Mon–Sat 10am–7pm, late night Thurs till 8pm and Sun 12pm–6pm

Faith doesn't seem to take itself, or its shoe designing, too seriously. Most styles are based on high-fashion shapes and shades, with an emphasis on affordability and accessibility – such as the patchwork and antiquated looks coming in for summer. There are cork, rope and wooden platforms too, should you have the urge.

For branches, call: 0800 289 2971.

Foster and Son

83 Jermyn Street SW1
Tel: 0171 930 5385
Open: Mon–Fri 9am–5pm and Sat 9am–3.30pm

See page 206.

Hobbs

8 South Molton Street W1
Tel: 0171 495 1557
Open: Mon–Sat 10am–6.30pm and late night Thurs till 7pm

See page 215.

James Taylor and Son

4 Paddington Street W1
Tel: 0171 935 4149
Open: Mon–Fri 9am–5.30pm and Sat 10am–1pm

In 1857, James Taylor walked from Norfolk to London to start a business in the then-fashionable Great Portland Street. Several generations later, his bespoke shoe business is still going strong, retaining the original craftsmanship and many original designs. A distinguishing element is the Sherlock Holmes Collection (the shop is around the corner from Baker Street), an interpretation of late-Victorian designs, with names such as the Dr Watson Walker and the Lestrade, designed for tourists and detectives, presumably.

John Lobb

90 Jermyn Street SW1
Tel: 0171 930 8089
Open: Mon–Sat 10am–6pm and late night Thurs till 7pm

See page 205.

Parallel

22 Marylebone High Street W1
Tel: 0171 224 0441
Open: Mon–Sat 10am–6pm

Parallel is a store to watch, carrying an impressive range of Italian, French and Spanish names, such as the romantically titled Un Dimanche à Venise. Other names include Alberto Zago, Enrico Coveri and Gianni Bravo. What is equally impressive is the price, from £45. Men have their own branch opposite.

Men's at: 96 Marylebone High Street W1, tel: 0171 486 6440.

Ravel

184–188 Oxford Street W1
Tel: 0171 631 4135

Open: Mon 10.30am–7pm, Tues–Wed and Fri 9.30am–7pm, Thurs 9.30am–8pm, Sat 9.30am–6pm and Sun 12pm–6pm

Ravel improves by the season, turning out spot-on shoes for a spot-on price. The company is currently preparing for the millennium by redesigning its stores, and accessories will be the latest addition. For spring, the catwalk knock-off comes into its own, so look here before you spend a month's salary at Prada.

For branches or mail order, call: 0171 631 0224.

Robert Clergerie

67 Wigmore Street W1
Tel: 0171 935 3601

Open: Mon–Sat 10am–6pm and late night Thurs till 7pm

Fashionoids can spot a Clergerie heel at thirty paces. The charming Frenchman, who came to shoe design almost by accident, continually produces a balanced, basic collection of footwear that is architectural in look and comfortable by nature. The signatures: that curvy heel, or men's styling for women with crepe or latex soles, likely to set you back around £110–£300.

Roland Cartier

175–179 Oxford Street W1

CLOSED

Launched in 1976, Roland Cartier has a reputation for elegant evening shoes at high-street prices.

For branches, call: 0116 280 1433.

Sacha

147 Oxford Street W1
Tel: 0171 434 1467

Open: Mon–Sat 9.30am–6.30pm, late night Thurs till 8pm and Sun 12pm–6pm

Clubby street shoes for men and women at moderate prices. More chunky than Campbell's soups.

For branches, call: 0171 434 1467.

Shellys

266–270 Regent Street W1
Tel: 0171 287 0939

Open: Mon–Sat 9.30am–6.30pm and late night Thurs till 7.30pm

Shellys staff are not the most helpful in the world, but with the number of demanding customers that pass through the store each day, it's no wonder they look so hassled. Oxford Circus is the capital's most chaotic place to shop, and Shellys is no exception – after you have waited half-an-hour for your chunky-heeled shoe or winklepicker boot to be brought out, you are hard pressed to track down your sales assistant in order to complete the pair. A better idea is to visit one of Shellys' quieter shops – but not the Covent Garden branch, which is, if anything, even busier.

For branches, call: 0181 450 0066.

Shoe Express

72 Oxford Street W1
Tel: 0171 436 8791
Open: Mon–Sat 9am–7pm, late night Thurs till 8pm and Sun 11am–5pm

Well, it's not exactly Jimmy Choo, but if you're not fussy about what you put on your feet and you are working to a budget, then Shoe Express does the job. All the styles are displayed in pairs in their boxes in a sort of self-service, no-staff-required way. They're shoes, they're express and they're cheap – if you're lucky, you might even get change out of a tenner.

For branches, call: Talking Pages.

The Small and Tall Shoe Shop

71 York Street W1
Tel: 0171 723 5321
Open: Mon–Sat 10am–5pm and late night Thurs till 7pm

See page 191.

Trickers

67 Jermyn Street SW1
Tel: 0171 930 6395
Open: Mon–Fri 9.30am–5.30pm and Sat 9.30am–5pm

See page 204.

Soho and West Soho

Jones the Bootmaker

15 Foubert's Place W1
Tel: 0171 287 5301
Open: Mon–Sat 10am–6.30pm and late night Thurs till 7.30pm

Although originally established in 1857, the Jones you see today was relaunched in 1987 in an attempt to move into a more fashion-conscious market while retaining the company's heritage. The move has worked well; Jones now appears regularly in *Vogue*, and you can find several key directional styles for men and women in among the traditional brogues, loafers and boots. Look for precious summer sandals and the Bootleg Boot, inspired by The Beatles. The sister store, Church's, sticks to more classic lines. Prices from £70 for ladies' shoes, £80 for men's.

For branches, call: 01323 649408.

Soho Shoes

73 Brewer Street W1
Tel: 0171 734 4848
Open: Mon–Fri 10am–6.30pm and Sat 10am–6pm

Selling traditional bench-made shoes at a fraction of bespoke prices, Soho Shoes carries Trickers' St James's collection, John Spencer, Allen Edmunds and Alfred Sargeant for men and women. Prices start at £90, a quarter of what you would expect to pay for made-to-measure shoes elsewhere, but with the same clever craftsmanship and meticulous attention to detail.

Underground Shoes

22 Carnaby Street W1
Tel: 0171 494 2338
Open: Mon–Sat 10am–6.30pm and late night Thurs till 7pm

"Made in England" is the selling point for these shoes, reflected in the many Union Jack designs – not a look that is necessarily to everyone's taste. The shoes are, in the main, designed for club wear, with platforms, wedges, stilettoes and tough-stuff boots with those all-important steel-toe caps. If you're a Fifties freak, ask about the range of brothel creepers. If you want elegance, look elsewhere.

South-west

Cara

7 Sheen Road, Richmond TW9
Tel: 0181 940 6441
Open: Mon–Sat 10am–6pm and Sun 12pm–5pm

Cara's own-label shoes have found the elusive Holy Grail of modern retailing: they are both smart and stylish. Ranges from Guess? and Laceys make up the mix, with prices from £39.95 for a basic loafer to £135 for ankle boots. Although mainly a shoe shop, there's a small clothing section at the back that sells "impulse buy" must-haves from WoolfeEurope, Assets (knitwear) and Great Plains.

St Cassien

70a High Street, Wimbledon SW19
Tel: 0181 241 0002/241 0003
Open: 10am–6pm seven days a week

Stop here for men's shoes by Charles Jourdan, Fratelli Rossetti, Grenson and Jeffrey West, underwear by Boss and socks by Burberry; women's stock includes shoes by Emporio Armani, Fratelli Rossetti and Un Dimanche à Venise, with prices from £79 to £170 for skinny, long boots.

Also at: Cabot's Place East, Canary Wharf E14, tel: 0171 363 6161.

All Over the Shop

CF (Cruise Flannels)

186 Chiswick High Road W4
Tel: 0181 994 1028

Open: Mon–Fri 10am–6pm, late night Thurs till 6.30pm and Sat 9.30am–6.30pm

Cruise Flannels is a hybrid of two successful Northern retailers, Cruise and Flannels, with outlets in Manchester, Nottingham, Newcastle and Glasgow. This – the first London branch run by a very enthusiastic team, including manager and all-round nice guy Gary White – sells an extensive selection of shoes from Rider Burns, Katharine Hamnett, Jeffrey West, Guess? and Moschino. The store also carries a near-complete stock of Patrick Cox, Wannabe and PC (the second diffusion range), and has the advantage of being able to request further sizes from the other branches, delivered within a couple of days.

KWGS

27 Turnham Green Terrace W4
Tel: 0181 747 1771

Open: Mon–Sat 10am–6pm

What KWGS stands for is, according to owner Simon Marsh, too rude to print. We can, however, let on that this laid-back shop sells outdoor, street shoes and trainers by Travel Fox, Base, Bronx and Jack Morgan, alongside unisex accessories by Hooch, Hussy and Custard Shop. Actually, the guys in the shop are so laid-back that they're practically vertical; no hard-sell here.

Shipton and Heneage

117 Queenstown Road SW8
Tel: 0171 738 8484

Open: Mon–Fri 9am–6pm and Sat 10am–2pm

In the style Gobi between Battersea and Clapham, Shipton and Heneage makes traditional gentlemen's shoes that can be ordered via mail order. There are two main ranges: prices start at £75 for the Grade range, £125 for Premium.

Accessories

Bond Street

Aigner

Leather and jewellery

119 New Bond Street W1

Tel: 0171 499 4041

Open: Mon–Fri 10am–6.30pm, late night Thurs till 7pm and Sat 10am–6pm

This is a new shop, stocking Aigner's well-known brand of luxury leather goods – bags, belts, boots and shoes – together with silk scarves, ties, costume jewellery and fragrance. A concise fashion line for women (business suits and upmarket weekend clothes) completes the concept from this Munich-based company, slated to open 118 further boutiques across the world by the end of 1997. Phew.

Asprey

Jewellery and luxury goods

165–169 New Bond Street W1

Tel: 0171 493 6767

Open: Mon–Fri 9.30am–5.30pm and Sat 10am–5pm

Asprey was founded in 1781 by William Asprey and is now deemed to be one of the most luxurious shops in the world, frequented by European royalty and Indian maharajas and look-but-don't-buy shoppers alike. Ornamental lamps in diamond-encrusted quartz may not be everyone's cup of Darjeeling, but you have to admire the craftsmanship that goes into creating such costly bric-a-brac. Of course, Asprey's reputation for high-class jewels is unrivalled, and this is where arbiters of taste can drink their fill. Not a place for the jeans-and-T-shirt brigade.

Cartier

Jewellery

175 New Bond Street W1

Tel: 0171 493 6962

Open: Mon–Fri 10am–6pm and Sat 10am–5pm

Cartier is known for huge rocks and big prices, and as the *only* place to buy an engagement ring. Or at least, that's what you can tell your fiancé. Iman wears a Cartier Tank watch, Jerry Hall has a Cartier charm bracelet, and Richard Burton gave a 69-carat Cartier diamond to Elizabeth Taylor for one of her many birthdays. As *Vogue* said recently: "The right people wear it, and if you want to be one of them, you'll wear it too." Current Cartier favourites include Love Bangles, Rolling Rings in three colours: red, white and yellow gold, and – of course – the Mimi Rings. The new collection, La Création, includes a necklace called Luminance, which is reversible – plain white gold for day, flip it over and, *voilà*, you've got diamonds for evening! Brilliant.

Also at: 188 Sloane Street SW1, tel: 0171 235 9023.

Demas

Jewellery

31 Burlington Arcade W1
Tel: 0171 493 9496
Open: Mon–Fri 10.45am–4.45pm, Sat 10.45am–12.45pm

You will find a trove of pretty Georgian and Victorian antique and costume jewellery at Demas, with a faithful clientele who have visited the shop throughout its 45-year history. No Ratner's-style rows of rings here, but an eclectic jumble which is incomparably more exciting to truffle through.

Frederick Fox

Hats

87–91 New Bond Street W1
Tel: 0171 629 5706
Open: by appointment only

From his third-floor atelier, Australian-born Mr Fox provides grand gestures of style to Joan Collins, Diana Rigg, Ivana Trump – and also, for the last 28 years, to the Queen. In between celebrity appointments, he designs marvellous millinery: coloured silk hats perch like exotic birds around the room, while crin and straw hats festoon tables and spill from cupboards (this season the major spillage will be in orange and pink). Fox also made the hats for *2001: A Space Odyssey*, and for the Red or Dead catwalk shows. Should the Queen be told?

MCM

Leather goods

4 Old Bond Street W1
Tel: 0171 629 6727
Open: Mon–Sat 10am–6pm and late night Thurs till 7pm

Michael Cromer, founder of MCM, is a former model and actor who recognised a gap in the leather goods market for a fine-quality range of suitcases and set about filling it. He also took on Cindy Crawford to invest his ad campaign with a touch of Supermodel glamour. Now the collections incorporate more than 300 products, from sporty bags to discreetly embossed signature pieces in coloured leather – the latter finding favour, unwittingly, with the New York hip-hop set.

Rolex

Watches

5 New Bond Street W1
Tel: 0171 493 2716
Open: Mon–Fri 9.30am–5.30pm and Sat 10am–5.30pm

Probably the most desired, not to mention knocked off, name in wrist décor, Rolex is the kind of purchase you do not enter into lightly (the annual overhaul alone costs a small fortune). But if you want to make sure you own the genuine article, it pays to buy here.

Tiffany and Co

Jewellery

25 Old Bond Street W1

Tel: 0171 409 2790

Open: Mon–Sat 10am–5.30pm

Tiffany and Co is America's leading jeweller, founded in 1837 by Charles Lewis Tiffany. Home to 400 master jewellers dedicated to creating enduring designs, the company recently celebrated ten years in London with an exhibition of Elsa Peretti's work. The Tiffany cross and the silver coffee-bean necklace are worn on some of the most elegantly fashionable necks in the world. Jewellery fanatics will find everything they dream of here. Apart from breakfast.

Camden

Custom Leather/Sue Engels

Leather goods and shoes

Unit 72 Camden Lock, Chalk Farm Road NW1

Tel: 0171 482 1407

Open: Sat–Sun 11am–6pm, call first for weekdays

In the relative calm of West Yard (calm and Camden do not tend to go together) are Henry Tomkins for hand-crafted leather briefcases, satchels and travel bags and Sue Engels for leather shoes and sandals. Both offer off-the-peg and made-to-measure designs. Prices from £25 for bags and £50 for shoes.

Roger Stone

Jewellery

68 West Yard, Camden Lock NW1

Tel: 0171 267 7056

Open: Wed–Sun 10am–5.30pm

One of Camden's few remaining secrets, Roger Stone's silver jewellery is exquisitely hand-crafted and any design can be made to order in a fortnight. Some of the most popular pieces include the daisy-chain necklaces, earrings and bracelets, jigsaw rings and unisex engraved rings. Don't tell your friends.

Chelsea

Anya Hindmarch

Handbags

91 (upstairs) Walton Street SW3

Tel: 0171 584 7644

Open: Mon–Fri 9.30am–6pm and Sat 10am–4pm

See page 219.

Arabesk

Jewellery

156 Walton Street SW3

Tel: 0171 584 3858

Open: Mon–Sat 10am–6pm

See page 219.

Butler and Wilson

Jewellery

189 Fulham Road SW3

Tel: 0171 352 3045

Open: Mon–Sat 10am–6pm and late night Wed till 7pm

Butler and Wilson started out as a stall in Portobello Market, selling antique art deco jewellery. From these modest beginnings, the team soon began to design its own collections. It still carries a selection of antique pieces, but the contemporary ranges of costume jewellery are the ones that make it into magazines.

Also at: 20 South Molton Street W1, tel: 0171 409 2955.

Cox and Power

(&)

Jewellery

95 Walton Street SW3

Tel: 0171 589 6335

Open: Mon–Sat 10am–6pm

See page 219.

Detail

(&)

Jewellery

4a Symons Street SW3

Tel: 0171 730 8488

Open: Mon–Sat 10am–6pm

The fair ladies of the fashion press are nuts about this shop. Frances Robinson, one half of the team behind Detail (her husband, Eamon McMahon, is the other half), produces witty pieces that will make your heart sing. In among the enamel and rose-gold jewellery is a range of chunky ID bracelets and rings, starting from £50. Be careful, top prices reach into the thousands, so don't fall in love too fast.

Farah Lister

Jewellery

137 Fulham Road SW3

Tel: 0171 823 9878

Open: Mon–Sat 10am–6pm

Lister's bold, captivating jewellery is for bold, glamorous women. She uses beads and Venetian glass with gold to create costume necklaces (from £100) and earrings (from £35 to £125).

Henrys

Luggage
143 Fulham Road SW3
Tel: 0171 581 1321
Open: Mon–Sat 9.30am–6pm

Henrys stocks smart-set luggage, as seen at all the best hotels. Look out for the Mandarina Duck label – it's great.

Kiki McDonough

Jewellery
77c Walton Street SW3
Tel: 0171 581 1777
Open: Mon–Fri 9.30am–5.30pm and Sat 10am–1pm

See page 219.

Merola

Jewellery
178 Walton Street SW3
Tel: 0171 589 0365
Open: Mon–Sat 10am–6pm

See page 220.

Van Peterson Designs

Jewellery
194–196 Walton Street SW3
Tel: 0171 584 1101
Open: Mon–Sat 10am–6pm, Wed 10am–7pm and Sun 12am–5pm

See page 220

City and East End

Fred Bare

Hats
118 Columbia Road E2
Tel: 0171 739 4612
Open: 10am–2pm Sun only

Fred Bare millinery is available in most department stores – but if you want to see work in progress, visit the shop, which is open just once a week to catch the myriad visitors to the Columbia Road flower market. The two designers behind the label have been in business for more than a decade and provide witty, woolly, fluffy, funky hats of all shapes and sizes – including puffa hats. Twice a year Fred Bare discounts the lot in a warehouse sale; call for dates.

Hide All

(&)

Outdoor wear and leather

43 Shad Thames, Tower Bridge SE1
Tel: 0171 403 2600
Open: 10.30am–5.30pm seven days a week

Concentrating on hand-crafted leather goods and outdoor clothing, Hide All first set up shop in Greenwich Market, where the original outlet is still located. It stocks Barbour and Driza Bone waxed coats, padded waistcoats and riding jackets, with prices from £39 to £169. The leather goods include The Bridge from Italy, the very English Papworth, Chesneau from Ireland, and Hidesign.

Also at: 9 Greenwich Market SE10, tel: 0181 858 6104.

Lesley Craze Gallery

(&)

Jewellery

34–35 Clerkenwell Green EC1
Tel: 0171 608 0393
Open: Mon–Sat 10am–5.30pm

Clerkenwell Green boasts a thriving community of interesting retailers, few more so than Lesley Craze, whose gallery-shop showcases the work of over 100 British jewellery designers. You will find a wealth of talent, with prices starting at £100. If you have a lower budget, Craze 2 is the more frivolous end of the business, with colourful, semi-precious, often crazy jewellery from £20.

Sombrero

(&)

Hats

105a Commercial Street E1
Tel: 0171 377 6324
Open: Mon–Fri 9.30am–5.30pm and Sun 9am–2pm (closed Sat)

The happiest hatters in town, Sombrero can conjure up any design you desire. One of the first shops to appear in the Spitalfields development, it has led the way for others to follow, making this a great area to find a truly individual purchase. Sombrero will sell any design you see in the shop or will make to order in any fabric and style – with prices in everyone's range.

Covent Garden

Accessorize

Jewellery, hats, scarves and bags

Unit 22 The Market WC2
Tel: 0171 240 2107
Open: Mon–Sat 10am–8pm and Sun 11am–7pm

This is an increasingly worthwhile shop for throwaway accessories. The colour stories are always in step with the season, so you can bank on plenty of prettiness in store this summer, particularly given that Accessorize is a division of Monsoon. The evening bags for under £15 are perfect – although the jewellery isn't – and the straw hats are just the thing for summer picnics.

Crazy Pig Designs

Jewellery

38 Shorts Gardens WC2

Tel: 0171 240 4305

Open: Mon–Sat 10.30am–6.30pm

What brings The Rolling Stones, Ozzie Osbourne and Dave Stewart to this upbeat shop? Chunks of solid silver wrought into ET aliens, skulls and Batman insignia, that's what. Ageing rock legends aside, Crazy Pig stocks T-bar chains and ID bracelets which are a sight more sensible, with prices from a mere £10. The cheery team also undertakes commissions, so if you have an idea, or a stone you want set, then pop in.

Janet Fitch

Jewellery

37a Neal Street WC2

Tel: 0171 240 6332

Open: Mon–Sat 11am–7pm and Sun 1pm–6pm

See page 210.

Octopus

Gifts and bags

54 Neal Street WC2

Tel: 0171 836 2911

Open: Mon–Sat 10.30am–7.30pm and Sun 12pm–6pm

See page 210.

Stephen Jones

Hats

36 Great Queen Street WC2

Tel: 0171 242 0770

Open: Tues–Fri 12pm–7pm and Sat 11am–5pm

As Vivienne Westwood once said, "When a lady wears a Stephen Jones hat, she is an elegant lady and not just a lady wearing a hat" – a fitting tribute to one of our most respected and enduring milliners, whose salon has been the toast of WC2 for over 17 years. As well as his own whimsical creations (perky flowerpot hats, mini bowler hats, vast dishes of feather and net), he has developed collections for Jasper Conran, Comme des Garçons, Jean Paul Gaultier and Jil Sander, and examples of his work can be found in the permanent collections of the Victoria and Albert Museum and the Brooklyn Museum in New York.

The Hat Shop

Hats

Now 14 Lamb Street E1
Tel: 0171 247 1120
Open: 10.30am–6.30pm Mon–Sat

See page 211.

Greenwich

Autumn and May

Jewellery

3 Greenwich Market SE10
Tel: 0181 293 9361
Open: seven days a week 10.30am–5.30pm

Specialising in amber, semi-precious stones and design-led jewellery, Autumn and May has now introduced designer pieces displaying meticulous attention to detail and quality. New too is a range of amber set in gold, and a commission service allowing clients to have jewellery made to individual requirements.

Hampstead and Highgate

Tanners

Leather goods

23 Hampstead High Street NW3
Tel: 0171 431 1572
Open: Mon–Sat 10am–6pm and Sun 11am–6pm

Tanners, with four London branches, is gift city. As well as a good own-label collection, there are countless leading names in leatherwear, such as Mulberry, The Bridge and Schneiders. Underwear, socks and accessories from Paul Smith complete the picture. Owner Peter Bennet also carries out repairs to the own-label collections at his Turnham Green shop.

Also at: 8 Hill Street, Richmond, tel: 0181 332 1655, 2 Turnham Green Terrace W4, tel: 0181 994 4762, and Cabot Place East, Canary Wharf E14, tel: 0171 513 0188.

Highbury and Islington

Estilo

Jewellery

103 St Paul's Road N1

Tel: 0171 359 8279

Open: Mon–Fri 9.30am–6pm and Sat 10am–5.30pm

Estilo specialises in silver jewellery culled from across the globe, particularly from South and Central America.

Dream Time

Jewellery

Shop 7, Ground Floor Georgian Village, 30–31 Islington Green N1

No phone

Open: Wed 7am–3pm and Sat 8.30am–4pm

The Georgian Village is an indoor antiques market that only opens on Wednesday and Saturday, leaving the traders free for the rest of the week to track down their unique stock. Dream Time is the best unit for wonderful period costume jewellery from 1900 to 1950. The appeal is born of an element of humour: wacky fruit necklaces and earrings, and Christmas-tree brooches (a surprising best seller in the winter). Prices can be anything from £5 to £300, but if you mention the word cash you'll be offered a 10% discount.

Eclectica

Jewellery

2 Charlton Place N1

Tel: 0171 226 5625

Open: Mon–Sat 11am–6pm

This tiny shop just off Upper Street specialises in antique necklaces, earrings, and jewellery sets from the turn of the century to the present day. Most items originate from the United States and Europe, lovingly restored to their original condition. Much of the jewellery is bright, colourful and doesn't take itself too seriously; the same can be said of the sequinned fruit and *Saturday Night Fever* disco balls that can be made to order. Every home should have one.

Stephen Einhorn

Jewellery

210 Upper Street N1

Tel: 0171 359 4977

Open: Mon–Sat 10am–6pm

Shop here for anything from individual pieces of jewellery to furniture and even bath taps – all with an obscure twist, such as Einhorn's signature skulls. The jewellery is made on a commission basis and takes around six weeks to complete, although you can buy anything you see in the showroom. There is also a mail-order service with an extensive range of off-the-shelf pieces.

Kensington

The British Hatter

Hats

36 Kensington Church Street W8
Tel: 0171 361 0000
Open: Tues–Sat 10.15am–5.30pm

Pamela Bromley believes that colour co-ordination in millinery is a redundant concept, and steers her customers towards a mix-don't-match approach. For winter, there are cloches and velvet hats trimmed with organza; in summer, designs are lighter and more ornate. There are hats for hire, £25 for three days.

Also at: Riverside Centre, High Street, Kingston KT1, tel: 0181 546 0214.

The Hat House

Hats

7 Kensington Mall W8
Tel: 0171 727 3859
Open: Tues–Fri 10am–6pm and Sat 10.30am–5pm

Tucked away in a little lane off Kensington Church Street, Sharon Williams will match your chosen design to any outfit, and the resulting hat will be ready in two to four weeks. If you can't wait that long, there are ready-made collections in stock (prices from £75 to £295) and bags to match (from £98). If all you need is a new look for a worn favourite, a renovation service will restore your old hat to its former glory. Ascot, here you come.

Manguette

Jewellery

40 Gordon Place, Holland Street W8
Tel: 0171 937 2897
Open: Mon–Sat 11am–6pm

Maguette, here for 15 years, specialises in amber and fresh-water pearls. The styles are classic, although a few surpirses are in store, such as the liquid silver chokers that are deliciously modern. Average prices are £250–£500.

Knightsbridge

The Bridge

(&)

Leather goods

53 Beauchamp Place SW3
Tel: 0171 589 8055
Open: Mon–Sat 10am–6pm and late night Wed till 7pm

Most of the accessories here are hand-made from butter-soft Florentine hide. The entire stock – from key-rings, wallets and Filofaxes to bags, briefcases and trunks – is designed by Fernando Biagioni and produced in Italy, the home of luxuriant leather. Prices start at £12 (you guessed it, that's the key-ring) and go up to a whacking £8,000. A beautifully crafted handbag costs around £150.

Coach

Handbags

8 Sloane Street SW1
Tel: 0171 235 1507
Open: Mon–Sat 10am–6pm and late night Wed till 7pm

Serviceable leather handbags are the forte of this 50-year-old American company based in Manhattan.

Cobra and Bellamy

Jewellery

149 Sloane Street SW1
Tel: 0171 730 9993
Open: Mon–Sat 10.30am–6pm

Launched in 1980 by partners Veronica Manussis and Tania Hunter, Cobra and Bellamy produces several mouthwatering ranges using silver, amber and jet. The own-line watches, *faux* pearl necklaces, brooches and earrings are complemented with the work of Barbara Bertagnolli, who designs collectable silver and 24-carat gold jewellery set with gemstones and exclusive to Cobra and Bellamy.

Dower and Hall

Jewellery

60 Beauchamp Place SW3
Tel: 0171 589 8474
Open: Mon–Sat 10.30am–6.30pm

Dower and Hall design their own quiet jewellery, balanced with up-and-coming collections from Sarah Pulvertaft, Diana Porter and Sally Ann Lowe. The wedding and engagement rings make a break with tradition, combining white with yellow gold, silver with yellow gold, or white gold with platinum.

Folli Follie

Jewellery

45 Beauchamp Place SW3
Tel: 0171 589 0552
Open: Mon–Sat 10am–6pm and late night Wed till 7pm

This is a specialist jewellery retailer whose stock is designed by Michel Comté and produced in Greece for export all over the world. Particularly popular with the Japanese, the bi-annual collections include silver and gold pieces set with semi-precious stones. There is also a Folli Follie perfume and after-shave, with, we are told, a "sparkling" aroma.

Georgiana Scott

Jewellery

11a Brompton Arcade SW3
Tel: 0171 591 0771
Open: Mon–Sat 10am–7pm

Georgiana Scott's clever combinations of silver and gold can be made to your own design. Don't be afraid to chat to the manager, as many of the rings are held under the counter.

John Boyd

Hats

16 Beauchamp Place SW3
Tel: 0171 589 7601
Open: Mon–Sat 9.30am–5pm

If you've got a spare couple of hundred pounds and a wedding in the diary, John Boyd is worth a visit. His team can make a co-ordinating hat for the big day in a fortnight – all they need from you is a vague idea of what the finished product should look like. He has been in the business since 1949, so should know the ropes by now, but suggestions from the floor are always welcome.

Kenneth Jay Lane

Jewellery

58 Beauchamp Place SW3
Tel: 0171 584 1985
Open: Mon–Sat 9.15am–5.30pm

Pearls, pearls, pearls – as worn and adored by Barbara Bush, Shirley Bassey and Jerry Hall. Watch as Jerry flips her blonde locks 180 degrees over her head to reveal an earlobe complete with its Kenneth Jay Lane dangly earring. The designer is based in New York and Florida, where he tinkers with some of the finest jewellery ingredients in the world to come up with his sumptuous collections, both real and *faux*. Prices from £10 to £600.

Also at: 30 Burlington Arcade W1, tel: 0171 499 1364.

Louis Vuitton

Leather goods

198–199 Sloane Street SW1
Tel: 0171 235 3356
Open: Mon–Sat 9.30am–6pm and late night Wed till 7pm

From St Moritz to St Ives, from Gstaad to Golders Green, the Louis Vuitton signature monogram canvas spells *expense*. Globetrotters who can afford it trot the globe with a complete set of Vuitton trunks and vanity cases, which travel shrouded in plastic to preserve the luxuriant sheen of the fabric. The Eighties were good to Vuitton, as fashion went label crazy and the LV became one of the handful of important initials to brandish in public. After a fallow period, the monogram is back on the most-wanted lists – particularly if you can get your hands on a vintage handbag. Company chairman Bernard Arnault is the power broker behind the new British designers signed to sister companies Christian Dior and Givenchy. This year, Arnault's worst-kept secret is that American funky designer Marc Jacobs is joining Vuitton to produce a clothing range. Can Arnault out-Gucci Tom Ford? Watch and see.

Also at: 149 New Bond Street W1, tel: 0171 409 0155.

McKenna and Co

(&)

Jewellery

28 Beauchamp Place SW3
Tel: 0171 584 1966

Open: Mon–Sat 10am–5.45pm

This is a family-run business dealing in fine antique and period jewellery, with some new ranges from designers such as Charles Garnier. From Georgian, Victorian and Edwardian to art deco and nouveau pieces, the shop is a real treasure trove of delights. Don't be put off by the buzzer entry system, the staff are friendly and willing to help.

Notting Hill

Bill Amberg

Handbags

10 Chepstow Road W2
Tel: 0171 727 3560

Open: Mon–Tues and Fri–Sat 10am–6pm, late nights Wed and Thurs till 7pm and Sun 12pm–5pm

Billy Handbag, as he is known to his fans, makes beautiful bags, shown off to their full advantage in his newly opened first shop. Here you can order spe-cific pieces of luggage (from collections past and present), furniture or even leather flooring should you require it. An on-site studio undertakes private commissions, while the deftly displayed off-the-shelf collections are fast introducing a whole new audience to the Bill Amberg name.

Dinny Hall

Jewellery

200 Westbourne Grove W11
Tel: 0171 792 3913

Mon–Fri 10.30am–6.30pm and Sat 10am–6pm

Dinny is another favourite face in W11. This, her first shop, opened in 1992 after a decade spent supplying Liberty, Harvey Nichols and Browns with her modern, more-ish jewellery. A past winner of the British Accessory Designer of the Year, she will make commissions to order if you're not entranced by the collection on display.

Also at: 54 Fulham Road SW3, tel: 0171 589 9192.

Frontiers

Jewellery

37–39 Pembridge Road W11
Tel: 0171 727 6132
Open: Mon–Sat 11am–6.30pm

Frontiers sells ethnic jewellery from Africa, Asia and South America, plus loose beads so you can make your own at home.

Gilly Forge

Hats

14 Addison Avenue W11
Tel: 0171 603 3833
Open: Mon–Fri 9am–5pm by appointment

Hidden away, but well worth discovering, Forge's workshop is as bright and pretty as the hats she makes. In summer, the main styles are bound for Ascot and garden parties: fine-straw, wide-brimmed Panamas and crin creations. In winter, things get cosy, with oodles of fake fur and felt. Choose from an off-the-peg style (stocked at Harrods and Harvey Nichols), or visit the studio for the made-to-measure service, costing around £350 and ready in 10 days.

J & M Davidson

Leather goods

62 Ledbury Road W11
Tel: 0171 243 2089
Open: Mon–Sat 10am–6pm

See page 207.

Lulu Guinness

Bags

66 Ledbury Road W11
Tel: 0171 221 9686
Open: Mon–Sat 10am–5pm

See page 208.

The Cross

Hats, bags and scarves

141 Portland Road W11
Tel: 0171 727 6760
Open: Mon–Sat 10.30am–6pm

The Cross is the wild-fire whisper of the moment, a cool, calm, white space tucked away in one of the most tranquil areas of London. Much of the stock is the work of individual designers such as Emma Bernhardt (who makes groovy shopping bags from fabrics sourced on trips to Central America) and Lyme (whose straw baskets were the defining mark of the fashion editor last summer). The Jackson label is the work of identical twins, who have their own clothing range to accompany a line of funky customised flip-flops. Finally, RCA graduate Asta Barrington makes throws and scarves that are all set to be the Next Big Thing. One visit and you'll know you saw it here first.

Solange Azagury-Partridge

(&)

Jewellery

171 Westbourne Grove W11
Tel: 0171 792 0197
Open: Mon–Sat 11am–6pm

Solange Azagury-Partridge's fascination with jewellery began after working with Butler and Wilson's dealer Gordon Watson. The engagement ring she designed for herself elicited innumerable enquiries, and led her to set up in business. Seven years on, her brand of bold gold jewellery studded with precious stones has won the favour of David Bailey, Elle MacPherson and Madonna. This, her first shop, opened in 1995 and is a reflection of her inimitable sense of style, with its Jaffa-orange leather floor, gold-leaf cases (designed by Tom Dixon) and padded velvet walls – an oversized jewellery box selling if-only jewellery.

Oxford Street and Regent Street

Agatha

Jewellery

4 South Molton Street W1
Tel: 0171 495 2779
Open: Mon–Sat 10am–6pm and late night Thurs till 7pm

See page 215.

Bates the Hatter

(&)

Hats

21a Jermyn Street SW1
Tel: 0171 734 2722
Open: Mon–Fri 9am–5.30pm and Sat 9.30am–4pm

See page 203.

Boodle and Dunthorne

(&)

Jewellery

128–130 Regent Street W1
Tel: 0171 437 5050
Open: Mon–Sat 9.30am–6pm

Boodle and Dunthorne, established in 1798 and now owned by the Wainwright brothers, specialises in diamonds – particularly spectacular engagement rings, which you can commission and insure for 12 months. There is also a large selection of Rolex and Patek Phillippe watches.

Also at: 58 Brompton Road SW3, tel: 0171 584 6363.

Bucci

Leather goods

16 Princes Arcade Jermyn Street SW1
Tel: 0171 734 1846
Open: Mon–Fri 9.30am–5.30pm and Sat 9.30am–4pm

Although Britain is not renowned for its high-quality leather goods, Bucci stocks two names that are – Papworth and Launer. Papworth specialises in hand-crafted briefcases and luggage in English bridle hide, Launer concentrates on handbags and wallets. Collections from Italy, France and Germany round off the stock, with prices from £42 for a belt to £1,700 for a crocodile-skin bag.

David Shilling

Hats

88 Marylebone High Street W1
Tel: 0171 487 3179
Open: by appointment only

Creating a three-feet-wide, black and white hat at the tender age of 12 for his mother to wear to Ascot was David Shilling's first introduction to the world of millinery. His witty, charming designs and travelling exhibitions have since earned him the title of the "original mad hatter" amongst the many who admire his work. If you need to ask the price then you're probably in the wrong place.

Garrard and Co

Jewellery

112 Regent Street W1
Tel: 0171 734 7020
Open: Mon–Sat 9am–5.30pm

This upstanding company is famous for outstanding jewellery. The prices match the quality, and the commissioning service is unrivalled – dream it up, set it on paper and the Garrard smiths will get to work.

Georgina von Etzdorf

Scarves

50 Burlington Arcade W1
Tel: 0171 409 7789
Open: Mon–Sat 9.30am–6pm

Luscious scarves, shawls and stoles in velvet, devoré and lighter-than-air chiffon are von Etzdorf's calling cards. The original designs are produced in watercolour before being transferred to the fabric, giving her products a fluid, individual look – and a high price (from £95). The wild beauty of the scarves has won her a huge following in the fashion industry, and has become the basis for a more comprehensive range including plush velvet jackets and delectable evening dresses, all in those rich, rare colours.

Mappin and Webb

Jewellery

170 Regent Street W1
Tel: 0171 734 3801

Open: Mon–Sat 9.30am–6pm and late night Thurs till 7pm

Mappin and Webb sells top-of-the-range baubles at top-drawer prices. The diamond rings are designed and set in its own workshop and can be made to suit engagements, anniversaries and Christmas presents. The company holds royal warrants as silversmiths to the Queen and the Prince of Wales.

Also at: 413 Oxford Street W1, tel: 0171 409 3377, 125–126 Fenchurch Street EC3, tel: 0171 626 3171, and 65 Brompton Road SW3, tel: 0171 584 9361.

Osprey

Leather bags

11 St Christopher's Place W1
Tel: 0171 935 2824

Open: Mon–Sat 10am–6pm and late night Thurs till 7pm

Osprey are the leaders in contemporary and alluring hand-made bags that are more affordable than you might think. A shoulder bag can be as little as £160, while a classic tote bag is £295. The Kelly bags are *almost* the genuine article.

Also at: 42 Beauchamp Place SW3, tel: 0171 823 8338.

Philip Somerville

Hats

38 Chiltern Street W1
Tel: 0171 224 1517

Open: Mon–Fri 9.30am–5.30pm

Philip Somerville moved from his Bond Street store to the charming Chiltern Place in 1995 after 21 years in the millinery trade. The key to his lasting success lies in the classic, beautifully created designs – wide-brimmed hats or perky pillboxes – that have been worn by some of Britain's most influential women, including the Princess of Wales, Margaret Thatcher and Joan Collins. The ultimate recognition came in 1994 with the appointment of a royal warrant.

Simon Carter

Sunglasses

15 Quadrant Arcade, 80–82 Regent Street W1
Tel: 0171 287 4363

Open: Mon–Sat 10am–6.30pm and late night Thurs till 7.30pm

"Villainous sunglasses" based on Bond baddies in tortoiseshell or coloured acetate are Carter's forte, with prices starting at £65. The already extensive cufflink collection has been expanded to include Sixth Form, Groovy and Wide Boy ranges in engraved enamel and pewter, all packaged in wide-boy black lizard boxes; the watch collection has grown too and now caters for women, with prices from £85.

Soho and West Soho

American Retro

(&)

Jewellery

35 Old Compton Street W1
Tel: 0171 734 3477
Open: Mon–Sat 10.15am–7pm

The move away from clothing and towards accessories has been a resounding success for American Retro. Key names remain – including John Smedley, Dolce and Gabbana, Helmut Lang and W< – but the slack has been dropped to make way for more contemporary jewellery designers such as Janice Taylor. The shop is still a good place to visit for camp cards, home ideas and books on style and popular culture. The imaginatively titled *How to Draw a Radish and Other Fun Things to Do at Work* should make those nail-bitingly boring afternoons in the office just fly by.

The Great Frog

(&)

Jewellery

10 Ganton Street W1
Tel: 0171 439 9357
Open: Mon–Sat 10am–6.30pm

The Great Frog's in-yer-face jewellery hawks cowboy vulgarity to the hidden rock star within all of us. Think heavy metal: chunky, hand-carved silver rings, necklaces, bracelets and chains crowded with skulls, moons and enamel "eyeballs", although any commission is welcomed. The ever-cool ID bracelets are perhaps more suitable for most tastes. Prices start at £30 and go up to £200.

Also at: 51 Carnaby Street W1, tel: 0171 734 1900.

Jess James

(&)

Jewellery

3 Newburgh Street W1
Tel: 0171 437 0199
Open: Mon–Fri 11am–6.30pm, Tues 12pm–6.30pm, Thurs 11am–7pm and Sat 11am–6pm

See page 213.

South-west

Stones

Jewellery

9 Golden Court, Richmond TW9

Tel: 0181 332 7870

Open: Mon–Sat 10am–6pm and Sun 11am–5pm

Stones is an open-door jewellery gallery housing over 25 different and mainly local contemporary designers. As well as the two own-label ranges, the designers include Diana Porter (specialising in silver and gold inscribed pendants, bracelets and rings), Leonardo Pieroni (for hand-forged, masculine chains and bracelets with primitive influences) and Marsha Hunt (diminutive daisy, crown and heart jewellery as pretty and petite as the artist herself).

Toko

Jewellery

56 Church Street, Twickenham TW1

Tel: 0181 891 4214

Open: Mon–Fri 10am–6pm and Sat 9am–6pm

It can be difficult to track down fabulous, funky jewellery, so Toko is a rare find. It sells hand-crafted sterling-silver pieces – some simple enough to be worn every day, others set with semi-precious stones such as amber, amethyst, topaz, agate and garnet for grand occasions. The huge range of delicate or hefty chokers starting at £27 will have jewellery lovers reaching for their credit cards.

Victoria

Erickson Beamon

Jewellery

38 Elizabeth Street SW1

Tel: 0171 259 0202

Open: Mon–Fri 10am–6pm and Sat 11am–5pm

See page 202.

Philip Treacy

Hats

69 Elizabeth Street SW1

Tel: 0171 259 9605

Open: Mon–Fri 10am–6pm

See page 202.

Reema Pachachi

Jewellery

79 Elizabeth Street SW1
Tel: 0171 730 8030
Open: Mon-Fri 10.30am-6pm

See page 203.

Selina Blow

(&)

Scarves and bags

42 Elizabeth Street SW1
Tel: 0171 730 2449
Open: Mon–Fri 10am–6pm and Sat 11am–5pm

See page 202.

All Over the Shop

Edwina Ibbotson

Hats

45 Queenstown Road SW8
Tel: 0171 498 5390
Open: by appointment only

Working mainly in straw, Ibbotson lends a touch of wit and sophistication to the millinery trade. She started out with the Clerkenwell Green Award Scheme, a city-based charity that backs young designers (see page 121). Classic but never conservative, her summer straws and satins are succeeded by velvets and felts in the winter – with prices from £200 to £400. The hats are complemented by Fiona Clare bridalwear, Bijoux Heart jewellery and a select band of hand-made gloves, handbags and shoes, all delicately displayed in this pretty shop.

Hat Block and Last

Hats

47 North Street SW4
Tel: 0171 498 3279
Open: Thurs–Sat 10.30am–5pm

Made-to-measure and ready-made hats are sold from this charming little shop in Clapham Old Town. At the initial fitting, designer Suzanne White asks that your chosen outfit is in attendance to allow her to match it. The service takes a minimum of three weeks to complete, depending on the requirements, and prices start at a mere £70. A range of cute knitted childrenswear and exquisite jewellery by Peppi Taylor make this a boutique to beat.

Herald and Heart Hatters

Hats

131 St Philip Street SW8
Tel: 0171 627 2414
Open: Mon–Fri 10am–6pm and Sat 10am–5pm

Perhaps best known for its contributions to *Four Weddings and a Funeral* and *101 Dalmatians*, Herald and Heart is nothing if not modest about the hats it creates. The biannual collections include trad designs in straw and felt, but special orders are undertaken if you can't find exactly what you want. Should Battersea be too distant (and unreachable), try Harrods, John Lewis and Debenhams. Prices from £30 to £300.

Sadle

Jewellery

23 Turnham Green Terrace W4
Tel: 0181 742 1178
Open: Mon–Sat 9.30am–6pm, late night Thurs till 6.30pm and Sun 11am–5pm

Most of the silver jewellery in this wholesale/retail shop is imported from Indonesia, Mexico and Poland, although a small percentage is designed in this country by Jacqueline Michelow. Prices range from £3.50 to £400.

Slim Barrett

(&)

Jewellery

Studio 6, Shepperton House, Shepperton Road N1
Tel: 0171 354 9393
Open: by appointment only

Irishman Slim makes jewellery for catwalks across the globe, and routinely stars in the pages of glossy magazines. His work – predominantly in gold or silver – suggests his Celtic roots, with intricate turned designs, dainty tiaras and glorious hair pins. The signature crown motif finds its way on to plenty of pieces, while his bridal headdresses are worn at the most elaborate weddings. He even turns his hand to making chandeliers, should you so desire.

Specialist Shops

Bond Street

Ballantyne Cashmere

(&)

Cashmere

153a New Bond Street W1

Tel: 0171 493 4718

Open: Mon–Sat 9am–6pm

The company kicked off in the Twenties with men's woollen stockings and golf hose. Demand led to the introduction of "Intarsia", an intricate weaving technique which is now the Ballantyne hallmark. Each season leading designers consult on the range (currently Alistair Blair from Louis Féraud) to produce the relevant styles, shapes and colours for the moment. This year's batch includes tunics, gently flared trousers, summer twinsets and wrap skirt suits in blue, yellow, pink and purple. The men's collection features sea-island cotton, super-fine merino wool and cashmere knits, with sports jackets, classic trousers and one- and two-button single-breasted suits.

Berk

(&)

Cashmere

46–49 Burlington Arcade W1

Tel: 0171 493 0028

Open: Mon–Sat 9.30am–5.30pm

If you like cashmere (show me a girl who doesn't), then you will appreciate Berk's three floors devoted to the wicked wool. Twinsets start at £338, with five new colours introduced each season to keep up with current trends. A surprising best seller is the animal-print Ballantyne sweater at an extravagant £820, selling at speed to foreign customers.

Also at: 6 and 20–21 Burlington Arcade W1, tel: 0171 493 6558, and 61 Brompton Road SW3, tel: 0171 589 8000.

Boisvert

Lingerie

16b Grafton Street W1

Tel: 0171 409 1721

Open: Mon–Sat 10.30am–6.30pm

If you are looking for the most seductive lingerie in the most luxurious surroundings, this ethereal boutique is the place to visit. Originally established in Neal Street, Suzanne Boisvert's business recently relocated to larger premises to cope with her phenomenal success, thanks in part to a renewed interest in precious, special underwear. As well as lingerie from La Perla, Malizia, Cadolle, Sybaris, Aubade, Folies and Chantal Thomass, the shop sells the best in corsetry, nightwear and swimwear. The interior is complete with "corset chairs" and chaises longues by Scottish design team Precious McBane.

Courtenay/Stanbury Cashmere ®

Lingerie and cashmere

22 Brook Street W1

Tel: 0171 629 0542

Open: Mon–Sat 10am–6pm and late night Thurs till 7pm

A little piece of heaven: Courtenay lingerie and Elizabeth Stanbury cashmere share space at this snug boutique. It also sells La Perla and Hanro, two of the most covetable lingerie labels known to womankind. As well as ready-to-wear cashmere, a couture service is on offer (crewnecks from £170, cardigans from £285 and cashmere jackets from – gulp – £1,500).

Fogal

Hosiery

36 New Bond Street W1

Tel: 0171 493 0900

Open: Mon–Sat 9.30am–6pm

One of the new breed of shops devoted to hosiery, Fogal is the perfect place to pick up a pair of tights to go with that little designer number. Prices start at £15 and can rocket to £395 for a cashmere-and-silk body. Fogal has a sample stand, so try before you buy. Your legs will thank you for ever more.

Formes

Maternity clothes

33 Brook Street W1

Tel: 0171 493 2783

Open: Mon–Sat 10am–6pm and late night Thurs till 7pm

The days of kaftans, bib collars and elasticated waists for pregnant women are long gone, thanks in part to companies such as Formes, which makes a point of being fashionable as well as functional. Prices range from £40 for trousers to £210 for a tailored suit.

For mail order, call: 0171 820 3456.
For branches, call: 0171 820 3434.

Holland and Holland ®

Outdoor

31–33 Bruton Street W1

Tel: 0171 499 4411

Open: Mon–Fri 9.30am–6pm and Sat 10am–5pm

Holland and Holland was established in 1835 and originally built its reputation on the rifle manufacture which still continues today. Modern ranges include outdoor clothing, tweed jackets, silks, field boots, weekend luggage and accessories. Wherever possible, the clothes are made in Britain from British materials and centre on authenticity of shape and detailing. In winter, expect to find tweeds; summer alternatives are based on an African safari look, with linen jackets and Panama hats. Call for a mail-order catalogue.

S Fisher

Knitwear

22–23 and 32–33 Burlington Arcade W1
Tel: 0171 493 6221
Open: Mon–Sat 9am–6pm

Knitwear is the only product available here, so don't go trying to find anything else on the shelves; but rest assured, the stock is the best available from companies such as Pringle and Johnstons of Elgin and The Hayrick. If you're a fan of John Smedley, this is the home of the biggest range in London – and if you don't see what you want, ask and it will arrive within 24 hours.

Swaine Adeney/Herbert Johnson

Outdoor and hats

10 Old Bond Street W1
Tel: 0171 409 7277
Open: Mon–Sat 10am–6pm

The ultimate traditional outfitters, Swaine Adeney has joined forces with the ultimate traditional milliner to form this top stop for country and weekend wear. Swaine Adeney designs clothes and accessories to last a lifetime (tailored tweeds, riding jackets, bespoke umbrellas, leather attaché cases and shooting sticks). Herbert Johnson, meanwhile, can complement any outfit with a matching hat or provide an off-the-peg service for hats on the run.

Trevelyan

Men's accessories

63 Burlington Arcade W1
Tel: 0171 499 7189
Open: Mon–Sat 9am–5.30pm

This one-man operation, run by Terry Grigg, is a compact shop, but despite the lack of space, it offers an impressive selection of shirts, cufflinks and motif ties. Claustrophobics should visit early in the day.

Camden

Henry and Daughter

Made-to-measure

17–18 Camden Lock Place, Middle Yard, Chalk Farm Road NW1
Tel: 0171 284 3302
Open: Mon–Fri 10am–6pm and Sat–Sun 9am–6pm

Twenties flapper dresses, Thirties Charleston frocks – Henry and Daughter stocks all this plus a made-to-measure service in evening wear and wedding dresses. You won't find anything run of the mill, as the majority of the patterns are based on archive styles and most dresses can be adapted to suit your taste. Prices start from £67.

Keturah Brown

Lingerie

85 Regent's Park Road NW1
Tel: 0171 586 0512
Open: Thurs–Sat 10am–6pm

Visitors to the Victoria and Albert's exhibition "Fifty Years of Fashion" this year will discover Keturah Brown representing contemporary English underwear. Others are well advised to pay a vist to the impressive shop, where indulgence is expected. The silk satin and crêpe de Chine bras, camisoles and French knickers with exquisite appliqué lace detailing are the stuff of fairy-tales. Three years ago, Charlotte Danziger joined the outfit with made-to-measure occasion wear (dresses from £120, suits from £320).

Sixteen 47

Larger sizes

69 Gloucester Avenue NW1
Tel: 0171 483 0733
Open: Mon–Sat 10am–6pm

In 1991, Helen Teague and Dawn French took inspiration from the fact that 47% of British women are size 16 and above (hence the name), and formed a company to cater to their needs. These are real clothes for real women, with simple lines in good-quality fabrics. The main line is split into small (up to size 24), medium (up to size 36) and large (up to size 47), and incorporates three lengths in trousers, skirts and dresses – all of them inspiring designs rather than functional clothing. The designer label, "French & Teague", is available at Liberty too, and now Sixteen 47 is available through Littlewoods Home Shopping Catalogue for sofa-based shoppers.

For mail order, call: 0800 600 400.

Chelsea

Body Contact

Lingerie and hosiery

177 Draycott Avenue SW3
Tel: 0171 589 1920
Open: Mon–Sat 9.30am–6.15pm and late night Wed till 6.30pm

A recent Mintel poll found that 85% of women buy their lingerie for comfort alone. The other 15% probably shop here, where unabashed luxury rather than comfort is the key. The three main labels are La Perla (big on the *mmmm* factor), Malizia (younger, fresher) and Marvel (the design-led line). Body Contact also stocks Cotton Club, Hanro, Marie Jo (very good for its extensive range of cup sizes) nightwear from Joelle and hosiery from Wolford. Reports suggest that the shop's Christmas fashion show is a good place to pick up great presents, and a rich husband into the bargain. What a shop.

Brora

Cashmere

344 King's Road SW3

Tel: 0171 352 3697

Open: Mon–Sat 10am–6pm

This is the first retail outlet from this mail-order operation, which plays on its bulk-sell roots to produce some of the most affordable Scottish cashmere around. Summer's colours are pastel and pretty, and you can pick up a pair of warm and woolly cashmere gloves for just £15.

Eda Lingerie

Lingerie

132 King's Road SW3

Tel: 0171 584 0435

Open: Mon–Sat 10am–6.30pm and late night Wed till 7pm

This boutique stocks an own-brand range of lingerie, swimwear and nightwear. From the silk and lace to cotton and Lycra, everything is made from English fabrics, with prices from £25. Better still, there is a fitting service available for anyone unsure of their vital statistics – did you know that up to 40% of women are wearing the wrong bra size? Visit Eda and give your chest a chance.

Knickerbox

Lingerie

28 Sloane Square SW1

Tel: 0171 823 4437

Open: Mon–Tues and Fri–Sat 9am–7pm, late nights Wed and Thurs till 8pm and Sun 11am–5pm

It's lingerie, it's serviceable, but Knickerbox lacks the covetable quality of the more personal boutiques – precisely because of its staggering high-street success. Like the carpets in motorway service stations and the towels in Holiday Inns, the look is the same across the board, whether you're in Slough or Sloane Square. That said, the ten-year-old company does what it does remarkably well. The clean, miniature shops are designed to be easy to use, efficient and modern. Their appearance reflects the underwear within, which plays on current trends and developments in technology to remain as pretty and distinctive as possible. Prices start from £9.99 for a bra and from £3.99 for briefs; matching sets of pyjamas, baby dolls, slips and French knickers are part of the package too.

For branches, call: 0171 284 1744.

Laurence Tavernier

Nightwear

77 Walton Street SW3

Tel: 0171 823 8737

Open: Mon–Sat 10am–6pm

See page 218.

Sam de Teran

(&)

Swimwear

151 Fulham Road SW3
Tel: 0171 584 0902

Open: Mon–Fri 10am–6.30pm, Sat 10am–7pm and Sun 12pm–6pm

Think swim, think gym, think sun, ski and seasonal sportswear, and you will have a pretty accurate idea of what Sam de Teran is all about. Her shop opened in November 1995 and is home to technically innovative, active clothing, which is hugely popular with Honor Fraser, Kylie Minogue, Lauren Hutton, Wendy Richards and Valerie Singleton. Sultans of style one and all. Futuristic, graphic ski wear (£399 for an all-in-one), Fifties-inspired resort wear and "mix-and-match" size swimwear (a great idea) are sold from a shop featuring an aquarium and changing rooms with latex curtains. You can buy, buy, buy while the video of *Days at the Beach* plays continuously in the background to inspire you in your task. Two further London shops are in the pipeline.

Tatters

Made-to-measure

74 Fulham Road SW3
Tel: 0171 584 1532

Open: Mon–Fri 10am–6pm and Sat 10am–5pm

Despite the name, Tatters specialises in upmarket designs not Cinderella rags. Two decades supplying exuberant, opulent evening wear and couture bridalwear have put Tatters at the head of its class. All design is carried out on the stand, ensuring an immaculate fit that is a rare find outside of Paris. The precision detailing – with corseted and ruched bodices and the delicate use of lace and devoré – makes a Tatters dress something special. You can buy off-the-peg, or if you prefer a tailor-made fit, made-to-measure takes around a month to complete (up to four months for luxurious wedding dresses). Prices start at £400 and go up to £4,000 for a more intricate design.

Workshop

Shirts

178a King's Road SW3
Tel: 0171 376 3535

Open: Mon–Sat 10am–6pm, late night Wed till 7pm and Sun 12pm–5pm

Quite simply, Workshop makes the best-possible basic range of shirts for every woman's every need. Choose from cotton Oxford city shirts at £35 or velvet shirts that put the M&S version in its place, or go for the more pricey limited-edition ranges. Each one comes in a number of different fabrics (brushed cotton, satin, crushed velvet, linen) and colours. And if you don't live near a branch of Workshop, don't panic – you can get hold of a copy of the mail-order catalogue by calling 0171 738 9477.

Also at: 52 Bow Lane EC4, tel: 0171 236 0327, and 1 Cabot Place East, Canary Wharf E14, tel: 0171 513 0333.

City and East End

Couch and Hoskins

Tailoring

21 Eastcheap EC3

Tel: 0171 626 3831

Open: Mon–Fri 9am–5pm

As well as traditional tailoring expertise, Couch and Hoskins has a number of more up-to-date services up its sleeve to set it apart from the rest. You can have country tweeds or even a smoking jacket made, not just the classic bespoke suit. And for the aspiring City lad who is strapped for cash, there's a banker's order system where you can pay for your suit over eight months with no interest added – HP suiting comes to town.

Ede and Ravenscroft

Ceremonial

93–4 Chancery Lane WC2

Tel: 0171 405 3906

Open: Mon–Fri 8.30am–6pm and Sat 10am–3pm

Ede and Ravenscroft has a heritage that stretches way back to the reign of William and Mary. In that period, the company has fashioned robes and costumes for coronations, state openings of Parliament and academic ceremonies, and men's and women's wear for social or sporting events.

J Amesbury and Co

Bespoke shoes

32 Elder Street E1

Tel: 0171 377 2006

Open: by appointment

In the basement of Timothy Everest's tailoring business is one Jason Amesbury, bespoke shoemaker. Originally a saddler, Jason has a sound grasp of classic leather styles, such as Oxford brogues, but can also turn his hand to more adventurous styles. The whole process takes around four months from first fitting to final setting, with prices starting from £750.

The Suit Room

Tailoring

29a Royal Exchange EC3

Tel: 0171 623 9899

Open: Mon–Fri 10am–6pm by appointment

It may be tight on space, but The Suit Room is bursting with ideas for well-dressed gents. The ready-to-wear is by Roy Robson, a German company whose suits start at £150 and go up to a 56-inch chest size; there is also a made-to-measure laser service, with prices from £320.

Thresher and Glenny

(m)

Tailoring

50 Gresham Street EC2
Tel: 0171 606 7451
Open: Mon–Fri 9am–5.30pm

Men's outfitters and makers of legal dress, Thresher and Glenny is over 200 years old, and now has a list of products and services that includes dress shirts, blazers, braces, boxer shorts, bespoke suiting, socks, ties and ready-to-wear. Also on the premises is Harry B Hart, the City bench-made shoemaker.

Timothy Everest

(m)

Tailoring

32 Elder Street E1
Tel: 0171 377 5770
Open: Mon–Fri 9am–6pm and Sat 9am–4pm by appointment

After answering an advert in the *Evening Standard*, Timothy Everest started working for Tommy Nutter in Savile Row. Today, Everest meets clients at his stunning three-storey Spitalfields store, and provides them with a level of service that is reminiscent of Savile Row, but is accompanied by (here's a first) a wicked sense of humour. This year sees the introduction of a ready-to-wear collection for anyone with no time to wait.

Covent Garden

Assets

(&)

Knitwear

29 Floral Street WC2
Tel: 0171 240 3055
Open: Mon–Sat 10.30am–6.30pm and late night Thurs till 7pm

Relatively unknown outside fashion circles, Assets is a division of Tin Lung Knitwear, established in Hong Kong in 1976. With its own factory in Tyne and Wear and a team of British designers headed by Amanda Beckham, the company produces understated (yet undeniably fashionable) knitwear for men and women. Cotton, silk, linen and cleverly recycled yarns are used; this spring, the mood is blue, for knitted dresses, high-shine silk ribs and viscose chenille.

Bumpsadaisy

Maternity clothes

43 Covent Garden Market WC2
Tel: 0171 379 9831
Open: Mon–Sat 10am–6pm and late night Thurs till 7.30pm

Only 1% of the population is pregnant at any one time, but Bumpsadaisy is intent on getting all of them into specially designed pregnancy kit. Business suits are available for women who can't bear to leave the office until the last minute; skirts have adjustable elastic sides and are cut higher at the front so as to sit at the correct length; and there are masses of little extras to make the nine months easier – support tights to promote circulation, maternity belts to prevent back pain... But best of all, there's an evening wear hire service, with prices from £30 to £80 for a three-day hire. And finally, there is also a comprehensive underwear range, with a fitting recommended after 12 weeks.

Cashmere by Design

Cashmere

64 Neal Street WC2

Tel: 0171 240 3652

Open: Mon–Sat 10am–6.30pm and Thurs 10.30am–7pm

See page 212.

Jungle

Surplus

21 Earlham Street WC2

Tel: 0171 379 5379

Open: Mon–Sat 10am–6.30pm (occasionally on Sun, depending on Sat night)

Eli Shababo, who has been in the fashion business for 15 years, opened this shop just off Seven Dials in 1995. He buys army and government surplus gear (brilliant combats, quilted trousers, camouflage kit and prison shirts) and then customises the lot by dying, ripping, sewing and generally putting them through the mangle before selling them (cheap, cheap, cheaply) to the public.

Lingerie Brazil

Lingerie

Thomas Neal's Centre, Earlham Street WC2

Tel: 0171 379 3635

Open: Mon–Sat 10am–7pm and Sun 12pm–6pm

What's Brazil got that we haven't got? Yep, dental-floss bikini bottoms. And they know how to make a decent pair of pants too, if Lingerie Brazil is anything to go by. According to Liz in the shop, these knickers (£12.95) will last at least three years. The bras (£21.95) are sexy, colourful, comfortable, and look even better on than off. A full swimwear range – including those Rio-revealer bikini bottoms – brings a little South American chutzpah to chilly old London.

Sports Locker

Sportwear

17–18 Floral Street WC2

Tel: 0171 240 4929

Open: Mon–Sat 10am–7pm and Sun 1pm–5pm

The idea of having two stores of the same name adjacent to each other is an American concept, and one which works well for Sports Locker. Each shop's stock attracts a different customer: the serious fitness enthusiast to number

17 and the body-beautiful "vanity case" to number 18, where there is a strong showing of street and clubwear labels. Expect names such as Champion and Russell Athletic, and an own-label collection renowned for its attention to detail.

Also at: 53 Pembridge Road W11, tel: 0171 221 9166.

Hampstead and Highgate

Hug

Lingerie

87 Heath Street NW3
Tel: 0171 794 8006

Open: Mon–Thurs 9.30am–6pm, Fri–Sat 10am–6.30pm and Sun 12pm–6.30pm

The aptly named Hug is an independent lingerie retailer specialising in La Perla, Marvel, Emporio Armani and Aubade, plus swimwear by Domani and Gottex and a selection of Wolford tights.

Ebenezer Mission

Made-to-measure

67 Highgate High Street N6
Tel: 0181 347 9409

Open: Tues 11am–5.30pm, Wed–Thurs 10am–5.30pm and Fri–Sat 10am–6pm

Vittoria Piras's exquisite designs are as close to couture as London gets, with a variety of period-inspired samples which can be made up in any of 100 colours in wool, silk or cashmere (depending on the time of year). There is also a millinery service, starting at a mere £100 for a simple hat. A must for anyone fearful of wearing the same dress as another guest at a wedding.

Highbury and Islington

Barry Yarrow

Tailoring

137 Upper Street N1
Tel: 0171 226 9342

Open: Mon–Fri 9.30am–5pm and Sat by appointment

The walls of Barry Yarrow's shop, papered with letters from clients past and present, authenticate his reputation as one of the most adaptable tailors in town, offering an exclusively made-to-measure service to lawyers, judges and professionals from all over the world. Barry left school at the age of 14 with aspirations to become a brain surgeon, but tailoring seemed to be the more practical option. Forty years on, he is surviving – even thriving – where others have failed. The suits, needless to say, are cut with the precision of the scalpel.

Charlie Allen

Tailoring

186 Upper Street N1
Tel: 0171 359 0883
Open: Mon-Sat 10am-7pm

Visit Charlie Allen for avant-garde tailoring, based on formal fabrics and a taste for the unexpected, such as a groovy pink chalkstripe. If you are not drawn in by the alluring window displays (which have won some curious awards), then you will certainly be inspired by the interior of the shop, with its part-library, part-art-gallery atmosphere. Along with Richard James, Timothy Everest and Mark Powell, Allen is one of a refreshing new breed of London tailors. Prices for made-to-measure start at £750; off-the-peg, which is set to expand, starts at £350.

Design Also

Lingerie

101 St Paul's Road N1
Tel: 0171 354 0035
Open: Mon–Sat 11am–7pm

I walked into Design Also a 36B, and came out a 32D – proving the theory that 40% of British women wear the wrong bra size. The sizes here range from 30–38 in D–HH cup and 32–38 in A–HH cup. The styles are pretty, sexy and flattering, from Fantasie, Ballet, Impressions and Rigby and Peller. The accompanying range of accessories includes made-to-measure hats, hosiery in a multitude of colours and patterns (but strictly no American tan) and bra-sized swimwear.

Klass Designs

Made-to-measure

2 Shillingford Street N1
Tel: 0171 704 9654
Open: Mon–Fri 9am–6pm and Sat 10am–5pm

This is one of the most unusual shops in London. If you fancy yourself as a fashion designer but don't have the facilities to try, Klass can help. The company promises to create any made-to-measure outfit you desire, from a rough sketch or just an airy idea in your head. A brainwave in the bath can be translated into reality in as little as a fortnight. Prices (excluding fabric) start at £125 for a woman's jacket, £30 for a shirt and £40 for trousers, and can reach £550 for a man's coat. There is also a miscellaneous selection of ready-to-wear always available, and a full alterations and repairs service.

Kensington

Deliss

Bespoke shoes

15 St Albans Grove W8
Tel: 0171 584 3321

Open: Tues–Fri 9.30am–5.30pm and Sat 12pm–5pm

George V Deliss has been trading in bespoke shoes for 33 years, although much of the work is now carried out by his wife Mary. For a perfectly individual pair of high heels or flatties, a last is made (this costs around £300) and the shoes will then set you back around £470 (men's) and £390 (women's).

House of Suzuya

Japanese clothes

99 Kensington Church Street W8
Tel: 0171 243 1199

Open: Mon–Sat 10am–6pm

House of Suzuya specialises in the hire of Japanese wedding outfits and kimonos. Ninety per cent of the customers are Japanese women who live in London, so designs are tailored to their requirements; if you are over a size 12, forget it. Prices for a three-day hire start at £500 for wedding dresses, £360 for morning coats and £80 for a spectacular kimono.

Knightsbridge

Bjorn Borg

Lingerie

70 Sloane Avenue SW3
Tel: 0171 581 0150

Open: Mon–Sat 10am–6pm, late night Wed till 7pm and Sun 12pm–5pm

The Swedes are well known for removing their own and each other's clothes at every opportunity – and now we know why: they are desperate to display their Bjorn Borg pants, all bearing the famous tennis player's signature. The company also produces one of the quirkiest, smirkiest mail-order catalogues around, proving that all that you hear about Sweden is true. Call for a copy; it's steamy.

Bradleys

Lingerie

57 Knightsbridge SW1
Tel: 0171 235 2902

Open: Mon–Fri 9.30am–6pm and Sat 10am–6pm

Jenny Eikan has been running this glamorous lingerie store for 26 years and in that time has established a regular clientele that includes royalty and film stars. The stock isn't cheap (around £85 for a bra), but what you pay for is the intimate service and quality of the garments. The shop, which feels old-fashioned and vaguely frumpy, stocks a full range of swimwear, nightwear and bodies from La Perla, Carnival, Patricia and Lettermann. Look out for the cupboard at the back of the shop where staff will reveal a selection of *trousseaux* with matching mules – enough to make any aspiring Cinderellas turn into a pumpkin in delight.

Edward Sexton

Tailoring

26 Beauchamp Place SW3

Tel: 0171 838 0007

Open: by appointment only

Bespoke master tailor to the famous and infamous, Edward Sexton has been inventing refined designs since 14 February 1969, although he was based in Savile Row with Tommy Nutter until three years ago. He will provide a made-to-measure service for men or women in five weeks and prices start at £1,400. His diverse client list includes Diana Rigg, Linda McCartney and Maggie Smith. Stella McCartney, now chief designer at Chloe in Paris, learned her tailoring skills here.

Janet Reger

LIngerie

2 Beauchamp Place SW3

Tel: 0171 584 9360

Open: Mon–Sat 10am–6pm

Reger enveloped Joan Collins in lace and satin for *The Bitch*, and ever since has been the prime location for sexy, seductive lingerie. The bras and slips smack of soft lighting and heavy breathing, making the shop a stop-off for men buying their wives complicated lingerie for Christmas and birthdays. Reger is now the exclusive British stockist of "Curves" (fake breasts to you and me). So if you're not happy with what nature gave you, you can avoid the pain of surgery and invest in stick-ons, £169 (plus £5 p&p).

For mail order, call: 0171 584 9360.

Harvie and Hudson

Made-to-measure

55 Knightsbridge SW1

Tel: 0171 235 2651

Open: Mon–Sat 9.30am–6pm

This is the smaller and more casual sister branch of the two Harvie and Hudson shops in Jermyn Street. The family business – established in 1949 and now run by the founder's son, Andrew Hudson – offers both a ready-to-wear and made-to-measure service for shirts. The store also stocks brocade waistcoats, bathrobes, ties and braces; down the spiral staircase is the "weekend" range, where Roger Moore buys his signature poloneck sweaters.

Also at: 77 Jermyn Street W1, tel: 0171 930 3949, and 97 Jermyn Street W1, tel: 0171 839 3578.

Ray Ward Gunsmiths

Outdoor

12 Cadogan Place SW1
Tel: 0171 235 2550
Open: Mon–Fri 9am–6pm and Sat 10am–5pm

Traditional tweeds and hardy cords from Barbour, Viyella, John G Hardy and Hoesmann to complement the equally disturbing collection of guns.

Rigby & Peller

Lingerie

2 Hans Road SW3
Tel: 0171 589 9293
Open: Mon–Sat 9am–6pm and late night Wed till 7pm

The finest "establishment" lingerie and underwear boutique in the UK, Rigby & Peller has been measuring, fitting and pampering women for more than half a century. The company has corseted the Queen since 1960. June Kenton, who designs the own-label collection and maintains the all-important customer contact throughout the shop, is well aware of the importance of a well-fitting bra, so all her staff are trained to a high standard and each customer receives individual service. Further labels include Primadonna, Lejaby and Marie-Jo, and a new range of breast enhancers. As there is often a two-hour wait for a fitting, save time by visiting the more recently opened flagship store instead.

Also at: 22a Conduit Street W1, tel: 0171 491 2200.

Spaghetti

Made-to-measure

32 Beauchamp Place SW3
Tel: 0171 584 0631
Open: Mon–Fri 9.30am–6pm and Sat 10am–6pm

Nadia La Valle's little boutique boasts spaghetti-print walls – a clue, perhaps, to her origins. The clothes are noticeable too, with their elaborate beading and embroidery details, but so is the price. Expect to pay anything beyond £1,350.

Tian Art

Eastern lifestyle

36 Beauchamp Place SW3
Tel: 0171 823 8878
Open: Mon–Sat 10.30am–6.30pm

The aptly named Tian Art (*tian* meaning heaven) is a five-storey artistic lifestyle store bringing a piquant Asian flavour to the West. The fashion, housed among paintings and artefacts, is designed by Flora Cheong-Leen. She likens her art to that of Bonsai – "a ritual and a ceremony, each design is unique, classic, standing on its own". Whoever said there was no room for modesty in fashion?

Notting Hill

Anne Higgins

Knitwear

139 Portland Road W11

Tel: 0171 243 0834

Open: Tues 11am–6pm and Mon–Sat by appointment

Art in knits, if you like, from Higgins, who regularly sweeps off on foreign voyages of discovery to glean inspiration for her work. Prices start from £35 for a Horny Hat (a hat with horns, that is) and rise to £800 for a full-length coat. Nothing is made to size, so you just have to cross your fingers and hope. If it doesn't fit, hang it on your wall.

The Shirtsmith

Shirts

38b Ledbury Road W10

Tel: 0171 229 3090

Open: Mon–Fri 10am–6.30pm and Sat 11.15am–5.30pm

See page 207.

Oxford Street and Regent Street

Barrow and Hepburn

Specialist luggage

25 Bury Street SW1

Tel: 0171 925 2578

Open: Mon–Fri 9am–5pm

The Queen has her purses made for the Maundy ceremony at Barrow and Hepburn, the company that produces dispatch boxes used by monarchs and government ministers to carry official papers. It also designs and manufactures a luxurious collection of hand luggage, attaché and briefcases, portfolios and wallets in British bridle leather from its factory in Peckham.

Benson and Clegg

Trimming

9 Piccadilly Arcade W1

Tel: 0171 409 2053

Open: Mon–Fri 8.30am–5pm and Sat 8.30am–12pm

This cosy little shop is crammed with every conceivable "trimming" detail, be it for university, school or the forces. It is packed with buttons, cufflinks, ties and blazer badges and holds a royal warrant to the Prince of Wales. You can also have your own design or corporate logo incorporated into any of the products – the staff are delighted to assist.

Budd Shirtmakers

Shirts

1a and 3 Piccadilly Arcade SW1
Tel: 0171 493 0139

Open: Mon–Thurs 9am–5.30pm, Fri 9am–5pm and Sat 9am–12.30pm

You cannot help but be charmed by the Piccadilly Arcade and in turn by the shops within. Budd is an immensely cheerful shirtmaker that also stocks pyjamas, ties and socks. The made-to-measure service is initially cut on the premises by Mr Butcher (a man of few words but talented fingers) before being sent to the work room in Andover for completion. The original owner, who apparently declared the business bankrupt after one too many down at the Red Lion, must have wondered where he went wrong.

Damart

Underwear

235 Regent Street W1
Tel: 0171 629 6475

Open: Mon–Sat 9.30am–5.30pm

These are the kind of underthings that your granny might wear – they keep out the cold but aren't going to set any passions alight. But Damart is making every effort to appeal to a younger punter, with a new range of thermals that is positively racy. Suckers for a trend will probably shock their grannies by wearing them with nothing but a pair of slingbacks.

Favourbrook

Men's accessories

18–21 Piccadilly Arcade SW1
Tel: 0171 491 2337

Open: Mon–Fri 9am–6pm and Sat 10am–6pm

Imagine the wacky waistcoats worn by gregarious Gareth in *Four Weddings and a Funeral* and you will have a pretty good idea of the concept behind Favourbrook. The clothing here is based on traditional styling (Nehru jackets, frock coats and smoking jackets made in contemporary and period fabrics) and makes passable if pompous alternative wedding outfits.

General Leather Company

Leather clothes

56 Chiltern Street W1
Tel: 0171 935 1041

Open: Mon–Fri 10am–6pm and Sat 10am–5pm

"Everything they make fits me like a glove," says Lennox Lewis of the General Leather Company, just one of a long list of sports, music and media stars who keep coming back to have leather and suede jackets, shirts, trousers and skirts made to measure. Partners Peter Goodall and Alan Sprooles have been designing and manufacturing both wholesale and "one-offs" for TV and film since 1971. They have recently worked for Margaret Howell, Caroline Charles, Paul Smith, Katharine Hamnett and Ally Capellino. Prices are amazingly reasonable for such personal service, with jackets starting at £450 and trousers at around £175.

Long Tall Sally

Larger sizes

21 Chiltern Street W1

Tel: 0171 487 3370

Open: Mon–Wed, Fri 9.30am–5.30pm, Thurs 10am–7pm and Sat 9.30am–5pm

Long Tall Sally caters for women who are 5 feet 8 inches and taller in sizes 12–20. The clothes aren't exactly trendy but they do offer an alternative to trousers that are too short and sleeves that stop at the elbow. If you can't make it to the shop in Chiltern Street, a mail-order service is available. Every eight weeks, if you are on the mailing list, you will be sent an updated brochure.

For mail order, call: 0181 689 9000.

N Peal ®

Cashmere

192 Piccadilly W1

Tel: 0171 437 0106

Open: Mon–Sat 10am–6.30pm

N Peal, synonymous with creative design in cashmere, began in retail with two speciality boutiques in the Burlington Arcade in 1936 and now has four stores, plus branches in San Francisco and New York. Designer Gillian Hunter works on creating a "total image" and has introduced silk, wool and cotton designs to widen the cashmere brief and give the collection a more progressive edge.

Also at: 37 and 71 Burlington Arcade W1, tel: 0171 493 9220 (number 37), and 0171 493 0912 (number 71).

Rogers and Rogers

Larger sizes

Unit 7 The Plaza, 120 Oxford Street W1

Tel: 0171 580 3558

Open: Mon–Sat 10am–7pm and late night Thurs till 8pm

This is the Jeffrey Rogers collection for girls in sizes from 16 to 24. Rather than consisting of unflattering or unfashionable balloon dresses, the collections are as up-to-date as the main line, which is great news for a high street that has been waiting years for an affordable, youthful range for larger sizes.

For branches, call: 0171 208 4300.

The Small and Tall Shoe Shop

Unusual sizes

71 York Street W1
Tel: 0171 723 5321
Open: Mon–Sat 10am–5pm and late night Thurs till 7pm

The Small and Tall Shoe Shop does exactly what its name suggests, catering for women with tiny feet (sizes 12–3) and plates of meat (sizes $8\frac{1}{2}$–12). The prices aren't cheap, because the shoes are Italian and stock is kept low.

The Sock Shop

Socks and hosiery

257–259 Oxford Street W1
Tel: 0171 493 4039
Open: Mon–Sat 8.30am–7pm, late night Thurs till 8.30pm and Sun 10am–4pm

The largest specialist sock retailer in the UK now has 75 shops to its name – most of them in airports and train stations, well-placed to grab our attention when we are at our most vulnerable.

For branches, call: 01524 271071

Wolford

Hosiery

3 South Molton Street W1
Tel: 0171 499 2549
Open: Mon–Sat 10am–6pm and late night Thurs till 6.30pm

See page 215.

Savile Row

Anderson and Sheppard

30 Savile Row W1
Tel: 0171 734 1420
Open: Mon–Fri 8.30am–5pm

This discreet tailoring business, which prefers to keep as low a profile as possible, is best known among customers for soft styling. Alexander McQueen cut his teeth here, constructing smart suits for Prince Charles.

Blades of Savile Row

8 Burlington Gardens, Savile Row W1
Tel: 0171 734 8911
Open: Mon–Sat 9.30am–5.30pm by appointment

Blades offers a unique "easy order" system: a computerised made-to-measure service that eliminates several hours of expert labour and results in fast-track, more economical gentlemen's suits. The usual made-to measure and bespoke tailoring options start at a reasonable £395 and £895 respectively.

Dege

10 Savile Row W1
Tel: 0171 287 2941
Open: Mon–Fri 9.15am–5.15pm and Sat 9.30am–12.30pm

Makers of civil, military, sporting and ladies' bespoke tailoring since 1865, Dege now relies heavily on foreign visitors to make up a significant part of its business. Tailors Robert Whittaker and William Skinner make an annual trip to the States, visiting hotels and homes to bring the world-renowned Savile Row service to their American customers. Back in England, a bespoke two-piece suit starts at £1,500 and takes from six weeks to complete.

Denman and Goddard

13 New Burlington Street W1
Tel: 0171 734 6371
Open: Mon–Fri 9am–5.30pm and Sat by appointment

Much of the work in progress is carried out on site, making Denman and Goddard an interesting place to peer into. The three current partners each have more than 20 years' experience in Savile Row, so can cope with any request in men's and women's tailoring and shirtmaking. Suits start at £1,400, shirts at £110.

Davies and Son

32 Old Burlington Street W1
Tel: 0171 434 3016
Open: Mon–Fri 9am–5pm by appointment

Besides diplomatic and bespoke tailoring, Davies and Son makes many of the tailored costumes for Madame Tussauds, such as the latest Jacques Chirac outfit. To non-wax customers, bespoke suits start at £1,300.

Gieves and Hawkes

1 Savile Row W1
Tel: 0171 434 2001
Open: Mon–Sat 9am–6pm and late night Thurs till 7pm

Other tailors in Savile Row would probably balk at being associated with Gieves and Hawkes, as the company is now an international chain with stores all over the world, losing something of the personal service that is the traditional fare in the Row. Nevertheless, the shop holds the most commanding position – at number 1, a former home of both the 3rd Lord Burlington and the Royal Geographic Society – and can boast a history that dates back to 1785. Today, the company offers a modern slant on tailoring, using lighter-weight cloths and featuring casualwear, country wear and gentlemen's accessories.

Hardy Amies

14 Savile Row W1
Tel: 0171 734 2436
Open: Mon–Fri 9.30am–5.30pm

The ladies' gentleman of English tailoring, Sir Hardy Amies is a shrewd businessman blessed with a scrupulously polite nature and a dapper dress sense that have made him a favourite designer to many a society figure. He is also famously indiscreet, and a master of the acid epigram. His heyday was between 1946 and 1955, when Vivien Leigh, Edith Evans, Diana Broughton and Deborah Kerr were among the customers who fell for his tea, day and cocktail dresses in sumptuous fabrics. Amies has dressed the Queen for over half a century – and has made the wardrobe for every royal tour since Princess Elizabeth's first trip to Canada in 1951. It is little wonder, therefore, that his style is revered throughout the world. London is his home, however, and where he now watches over his quiet empire. "I abdicated my position as her personal designer, with the Queen's blessing, when I was 80," he says, now a young 87. "She wouldn't have wanted a doddery old gent fussing around her."

Henry Poole

15 Savile Row W1
Tel: 0171 734 5985
Open: Mon–Fri 9am–5.15pm

The discerning Englishman has always looked to Henry Poole to meet his sartorial requirements with ease. The materials are finest British woollens, including Huddersfield worsteds, tweeds from the lowlands of Scotland, the Harris and the Shetland Isles, and flannels from the west of England. The company now sells as far afield as Japan, Hong Kong and Los Angeles, as well as closer to home, with a collection of sports jackets, blazers and trousers for Swaine Adeney of Piccadilly.

Huntsman

11 Savile Row W1
Tel: 0171 734 7441
Open: Mon–Fri 9am–5.30pm, closed for lunch 1pm–2pm

Huntsman is one of the most expensive of the Savile Row tailors, with prices starting at £2,200 for a suit. The cost is justified by the fact that the clothes are made from the finest Yorkshire worsteds, Irish linen and tweeds from Scotland, many of which are produced specially for the company in limited quantities, ensuring their exclusivity.

Hogg and J B Johnstone

19 Clifford Street, Savile Row W1
Tel: 0171 734 5915
Open: Mon–Fri 8.30am–5pm and any other time by appointment

When they say "any other time", they mean it at Johnstone – the tailors are on hand in the evenings or at the crack of dawn, and will visit your hotel or home if you are unable to get to the shop. The primary aim of the company, run by the only woman boss in Savile Row, is to offer premium-quality service to its customers, from sourcing fabrics to repairing and restoring much-loved but well-worn suits. Unsurprisingly, there's a women's tailoring service too.

James and James

11 Old Burlington Street W1
Tel: 0171 734 1748
Open: Mon–Fri 9am–5pm and any other time by appointment

Although James and James has a well-established clientele that has bought there since the Twenties, it is no stranger to technology. The computerised system and laser cutting service allow a suit to be made in half the usual time, making James and James a natural choice for the younger customer who demands immediate service. To celebrate 50 years of tailoring, the spot-light this year is on the hand-stitched suit, harking back to pre-sewing-machine days and costing an uncompromising £20,000.

Kilgour, French and Stanbury

8 Savile Row W1
Tel: 0171 734 6905
Open: Mon–Fri 9am–5.30pm

Most of the clothes produced here are made for export, so the company now has its own site on the Internet to publicise details of its frequent foreign trips. The shop also incorporates Bernard Weatherill Ltd, widely acclaimed as one of the finest bespoke sporting tailors, holding the royal warrants to the Queen, the Queen Mother and the Duke of Edinburgh.

Maurice Sedwell

19 Savile Row W1
Tel: 0171 734 0824
Open: Mon–Fri 9am–6pm and Sat 9am–2pm by appointment

Bespoke tailor Maurice Sedwell is a relative spring chicken in Savile Row, having established his business in 1938. Today, the company maintains the original expertise and meticulous all-round service (the average suit takes 70–80 hours to complete). Any unusual requests are happily entertained. The staff relate the story of a customer who commissioned one suit of 24-carat-gold-stripe cloth, and another made with his name woven vertically into the suiting to create a subtle stripe, a modest fellow, we can only asume.

Norton and Sons

16 Savile Row W1
Tel: 0171 437 0829
Open: Mon–Fri 9am–5pm

This is a specialist field-sports tailor, creating full outfits for the hunting, shoot-ing, fishing and riding set. Unlike some of the struggling businesses around Savile Row, Norton and Sons is going from strength to strength and has recently taken on more tailors to cope with demand.

Oswald Boateng

9 Vigo Street W1
Tel: 0171 734 6868
Open: Mon–Sat 10am–6pm

Boateng takes delight in fusing vibrant colours with obvious and hidden features (angled pockets, concealed buttons and loud linings), a rule-breaking approach reflected in the red velvet and bright-yellow interior of his shop. His witty takes on the often-sober business of bespoke suiting attract a curious cross-section of customers. Look out for the "Mission Impossible" undercover collection, with bowler hats, raincoats and umbrellas. For the English gent with a glint in his eye.

Richard James

31 Savile Row W1
Tel: 0171 434 0605
Open: Mon–Fri 10am–6pm and Sat 11am–5pm

As the suit continues to dominate trends in men's clothing, Richard James brings a fresh approach to an often stagnant industry. Elton John spent £15,000 here last winter, and brought his pal Gianni Versace in for a spending spree (the designer left with £35,000 of James's best). The business was set up in 1992 and is a constant reminder of the versatility that can be achieved within tailoring. Working closely with fabric mills to produce exclusive cloths, Richard and his partner Sean Dixon have struck upon a maverick, modern approach, popular with customers such as Patrick Cox, Manolo Blahnik, Christian Lacroix and Liam Gallagher. If only he made womenswear too – although that didn't stop Madonna buying a brown tweed coat here when she was in town for the premiere of *Evita*.

Tobias Tailors

32 Savile Row W1
Tel: 0171 734 2551
Open: Mon–Fri 9.30am–5.30pm and Sat by appointment

This is one of the smallest and most informal outfitters in the street, and consequently one of the most adaptable and speedy. Prices are also lower than elsewhere, with suits starting at £1,150, although this does not denote any reduction in quality or service. Tobias also sells shirts, ties and its own exclusive range of enamel and silver cufflinks made from pre-war English and overseas coins.

Welsh and Jeffries

20 Savile Row W1
Tel: 0171 734 3062
Open: Mon–Fri 9am–5pm

Welsh and Jeffries combines bespoke tailoring with riding, hunting and Highland garments such as kilts for those with a wee touch of Scottish blood. Since 1991, the company has also held the royal warrant as military tailor to the Prince of Wales, further establishing the calibre of its craftsmanship.

Soho and West Soho

Agent Provocateur

Lingerie
6 Broadwick Street W1
Tel: 0171 439 0229
Open: Mon–Sat 11am–7pm

Interest in "lingerie to lounge in" has exploded in the past two years, serviced by specialist shops such as this. Inside the lush boudoir rooms, shoppers will find high-octane underwear, from sussy belts and bum-lifters, to hourglass corsets, decorated nipple clamps, rhinestone belly chains and feather tiaras *à la Showgirls*. For more conservative tastes, there are delicate slips, negligées and bras in mouthwatering colours from top French labels, plus an own-label range from the owner (Vivienne Westwood's son Joe Corre). At the back of the boutique is a jewellery collection, designed by Erickson Beamon and sold exclusively here, based – in the nicest possible way, of course – on a fetish theme.

For mail order (a set of pin-up playing cards), call: 0171 494 1102.

Ann Summers

Lingerie
79 Wardour Street W1
Tel: 0171 434 2475
Open: Mon–Sat 10am–11pm and Sun 1pm–10pm

Smutty and stupid, Ann Summers is still a popular haunt for giggle girls. It's fine for one-night-wonder lingerie, plus little extras that are good for a laugh at hen nights, including naughty nurse and French maid outfits (from £15).

For branches, tel: 0171 437 1886.

Brian Clarke

Made-to-measure
2 Ganton Street W1
Tel: 0171 439 2606
Open: Mon–Sat 10am–6.30pm and late night Thurs till 7pm

Colour (brash) and styling (trash) are the bywords here, where both off-the-peg and made-to-measure services are available, with prices from £450 for a ready-to-wear suit. On our visit, Brian was putting the finishing touches to a Crombie coat for Jonathan Ross, but don't let that put you off.

Eddie Kerr

Tailoring
52 Berwick Street W1
Tel: 0171 437 3727
Open: Mon–Fri 9am–6pm and Sat 9am–1pm

In the often insipid world of men's tailoring, Eddie Kerr is a light at the end of the tunnel. He is as cheerful a chap as his celebrity clientele, which includes

Chris Evans, Jack Dee and Dale Winton. Eddie is also responsible for the transformations in *Stars in their Eyes*, so if you have a secret longing to look like Frank Sinatra or Marti Pellow then you know where to head.

John Pearse

Tailoring

6 Meard Street W1
Tel: 0171 434 0738
Open: Mon–Fri 10am–7pm and Sat 1pm–7pm

"We're well thought of," says John Pearse of his tailoring business, and it shows in his distinguished list of clients. His showroom is smartly kitted out and his suits are charmingly pretentious, with hand-painted ties and obscure shirts to set them off. Buying a suit here is a leisurely process – and costs around £1,000.

Sam Arkus

Tailoring

60 Berwick Street W1
Tel: 0171 437 2156
Open: Mon–Fri 9am–5.30pm and Sat 9am–1pm

Sam Arkus specialises in Sixties and Seventies tailoring, best displayed in the slim-cut single-breasted suit, costing around £500.

South-west

Femme Fatale

Lingerie

Tel: 0181 947 8588
64 High Street, Wimbledon Village SW19
Open: Mon–Sat 10am–6pm and Sun 11am–5pm

Model Tamzin Greenhill started Femme Fatale in February 1996 because she was crazy about luxe lingerie, but couldn't find it nearby. The boudoir-style interior, with its draped ceilings and chaises longues, makes shopping here an unexpectedly relaxing experience. You can browse in comfort through the leading names in lingerie, swimwear, nightwear and hosiery (Malizia, Cotton Club, Marie Jo, Gottex, Hanro and Huit). And if you leave without buying, you win the *Evening Standard* Award for Retail Restraint. Prices from £24 to £100.

Larger Than Life/Mums 2 Be

Maternity clothes and larger sizes

2–3 Mortlake Terrace, Kew TW9
Tel: 0181 332 6506/7661
Open: Mon–Sat 10am–6pm and late night Thurs by appointment

Larger Than Life is for women of sizes 14–30, whatever their requirements – from a business suit to an evening outfit. Mums 2 Be, despite a name that looks like a Prince track, provides seven collections of formal- and casual-wear that can be adapted according to your waistline to see you through an entire pregnancy. Both businesses also operate an evening and black-tie hire service, with prices starting from £20 for a three-day hire. There is an alterations operation too, including a tailoring service that allows you to convert a cherished maternity suit for everyday wear when you revert to the slimmer you.

La Senza

Lingerie

Unit 209 Centre Court Shopping Centre, Wimbledon SW19
Tel: 0181 946 8041

Open: Mon–Fri 9.30am–7pm, late night Thurs till 8pm, Sat 9am–6pm and Sun 11am–5pm

This is a Canadian luxury lingerie specialist, where shoppers can indulge in underwear, nightwear and bodywear, or gifts such as bath oils, soaps and lotions. Ranges include silk chemises from £18 and Ultra-lift bras in satin or lace at £18. For men, there are cotton boxers from £9. The changing rooms each have a towelling robe, so you can wander back into the store to select other garments to try on. Whatever next?

For branches, call: 0181 445 0099.

Vivace

Larger sizes

2 Bridge Street, Richmond TW9
Tel: 0181 948 7840

Open: Mon–Fri 10am–5.30pm and Sat 10am–6pm

If you're over a size 16 and forever complaining that you have absolutely nothing to wear, you obviously haven't shopped here. Just slightly off the beaten track, but well worth tracking down, Vivace stocks clothing that is not just flattering and well cut but reasonably priced too. You can pick up some unpretentious names such as Gerry Weber, Persona, August Silk and Bitte Kai Rand.

Victoria

Piklik

Nightwear

30 Buckingham Palace Road SW1
Tel: 0171 931 9941

Open: Mon–Fri 9.30am–5pm

A very silly name for a very sensible shop stocking 100% cotton women's nightwear. From short nightshirts at £18 to more elaborate full-length dresses at £49, the business has been on a roll for the past 15 years. Also available are kids' pyjamas, from £18.

Redwood and Feller

Tailoring

89 Rochester Row SW1
Tel: 0171 828 9519
Open: Mon–Fri 8.30am–5.30pm and Sat 9am–4pm

Eddie Rowland caters for everyone from rock stars to royalty in his busy, cosy shop/workroom. While Eddie deals with the men, his wife – a trained dressmaker – looks after the women, so couples can have matching outfits if *absolutely* necessary. Prices start from £750; allow six weeks and four fittings before the completed suit is ready to be taken out on the town with its opposite number.

Ready-to-wear at: 37 Tothill Street SW1, tel: 0171 222 4621.

All Over the Shop

Ages of Elegance/ Military Metalwork

(&)

Historical dress

480 Chiswick High Road W4
Tel: 0181 742 0730
Open: Mon–Sat 10am–6pm

Ever fancied a full-scale 1860s wedding dress, or an eighteenth-century Hussar's costume for a fancy-dress party? Dawn Wood (clothing) and Andrew Clark (metalwork) are the people to see. Their unique partnership allows them to research historical costume and reproduce designs with great accuracy, creating meticulous period clothing for any occasion. Many commissions come from museums and battle re-enactment organisations, but individuals and collectors dip in too. All the work is hand-stitched and patterns are developed from scratch, making the service expensive. But this is about as original as garments get.

Benny Dee

Underwear

112–114 Kilburn High Road NW6
Tel: 0171 624 2995
Open: Mon–Sat 9am–6pm and Sun 10am–4pm

Benny Dee stocks clearance underwear lines from high-street stores such as BHS, M&S and Knickerbox, plus a constant supply of hugely discounted Wonderbras, knickers and bodies. Prices start from as little as £1.99 for a cheeky, party-bound Ann Summers bodice, and rarely go much higher than £5.99.

Also at: 74–80 Middlesex Street E1, tel: 0171 377 9067, 4–6 High Road Wood Green N22, tel: 0181 881 8101, and 136–138 High Street Walthamstow E17, tel: 0181 520 4637.

Henrietta Park and Claire Stratton

Bespoke shoes and jewellery

40 North Street SW4

Tel: 0171 207 2941

Open: Tues, Thurs, Fri 12pm–6pm, Sat 11am–5pm or by appointment

Henrietta is responsible for bespoke shoes; Claire designs and produces a range of silver jewellery. Both trained in fine art at Goldsmiths, responsible for the sculptural style of the merchandise. Expect to pay £200–£250 for a pair of boots or shoes, £30 and up for jewellery.

Kelsey Bespoke Tailors

Tailoring

58 Lamb's Conduit Street WC1

Tel: 0171 404 1616

Open: Mon–Fri 9.30am–6pm and Sat by appointment

Serena Kelsey is a whizz with scissors, and has been making suits for celebs (such as Paul Weller and Ocean Colour Scene) for 11 years. Her team of tailors makes up the designs in matt velvet and stretch satin, although more conventional pin- and chalk-stripe suitings are also available. To complement her designs, she stocks ties by Duchamp, Dormeuil and Yves Saint Laurent, plus cufflinks and a range of Italian shirts.

Second Skin

Lingerie

17 Turnham Green Terrace W4

Tel: 0181 994 8118

Open: Mon–Sat 10am–6pm

If you don't find what you are looking for in this specialist fitness and underwear shop, you can pop downstairs, where owner Lysta Perry runs her own "workout workshop". Her stock is designed for the sort of body that is rarely out of the Step class, with lingerie by Mark David Thomlin, Sloggi, Calvin Klein, Hanro and Gossard. Admire your new-found body in the beautiful pewter mirrors (designed by Teresa di Raddo and priced from £70 to £400).

Best Streets

Elizabeth Street, SW1

If accessories are your passion, you'll find some of the most exquisite here in deepest Belgravia. Erickson Beamon's jewellery defies the competition, Lulu Guinness's bags are adorable and Philip Treacy's hats need no introduction.

30 **The Exchange**

Dress agency

Tel: 0171 730 3334

Open: Mon–Fri 10am–4pm

The Exchange donates 50% of profits to The Kidney Foundation. Clothes must not be more than two years old, but some of the stock in the shop looks decidedly Eighties (no bad thing, given that an Eighties revival is threatening to materialise). Regular names include Nicole Farhi, Ungaro and Versace. Investigations uncovered a Balenciaga original tucked away at the back.

38 **Erickson Beamon**

Jewellery

Tel: 0171 259 0202

Open: Mon–Fri 10am–6pm and Sat 11am–5pm

One of the best finds in the capital, Erickson Beamon is rapidly earning accolades as the finest modern jewellery retailer around, following recent work with Dries Van Noten and John Galliano. The own-label collection comprises Victorian-influenced structured collars, rings, tiny bags and halter tops, all constructed from the most delicate crystal beads. The airy boutique also stocks the work of Van der Straeten (gold chunky jewellery), Laura Lee (silver and gold with enamel, as seen at Valentino), pendants and torques by Tom Binns, and the feather-adorned work of Chanel's accessory designer Eric Haley.

42 **Selina Blow** (&)

Designer clothes, scarves and bags

Tel: 0171 730 2449

Open: Mon–Fri 10am–6pm and Sat 11am–5pm

Blow's unusual enclave of style is a purple-and-lime cavern, stocking an eclectic mix of desirables. Her speciality is lavish velvet jackets with Nehru collars (equally foppish menswear is available) while her chum Lulu Guinness makes quirky, dainty bags (her rose bucket bag is a best seller), Camilla Ridley follows up with exquisite printed scarves and The Jacksons provide funky accessories.

Lulu Guinness also at: 66 Ledbury Road W11, tel: 0171 221 9686, see page 208.

69 **Philip Treacy**

Hats

Tel: 0171 259 9605

Open: Mon–Fri 10am–6pm

Britain's millinery king has an equally regal interior in his shop in Elizabeth Street, although the designer himself is surprisingly bashful and unassuming.

His creations are wildly imaginative, streamlined and often aerodynamic; they grace the best catwalks, involving anything from a flash of feathers to a net veil swathed across the face. If the £200–£700 price tag is too steep, do as the fashion editors do and head for Debenhams, where you can pick up the diffusion range with prices under £70.

79 **Reema Pachachi**

Jewellery

Tel: 0171 730 8030

Open: Mon–Fri 10.30am–6pm

After studying jewellery design at The Central School of Art and Design and The Royal College of Art (where she was awarded the Anstruther Award for "outstanding work"), Reema Pachachi began designing her own range of architectural and textural jewellery. She works mainly in sterling silver set with precious and semi-precious stones, priced from £40–£700, although recently she has moved towards bold designs in 18-carat gold, which at £1,200–£10,000 are destined to become collectors' pieces. Her stud earrings with a selection of attachments (from £38) are favourites with the style pack.

Jermyn Street, SW1

Elegant, urbane and sophisticated, Jermyn Street is the gentleman of London's shopping line-up. Come here for superb shirts, hand-made shoes, just-so tailoring and an air of old-school charm.

18–19 **Herbie Frogg**

Tailoring

Tel: 0171 437 6069

Open: Mon–Sat 9.30am–6pm and late night Thurs till 7pm

Herbie Frogg is an outfitters with an off-the-wall streak, but all the standard fare is here too: cotton double- and single-cuff plain and striped shirts, from £35 upwards; suits and jackets in chalk-stripe, pin-stripe and Prince of Wales check. Almost next door (at number 21) is a second branch of Herbie Frogg (a made-up name), selling predominantly Hugo Boss.

21a **Bates the Hatter**

Hats

Tel: 0171 734 2722

Open: Mon–Fri 9am–5.30pm and Sat 9.30am–4pm

More of a tourist attraction than a shop, Bates the Hatter looks as though it hasn't changed an iota since the turn of the century, with its rows of faded hatboxes and cabinets full to the, er, brim with caps and hats of all shapes and sizes. Now run by Geoff Bates, who still offers the friendly and personal service learnt at his great-uncle Edward's knee, the shop carries a wide variety of traditional formal and casual headwear from top hats to boaters, Panamas to fedoras, tweed caps to trilbies. It's all wonderfully *Brief Encounter* and will have you reaching for your ration book.

23 **Hawes and Curtis**

Tailoring

Tel: 0171 734 1020

Open: Mon–Sat 9am–6pm

Once upon a time, this men's outfitters boasted seven shops and 177 staff; today, there are just two outlets left. The empire, we hear, is being rebuilt.

Also at: 9 Savile Row W1, tel: 0171 734 1505.

53 **New and Lingwood**

Men's accessories

Tel: 0171 493 9621

Open: Mon–Fri 9am–5.30pm and Sat 10am–5pm

A 150-year association with Eton has given New and Lingwood its reputation among blue bloods and bankers, who came here as fags in shorts to be fitted out in caps, socks, shirts and ties. Later, they return to the comfort zone for bespoke shoes and made-to-measure shirts.

67 **Trickers**

Shoes

Tel: 0171 930 6395

Open: Mon–Fri 9.30am–5.30pm and Sat 9.30am–5pm

Boasting personal service, an intimate touch, and a roll call of the great and the good, Trickers makes shoes to an existing or new design by a method that has remained unchanged over its 160 years in business. The process is precise and time-consuming, with the relief of each foot taken to ensure maximum comfort. It takes six months, but your feet will thank you for a lifetime.

71–72 **Turnbull and Asser**

Shirts

Tel: 0171 930 0502

Open: Mon–Fri 9am–6pm and Sat 9.30am–6pm

Turnbull and Assers produces the most beautifully made shirts in the world – as Albert Finney, Michael Caine and Robert Redford would testify. Ready-made clothing is sold in the Jermyn Street side, while around the corner, The Churchill Room (so called because Winston Churchill was a former client) offers a full made-to-measure service with prices starting from £100. The attentive staff will ensure that the fit is flawless and will subsequently keep your "credentials" on record should you choose to return. You will.

73 **Hilditch and Key**

Shirts

Tel: 0171 930 5336

Open: Mon–Fri 9.30am–6pm and Sat 9.30am–5.30pm

The friendly "nothing-is-too-much-trouble" attitude is a feature of many shops in Jermyn Street, and Hilditch and Key is no exception. Choose from made-to-measure, with prices starting at £125, or a stock special, which is made from an existing pattern in your choice of fabric, with prices starting at £99.50. Women's shirts can be made as a stock special in the same or lighter weight fabrics.

Also at: 37 Jermyn Street SW1, tel: 0171 734 4707.

83 Foster and Son

Bespoke shoes

Tel: 0171 930 5385

Open: Mon–Fri 9am–5pm and Sat 9am–4pm

This 150-year-old firm specialises in made-to-measure shoes, with a modern feel, from £915. There's ready-to-wear too, from £195.

85 Thomas Pink

Shirts

Tel: 0171 930 6364

Open: Mon–Sat 9.30am–6pm and late night Thurs till 7pm

Thomas Pink is the newest and, some say, the least authentic of the Jermyn Street shirtmakers. The business was started just 13 years ago by three Irish brothers in the Fulham Road and became a romping success almost overnight. Jeffrey Archer wears Pink shirts, as does Rowan Atkinson, Alan Bennett, Hugh Grant, John Cleese and most of the City boys who have made it, and a few who haven't yet. The philosophy is simple: high-quality cotton, a generous cut and a standard price of £47.50.

For branches, call 0171 498 2202.

90 John Lobb

Bespoke shoes

Tel: 0171 930 8089

Open: Mon–Sat 10am–6pm and late night Thurs till 7pm

Renowned worldwide for excellence, John Lobb makes bespoke shoes of indisputable quality. The prices (from £350) are high, but then so is the calibre of the leather, craftsmanship and service. If you can't make it to Jermyn Street, a John Lobb shoe fitter will visit your home (provided it is in central London) with a selection of 12 ready-to-wear styles in different width fittings. Appointments should be made through the shop one week in advance.

95 Russell and Bromley

Shoes

Tel: 0171 930 5307

Open: Mon–Fri 10am–6pm and Sat 10am–5pm

In keeping with the spirit of Jermyn Street, this branch of Russell and Bromley retains its traditional exterior and does the same with its stock, which consists of brogues and loafers, for men only.

For branches, call: 0171 629 6903.

101 **Coles**

Shirts

Tel: 0171 930 6448

Open: Mon–Fri 9.30am–6pm, late night Thurs till 7pm and Sat 9.30am–5.30pm

Coles was established in 1878, and today makes shirts for men and women in a variety of styles and fabrics (around 150 in all). Men's cost £44.50 and come with a choice of classic, cut-away, button-down or tab collars, and an impressive 22 different sleeve lengths, so no waiting for alterations. There is also a made-to-order service with prices starting at a very reasonable £79.95, ready in an average of six weeks. The stripes, incidentally, all match perfectly.

106 **T M Lewin and Sons**

Tailoring

Tel: 0171 930 4291

Open: Mon–Fri 9am–6pm and Sat 9.30am–5.30pm

Lewin's is the most contemporary shop on Jermyn Street, incorporating new colourways and designs through computer technology each season. A mail-order service with a full catalogue, produced since 1903 and circulated all over the world, is available for out-of-towners. The business also has a reputation as a leading supplier of specialist club, school and regimental ties, although you may be asked for proof of membership to obtain one.

Also at: 32–33 Blomfield Street EC2, tel: 0171 920 0782, 34–36 Lime Street EC3, tel: 0171 283 1277, and 27a Chancery Lane WC2, tel: 0171 242 3180.

112 **Piccadilly Man Shop**

(m)

Shirts

Tel: 0171 930 1927

Open: Mon–Fri 8.15am–5.30pm and Sat 9am–5pm

This is the UK's largest independent stockist of Van Heusen shirts, with prices starting at a mere £35. You can get your Jockey Y-fronts here too.

Ledbury Road, W11

Notting Hill may be famous for its tourist-packed market, but just around the corner lies Ledbury Road, one of the most inviting streets on the shopping map. Among the purveyors of antiques and the bustling bars, shops such as Oguri and J & M Davidson are the perfect antidote to crowd-trouble at Portobello.

38 **Roger Doyle**

Jewellery

Tel: 0171 727 5797

Open: Mon–Sat 10am–6pm

Roger Doyle, who has been designing and manufacturing jewellery since his apprenticeship with Cartier more than 25 years ago, produces unconventional work in silver and gold, picking up such accolades as The Diamonds International Award along the way. If you are not familiar with Doyle's style, then his compelling window displays will tell the tale – his approach is to put strange and wonderful coloured stones together in a way that works like a dream. Prices from £25.

38b **The Shirtsmith**

Shirts

Tel: 0171 229 3090

Open: Mon–Fri 10am–6.30pm and Sat 11.15am–5.30pm

As you enter The Shirtsmith, you are immediately immersed in a sea of purple carpet, shocking-pink cushions and amoeba-shaped light fittings. This distinctive interior is the brainchild of Justin Southgate of Bentheim Design, who also created the Roger Doyle shop next door. The designs within the riotous décor are thankfully a little more restrained, and include off-the-peg cotton shirts and bespoke trousers, dresses and jackets in natural fibres such as cotton, wool, linen (in summer) and silk. Pamela Frances will create an outfit in less than a month, and prices start at £250 for a jacket and £125 for a skirt.

57 **Nick Ashley** ⓜ

Designer

Tel: 0171 221 1221

Open: Mon–Sat 10am–6pm (closed August)

Ashley (son of Laura) is very big in Japan, where his sports-influenced menswear has made him a star. In this country, he retains a hands-on approach, and can usually be found in the shop carrying out his own style of "market research". His talent lies in creating classic designs from technical and performance fabrics such as Goretex, Polatex and Teflon-coated tweed. The results are engineered rather than designed, and all the manufacture is carried out in this country, so he makes no apologies for the hefty price-tag most of his garments carry (£300 for a Goretex jacket, £100 for a fleece body-warmer, £50 for moleskin trousers and £350–£950 for leather jackets). The clothes are simple, user-friendly and can be thrown into the washing machine after a hard day out on the fells.

62 **J & M Davidson**

Leather goods

Tel: 0171 243 2089

Open: Mon–Sat 10am–6pm

For 13 years, John and Monique Davidson have consistently produced high-quality, wickedly wantable leather goods, starting with belts and progressing into bags, luggage and wallets. The success of their precise, perfect leather lines has been the springboard for knitwear, outerwear and even bed linen. Her French flair and his British background combine to make a very personable, enjoyable shop; this season flat-front trousers, hipster maxi skirts and button-through dresses are the name of the game, and the bags, as ever, are delicious.

63a **Molly K**

Designer

Tel: 0171 229 7911

Open: Mon by appointment, Tues–Thurs 11am–6pm, Fri–Sat 10am–6pm

What Molly lacks in experience, she makes up for in enterprise and skill. From her shell-inspired shop (designed by Matt Stanwix), the young designer works on the stand or on real bodies to create highly experimental womenswear that – get this – is totally wearable. Off-the-peg or made-to-measure clothes start at £100 for a skirt, £75 for silk jersey separates and £300–£400 for evening wear: each piece worth every last penny.

64 **Oguri**

(&)

Designer

Tel: 0171 792 3847

Open: Mon–Sat 10am–5.30pm

Mr Oguri is a man of charm and talent, and his thoughtful shop in Ledbury Road takes some beating. The vibe is one of creative collaboration between art and fashion: the boutique is lovingly furnished with a constantly changing line-up of Fifties and Sixties cabinets, chairs and canvases. On the fashion front, things are kept simple and covetable, with mens- and womenswear in key fabrics and the must-have shapes of the season. A selection of early Sixties Balenciaga completes the past-meets-the-present theme. For locals, Oguri has become a firm favourite; for visitors, it is not to be missed.

66 **Lulu Guinness**

Handbags

Tel: 0171 221 9686

Open: Mon–Sat 10am–5pm

Best known for her amusing evening bags that grace the wrists of some of the most elegant English women, Lulu is now on to her second shop (the first is a collaboration with Selina Blow and Neisha Crosland in Elizabeth Street, see page 202). The best-selling, and most photographed, bag is the flower basket, an adorable little tub of velvet with a lid of silk violets or red roses. Guinness also designs the bags for Caroline Charles, Belville Sassoon and Bruce Oldfield, but if her main-line prices (from £150) are out of reach, look out for her designs in Debenhams, for around £30.

68 **J W Beeton**

(&)

Designer

Tel: 0171 229 8874

Open: Tues–Fri 11am–6.30pm and Sat 10.30am–6.30pm

Ledbury Road is diverse and laid back, and few shops exemplify this more acutely than JW Beeton. The ground floor is packed with cool menswear from John Rocha, 6876, Griffin, W< and Antonio Miro. The lower ground houses a dress agency for new and nearly-new designer clobber, such as Paul Smith, Yohji Yamamoto and Comme des Garçons, at a fraction of the original price.

178a Westbourne Grove **Vent**

Vintage

No phone

Open: Fri–Sat 11am–6pm

Don't let the address deceive you, Vent is actually in Ledbury Road. Simon, the lovely man behind this shop is, in fact, an architect, with a great sideline in vintage clothing and *objets trouvés*. The shop is crammed full of bits and pieces that he collected for years before deciding to turn his prized possessions into a business. There's no emphasis on a particular era, which allows Simon to sell anything that seems "right" for now. There is also a photographic record of stock and customers that have passed through the portals; greater love hath no man.

Neal Street, WC2

Neal Street – the main artery of Covent Garden's shopping centre – combines high-street names and unusual one-off shops. The result is a cool, cobbled street that throngs with visitors at the weekend. Watch your handbag.

17–19 **Karen Millen**

Mid-range

Tel: 0171 240 4401

Open: Mon–Wed, Fri 10am–7pm, late night Thurs till 8pm, Sat 10am–6.30pm and Sun 12pm–6pm

The ambitious and talented Miss Millen opened her first store in 1983 at the tender age of 21. Since then, her eye for design and head for business have steered her towards the big time – today there are stores across the country. The seasonal collections incorporate the latest developments in synthetic and natural fibres, combined with sharp tailoring, lean silhouettes and directional cuts in strong colourways (bright orange, ochre, nutmeg and ginger for summer).

For branches, call: 01622 664032.

21 **The Natural Shoe Store**

Shoes

Tel: 0171 836 5254

Open: Mon–Tues 10am–6pm, Wed–Fri 10am–7pm, Sat 10am–6.30pm and Sun 12pm–5.30pm

This cosy little shop sells natural, comfortable shoes such as Birkenstock and Simple. A range of mung beans and whale music would set off the shoes a treat.

37 **Birkenstock**

Shoes

Tel: 0171 240 2783

Open: Mon–Tues 10am–6pm, Wed–Fri 10am–7pm and Sat 10am–6.30pm

Designed by Royal College graduate John Eager, whose previous projects have included work for Paul Smith and Freelance, the Birkenstock interior features industrial and natural materials, reflecting the nature of the shoes. The cult sandals are available in Classics (suede, leather and nubuck, in earthy and bright tones, £56.95 and £52.95), Birkis (hard-wearing rubber-based sandals and clogs, £29.95–£42.95) and Vegan (containing no animal products, £42.95–£56.95). It's enough to get you marching for Greenpeace.

For mail order, call: 0800 132 194.

37a **Janet Fitch**

Jewellery

Tel: 0171 240 6332

Open: Mon–Sat 11am–7pm and Sun 1pm–6pm

Janet Fitch's stores are characterised by their quirky interiors, a skilful blend of modernity and traditional craftsmanship that highlights the jewellery from the most talented of young British designers. Styles range from tiny resin earrings set with miniature plants and shells, to the new nine-carat-gold collection set with diamonds, with prices from £10 to £400. Should you find yourself spoilt for choice, pick up a copy of *The Art and Craft of Jewellery* by Janet Fitch, which should point you in the right direction. If you can't be bothered with research, head straight for Jessica Briggs's daisy-chain necklaces, from £32.

Also at: 25a Old Compton Street W1, tel: 0171 287 3789, and 188a King's Road SW3, tel: 0171 352 4401.

41 **Sam Walker**

Vintage and leather

Tel: 0171 240 7800

Open: Mon–Sat 10am–7.30pm and Sun 12pm–7pm

Originally a vintage clothing store, Sam Walker is now divided into two sections with new ranges upstairs and second-hand and vintage downstairs. The shop is noted for leathers – with inventive names like Mustang Trucker (£495), Storm Raider (£595) and Highway Patrol (£445), based on original designs from the Forties. The Ben Sherman shirts, Fred Perry tops, Simon Carter accessories and John Smedley knitwear are just as cool. Downstairs, vintage suits, ties and dinner wear from the Forties to the Sixties await – some of which are unworn, in perfect condition, and available for a four-day hire at a third of the retail cost.

54 **Octopus**

Accessories

Tel: 0171 836 2911

Open: Mon–Sat 10.30am–7.30pm and Sun 12pm–6pm

If you are looking for a gift for the difficult friend who has everything, Octopus is a good place to begin. The business started as a barrow in King's Walk Shopping Centre two-and-a-half years ago and currently totals four shops, each stocking a novel cache of accessories designed by a small in-house team. Spring's mad mix includes bags in the shape of sheep, colourful furniture, flower bustiers and blown-glass jewellery filled with multicoloured liquid. The difficult friend will have never seen anything like it, guaranteed.

Also at: 25 and 28 Carnaby Street W1, tel: 0171 439 1950/2259, and 122 King's Road SW3, tel: 0171 589 7715.

55 Freelance

Shoes

Tel: 0171 379 7856

Open: Mon–Tues 10am–6pm, Wed–Fri 10am–7pm and Sat 10am–6.30pm

Roger Vivier, the master craftsman of French shoe design who has worked with Schiaparelli, Christian Dior, Yves Saint Laurent and Emanuel Ungaro in his time, now designs Freelance's elegant range of shoes. The store (which, for fashion buffs, has a Bill Amberg floor) also carries No Name, Spring Court and Jean Baptiste Rautureau, a beautiful congregation of precious shoes littered among wrought-iron fixtures and damask sofas.

57 Office

&

Shoes

Tel: 0171 379 1896

Open: Mon–Sat 10am–7pm and Sun 12pm–6pm

Office first took the lead in shoe retailing in 1983 with a concession at Hyper Hyper constructed entirely from office furniture (hence the name). Today, the main shops (here and in South Molton Street) showcase work by leading designers such as Karl Lagerfeld, Robert Clergerie and Nicholas Deakins; this season the visiting designers include Michel Perry, Maud Frizon, Stephane Kélian, Costume Homme and Jeffrey West. Better still is Office's own line of great-value, high-fashion shoes. Pop in for Seventies wedges, platforms, strappy sandals and cool mules in chocolate, camel, tan and lime.

For branches, call: 0181 838 4447.

58 The Hat Shop

&

Hats

Moved to 14 Lamb Street E1, tel: 0171 247 1120

Open: Mon–Sat 10.30am–6.30pm

The Hat Shop stocks every type of hat, from woolly caps at £20 to grand occasion designs in straw or crin at £200, and almost every style in between. Kids get novelty cartoon designs (£10.95) and cute hats with plaits (£19.50). As well as the own label, the shop promotes young designers (Fred Bare started out here) and buys unique styles from around the world. If you need an Australian bush hat, a Spanish riding hat or a French beret, come on down. A mail-order service is available on the number above.

60 Offspring

&

Trainers

Tel: 0171 497 2463

Open: Mon–Sat 10am–7pm and Sun 12pm–6pm

"Buzz junkie sneakers for adrenaline seekers" is the anthem of this Office-owned trainer store, according the sneaker full-time status as a fashion accessory rather than a sports necessity. The space-age interior designed by Toni Spencer gives the merchandise (everything from Airwalk and Nike to Reebok and Vans) an iconic status, and rightly so, judging by the hordes of open-mouthed buzz junkies who shop here.

62 Apple Tree

High-street

Tel: 0171 379 5944

Open: Mon–Sat 10am–7pm and Sun 11.30am–6.30pm

Apple Tree grew from small-time beginnings at Camden Market. Six years down the line, you will find affordable, directional clothing including an own-label range and well-chosen collections from small UK independents.

Also at: 190 King's Road SW3, tel: 0171 823 3551.

64 Cashmere by Design

Cashmere

Tel: 0171 240 3652

Open: Mon–Wed and Fri 10am–6.30pm, Thurs 10.30am–7pm and Sat 10am–6pm

The words cashmere and classic go together like bacon and eggs, but at CBD things get funky and fresh. The ribbed twinsets look great with slender pants (£165) or skirts (£139), and each season new colours are added to reflect trends and keep the cashmere company looking modern and more-ish.

For mail order, call: 0171 240 3652.

66 Nick Coleman

Designer

CLOSED

Graduating from St Martin's with John Galliano must have been a good omen for Coleman, but the two designers stand at opposite poles. Nick designs with experimental fabrics, such as MicroFibre and Tactel, to make hard-edged tailoring; this season, there's a move towards a more relaxed look. Fitted pieces for men and women in powder-blue, green and yellow cost from £200.

67 Daniel Poole

Street

Tel: 0171 240 5425

Open: Mon–Sat 10.30am–7pm and Sun 12pm–5.30pm

An odd shop, which has dubbed itself a "World Safety Systems Sports Shop". By rights, it ought to stock crampons and ice axes, but instead you'll find W< and the Daniel Poole collection of branded, bland merchandise.

Also at: 49 Old Compton Street W1, tel: 0171 287 0666, and 284 Westbourne Park Road W11, tel: 0171 229 3777.

70 Big Apple

Street

Tel: 0171 497 0165

Open: Mon–Sat 10am–7.30pm and Sun 11am–7pm

A ear-achingly noisy shop selling an equally loud mix of French-influenced street fashion and clubwear, from Free, L M Lulu, Diva, Onyx Sportswear and

Standard Deluxe. Prices range from £14.99 for own-label trousers and stretch T-shirts to £94 for a Bill Tournade shirt.

Also at: 98 Kensington High Street W8, tel: 0171 376 1404.

72 SF2

Mid-range

Tel: 0171 836 2576

Open: Mon–Sat 10.30am–6.45pm and Sun 12pm–5.30pm

A forward-thinking store, owned by S Fisher, which has been selling traditional menswear in Burlington Arcade since 1941 (see page 176). This new venture stocks the Method menswear collection, John Smedley and Global eyewear.

Newburgh Street, W1

Possibly the most mispronounced street name in London, Newburgh Street, on the edge of China Town, is the pretty, cobbled home to some of the best names in urban streetwear and cool jewellery. It's "burgh" as in Edinburgh, by the way.

2 John Richmond

Designer

Tel: 0171 734 5782

Open: Mon–Sat 10am–6pm

After a couple of years in the fashion doghouse, John Richmond is back, better than ever. There's a new femininity to his work (which he shows in Paris), with sharp, subtle tailoring in muted tones and pretty paisley transparents – a refreshing change from the Denim and Destroy collections we all loved to loathe.

3 Jess James

Jewellery

Tel: 0171 437 0199

Open: Mon–Fri 11am–6.30pm, Tues 12pm–6.30pm, Thurs 11am–7pm and Sat 11am–6pm

Whether you are buying or just browsing through the cabinets of predominantly silver jewellery, this shop is a box full of delights. It's great for Wright and Teague's famous engraved rings, Vass Ludacer from New York, and Jacqueline Rabun's battered silver rings, chokers and bracelets. If you can't make up your mind, buy Jess James "money", the jeweller's equivalent of a gift voucher.

7 Etcetera Projects

Mid-range

Tel: 0171 287 2792

Open: Mon–Tues and Sat 10.30am–6.30pm, Wed–Fri 11am–7pm

Visit Etcetera Projects for Japanese elegance and sizing from Jessica Wong, who produces made-to-measure for a perfect fit. Prices start at £130 for a basic, no-frills jacket.

8 **D'Uomo**

Mid-range

Tel: 0171 437 0492

Open: Mon–Sat 11am–6pm

One of the secret havens for fashion know-alls, this mellow, cathedral-style shop deals in uncluttered monochrome designs, which subtract rather than add details to enhance the form of the clothes. Concentrating on womenswear but branching into menswear, D'Uomo's subtle ideas are made from a mix of natural and man-made fibres. From £70 for shirts and trousers, £50–£200 for coats.

10 **Bond**

Street

Tel: 0171 437 0079

Open: Mon–Sat 10.30am–6pm

Laurent from Bond describes the stock as "directional menswear" – which translates as street/skatewear for Soho bohos. The shop opened in 1987, selling acid-house gear, and fast picked up a reputation as a leader in street style. Its current crop of labels includes Stussy, Xtra Large, Droors, Fuct and Holmes, as well as Bond's own label. Accessories cover Vans trainers, the controversial Black Flys precision opticals and a wealth of magazines and videos to keep you ahead of the scene.

13 **Don't Look**

Jewellery

Tel: 0171 287 2298

Open: Mon–Sat 11am–6pm

Display is the key to selling jewellery, but no one has shared this little gem with the staff here. Rings languish on uninspiring market-stall trays, pendants are draped in the window... but there's some decent silver jewellery at a decent price.

14a **Rock 'n' Roll Wardrobe**

Made-to-measure

Tel: 0171 439 1163

Open: Mon–Sat 10am–6.30pm

The infamous Rock 'n' Roll Wardrobe Slogan Tee (unprintable) has brought more than its fair share of trade to a shop which should be more noted for leather wear and Native American jewellery. Much of the business comes from Kaveh Savage's made-to-measure service, with prices from £300 for suits and £500 for leather jackets. The leather trousers are a great fit and a trifling £175.

17 (ground floor) **Sun Sun**

Mid-range

Tel: 0171 287 0909

Open: Mon–Sat 10.30am–6.30pm

Mike Shen, formerly of French Connection, started Sun Sun four years ago and opened this store in October 1996. The shop is designed to reflect the unhurried confidence of the clothes, with lilac and green walls and metallic silver curtains. The current range comprises great jackets from £250, trousers from £60 and coats from £86, all in lush fabrics such as velvet and moleskin. A womenswear range is in the wings – watch this space.

17 (first floor) **Mark Powell** (&)

Tailoring

Tel: 0171 287 5498

Open: Mon–Sat 10.30am–7pm by appointment

One of the best-known faces around his native Soho, Powell has also become one of the most successful bespoke tailors in London. As well as making perfect bespoke suits, worn by Naomi Campbell and Bryan Ferry (with prices from £750), he also turns his hand to ready-to-wear (£500), shirts (£75), ties (£50) and now shoes. Must be an insomniac.

South Molton Street, W1

A wide, pedestrian street in the West End, specialising in strong international designer labels, costume jewellery, shoes and hosiery. In summer, girls in sun-glasses sip cappuccino on the street while watching the fashion world go by.

3 **Wolford**

Hosiery

Tel: 0171 499 2549

Open: Mon–Sat 10am–6pm and late night Thurs till 6.30pm

Wolford is the Austrian hosiery specialist that has Lycra'd the legs of the masses for 50 years. This is the only place to find the entire range, from stockings to bodies and swimwear. With new deliveries each week, there's a constant stock turnover (the Follow Me tights sold out in a day) but if you don't see what you want, staff can get it within four days. The company is constantly researching ways to sculpt and hold the female form and produce a perfect silhouette.

4 **Agatha**

Jewellery

Tel: 0171 495 2779

Open: Mon–Sat 10am–6pm and late night Thurs till 7pm

For funky jewellery with one eye on the catwalk and the other on your purse, Agatha can't be beaten. The French-owned shop is a good place to unearth the accessory that will tranform last season's dress into this season's model.

8 & 47 **Hobbs**

Shoes

Tel: 0171 629 0750 (shoes); 0171 495 1557 (clothes)

Open: Mon–Sat 10am–6.30pm, late night Thurs till 7pm and Sun 12pm–5pm

Hobbs automatically conjures up images of a typically English place to shop, where both mothers and daughters can buy their entire annual wardrobe in a laid-back, unflustered atmosphere. This may be true, but lately the high-street chain has brushed up its trend antennae and has succeeded in bringing a bit of polish to its gentle, low-key formula. Hobbs shoes are mid-price, minimal-fuss and maximum-style, and the clothes take a go-anywhere route.

For branches, call: 0171 586 5550.

16 **Vertice**

Designer

Tel: 0171 408 2031

Open: Mon–Sat 10am–6pm and late night Thurs till 7pm

Vertice is fixed firmly in the early Seventies, so its moment has returned. The labels are mainly up-and-coming designers from across Europe, such as Mario Sorbo, Alessandrini, Kevin, and Belgium's designer-of-the-year Union Pour les Vêtements. Prices are kept low (shirts from £49) and the styles are understandable. Worth a visit on your beeline from Browns to Pellicano.

18 **Genny**

Designer

Tel: 0171 629 1080

Open: Mon–Sat 10am–6pm and late night Thurs till 7pm

Over the past 36 years, Arnaldo Girombelli's Genny empire has grown and diversified, to include heavy-weight labels Complice and Byblos alongside the original venture. The current collection, designed by the talented Rebecca Moses, is a sea of white, featuring jersey and linen in slim maxi skirts, tapered trousers and jackets. Keep an eye on this label: with American Richard Tyler at the helm of sister-name Byblos, Genny could be set for a pre-millennial overhaul.

21 **Electrum Gallery**

Jewellery

Tel: 0171 629 6325

Open: Mon–Fri 10am–6pm and Sat 10am–1pm

Electrum Gallery is a refreshing find, considering it was founded way back in 1971. The geometric, hi-tech interior can be confusing, but as you get your bearings you will discover an exciting range of sometimes sculptural, always exquisite jewellery from more than 80 individual designers. Most will undertake special commissions, often at no extra cost. The gallery also arranges special exhibitions four times a year.

23–27 **Browns**

Designer

Tel: 0171 491 7833

Open: Mon–Sat 10am–6pm and late night Thurs till 7pm

Arguably the best-known and best-loved of London's high-fashion emporia, Browns gets it right time and again – in fashion-land, you can't say Browns without saying *mmmm*. Joan Burstein, the inestimable woman behind the outfit, was the first to stock John Galliano and Hussein Chalyan, and is on a constant hunt for new design talent culled from across the globe. There is no strict fashion philosophy here, more an awareness of what's new, what's special and what has got "buy me" written all over it. Current labels hot from the catwalks include Anna Sui, Dries van Noten, Alexander McQueen, Eric Bergere, Missoni and Prada; for men there is Helmut Lang, Costume Homme, Nigel Curtiss and Jose Levy. Browns' reputation for being stuffy couldn't be further from the truth; try it and see, and keep an eye open for the sale dates – you might be surprised by the bargains on offer.

Also at: 6c Sloane Street SW1, tel: 0171 491 7833.

38–39 **Browns Focus**

Designer

Tel: 0171 629 0666

Open: Mon–Sat 10am–6pm and late night Thurs till 7pm

The new Browns Focus shop was to be called 4C (as in "foresee the future") but the address confused the punters and the name was changed. The intention remains the same, however: it's a street-wise concept store to introduce young designer names who look towards the millennium for inspiration. Labels such as Hysteric Glamour (T-shirts), Orla Kiely (bags) and Born Free (T-shirts with inflatable "accoutrements") are stocked alongside diffusion lines from D&G, Helmut Lang's bland Jeansline and Vivienne Westwood's Red Label. It is all directed at Browns customers in the making, who will mosey across the road to the main store as their salaries increase. Full marks, though, to Caroline Collis – daughter of Browns supremo Joan Burstein and originator of the Molton Brown hair and cosmetics business – who came up with the Focus notion; she has seen the future, and it has a label on it.

44 **Astuces**

High-street

Tel: 0171 493 1428

Open: Mon–Sat 9.30am–6.30pm and late night Thurs till 7.30pm

Astuces has been going for over three years and describes itself as "young classic Paris fashion for 18–25 year olds". With new stock arriving every week and a constant turnover of ideas, the shop is a good place to pick up catwalk styles at a fraction of the price – the most expensive jackets are £120. Times are tough, though, and Astuces recently closed its branches in Whiteleys and Wimbledon. Also available in the two remaining branches is a full range of Laceys shoes.

For branches, call: 0171 229 1815.

48 **Cable and Co**

Shoes

Tel: 0171 629 9969

Open: Mon–Sat 10am–6.30pm and late night Thurs till 7.30pm

Established in 1901, Cable and Co creates shoes of fine craftsmanship and the kind of quality that elsewhere went out with the ark. The bridal collection appears in the spring – a chance to choose beautiful, contemporary wedding shoes at a fraction of the price of their designer equivalent.

For branches, call: 0116 2801434.

62 **Romeo Gigli**

Designer

Tel: 0171 495 6730

Open: Mon–Sat 10am–6pm and late night Thurs till 7pm

The Gigli look goes in and out like the tide, and right now, it's a wee speck in the distance. But the empire is still multi-faceted, with footwear produced by Cesare Paciotti, a men's range, a perfume and a diffusion line called G Gigli. Summer looks at G Gigli include low-waist trousers in tropical prints; the main line puts a spin on adolescent mini-skirt suits and vivid silk and chiffon prints.

63 **Pellicano**

Designer

Tel: 0171 629 2205

Open: Mon–Sat 10am–6pm and late night Thurs till 7pm

Pellicano is the sort of shop that most people are too intimidated to enter, let alone browse around, but once you take that initial step through the door you will find that the staff are friendly and the clothes worth every penny. Many a young designer has started their career here, and those same designers have grown up with the shop. They include Martine Sitbon, Eric Bergere, Miu Miu, Jean Colonna, Bella Freud, Justin Oh, Owen Gaster and Copperwheat Blundell. Take the plunge, because if you want to see it first, you'll see it here.

68 **Celia Loe**

Smaller sizes

Tel: 0171 409 1627

Open: Mon–Sat 10am–6pm and late night Thurs till 7pm

The diminutive Victor Wong runs this little boutique for small women (5 feet 4 inches and under, sizes 8–14). Celia designs specifically for the smaller size, so the clothes not only fit but have the right proportions. Prices are cut down to size, too: suits from £150, blouses from £49 and dresses from £85.

Walton Street, SW3

Walton Street is well-to-do and ultra expensive – but is saved from pomposity by several marvellous one-off retailers. For pyjamas, lingerie and handbags, it takes some beating; just don't forget to polish your shoes before you set off.

77 **Laurence Tavernier**

Nightwear

Tel: 0171 823 8737

Open: Mon–Sat 10am–6pm

Paris-based Tavernier designs nightshirts and night-dresses that are almost too good to sleep in. Big on the snuggle factor are the striped cotton pjs for men and women; for hanging around the house reading the Sunday papers, there are jersey leggings and Cowardesque monogrammed dressing gowns.

77c **Kiki McDonough**

Jewellery

Tel: 0171 581 1777

Open: Mon–Fri 9.30am–5.30pm and Sat 10am–1pm

Jeweller Kiki McDonough started business in Elizabeth Street before moving to this shop six years ago. The jewellery – a favourite at the *Tatler* offices – is kept simple for everyday wear, with plenty of gold and a sprinkling of diamonds. There is also a range of cufflinks in feminine styles, from £135.

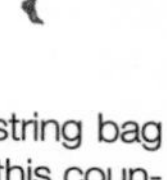

91 (upstairs) **Anya Hindmarch**

Handbags

Tel: 0171 584 7644

Open: Mon–Fri 9.30am–6pm and Sat 10am–4pm

At 18, Anya Hindmarch set off for Florence and returned with a drawstring bag and an idea. Ten years on, her bags have achieved cult status, both in this country and in Hong Kong, where she has a second shop. The bags are long on style, durability and practicality – and are currently beating Prada off pole position in the fashion editors' handbag stakes. A visit here is a visit to shopper's heaven.

95 **Cox and Power**

(&)

Jewellery

Tel: 0171 589 6335

Open: Mon–Sat 10am–6pm

This well-run, well-stocked, well-lit establishment specialises in "organic" betrothal rings in gold and silver, with matching earrings, necklaces and bracelets. Special pieces can be made to order at no extra charge. Prices start from £65 for hoop earrings to £4,250 for a red-gold ring set with an oval diamond. A good place to hunt out gifts for girlfriends.

156 **Arabesk**

Jewellery

Tel: 0171 584 3858

Open: Mon–Sat 10am–6pm

Arabesk is noted for hand-made, semi-precious jewellery inspired by ancient designs; look for the abstract, detailed chokers from the range of in-house designers, and the simpler, chunky necklaces and earrings that will go down a storm with London's lounge set. Commissions are undertaken, and can be completed within two weeks. Prices average between £150 and £300, although the real gold range can go up to £4,000.

170 **Bon Chic Bon Genre**

Mid-range

Tel: 0171 584 0545

Open: Mon–Sat 10am–6pm

With *Hello!* on the coffee tables, champagne in the cooler, and a gaggle of society ladies in attendance, BCBG sells dressy suits, cashmere coats and

Courrèges-inspired shifts – described by owner Marilyn Galsworthy as the kind of clothing you would find on the Left Bank in Paris. It's all pretty snobby stuff, but prices are significantly lower than their Parisian counterparts, with dresses at £185, trousers at £95 and coats at £350.

172 **Butterscotch**

Mid-range

Tel: 0171 581 8551

Open: Mon–Sat 10am–6pm

Ever wondered what "weekend wear" really means? Butterscotch should put you straight. The main label, Coup de Coeur, is a French line of fun pyjamas, nightshirts and dressing gowns for the whole family. Its good-quality ski range is cult property at Alpine resorts in winter, and the label's swimwear is out and about at Biarritz in summer. Poivre Blanc completes the French feel, with the kind of flowery leisurewear that tourists from Paris sport when ogling the Tower of London. Doesn't go down so well in Ladbroke Grove, mind.

178 **Merola**

Jewellery

Tel: 0171 589 0365

Open: Mon–Sat 10am–6pm

Maria Merola travels the country to track down precious period costume jewellery from the Twenties to the Fifties for her intimate shop. Few can beat her for glittering crystal, jet, bold beads and intricate wedding tiaras; a small selection of new pieces start from £17. Don't miss the vintage handbags.

190 **Bentleys**

(&)

Antique luggage

Tel: 0171 584 7770

Open: Mon–Sat 10am–6pm

What started as a hobby has turned into a full-time obsession for the owner of Bentleys, a small, jam-packed shop specialising in vintage leather luggage. Much of the stock is Victorian (attaché cases, racing handbags, crocodile vanity cases and Gladstone bags). There are also a number of collectors' pieces, such as a very early (and very covetable) Hermès handbag from around 1880, now a snip at £3,000, and a Louis Vuitton "wardrobe" – all set for a trip on the Orient Express if you've got £4,500 to spare.

194–196 **Van Peterson Designs**

Jewellery

Tel: 0171 584 1101

Open: Mon–Sat 10am–6pm, late night Wed till 7pm and Sun 12am–5pm

One of the success stories of the Eighties, Van Peterson is popular for bold "statement" jewellery in silver and gold, set with flamboyant citrines, rubies, rock crystal and topaz. Any design can be made to order (the price varies according to the stone) and a mail-order service allows you to purchase all this glamour and glitz from the comfort of your E-type Jag.

Top Tens

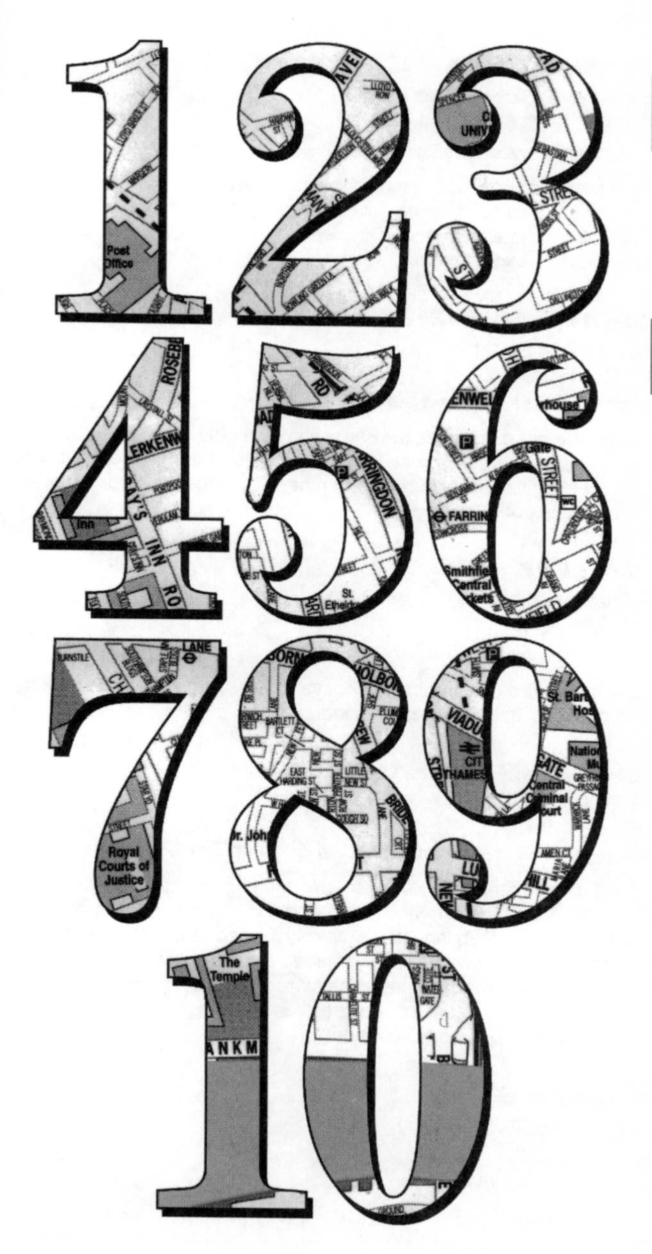
Post Office
Royal Courts of Justice
The Temple
Smithfield Central Markets
Central Criminal Court
St. Etheldreda
FARRINGDON
HOLBORN
VIADUCT
CITY THAMESLINK
INN
LANE
BARTLETT CT
EAST HARDING ST
LITTLE NEW ST
AMEN CT
HILL

Designer Discount Stores

Bicester Outlet Shopping

50 Pringle Drive, Bicester Oxfordshire
Tel: 01869 323 200
Open: 10am–6pm seven days a week

OK, so it's not in London, but a jaunt in the car down the M40 is not much to ask for 48 outlet shops, including Jaeger, Kurt Geiger, Aquascutum, Benetton, Hobbs, Whistles and Jigsaw. Bicester is one of the UK's new US-style shopping villages – expect more to spring up in the shires soon.

Browns Labels For Less

50 South Molton Street W1
Tel: 0171 491 7833
Open: Mon–Sat 10am–6pm and late night Thurs till 7pm

Browns Labels For Less carries the same names as the main store (Comme des Garçons, Missoni, Issey Miyake) at around 50% of the original cost. The men's version, originally around the corner, has now joined the womenswear in this one-stop shop.

Burberrys

29-53 Chatham Place E9
Tel: 0181 985 3344
Open: Mon–Fri 12pm–6pm and Sat 9am–3pm

The classic mac, the classic check – and all the sweaters, hats and sports jackets in between, at half the recommended price.

Designer Sale Studio

201 King's Road SW3
Tel: 0171 351 4171
Open: Mon–Fri 10.30am–6.30pm, Sat 10am–6pm and Sun 12pm–6pm

One of the capital's original designer sale shops, the store has recently moved to this flash location which manages to disguise the fact that the stock is far cheaper than any of its snooty neighbours. Womenswear is upstairs, menswear downstairs and labels include Moschino, Genny, Complice, Versus and Prada accessories (which, not surprisingly, sell out as quickly as they arrive). Most of the stock is from last season, but with discounts of up to 60%, who gives a hoot?

Designer Store

289 King's Road SW3
Tel: 0171 351 0880
Open: Mon–Sat 10.30am–6.30pm

Due to customer demand, the Store is moving away from simple sample stock and towards a more comprehensive selection of designer fashion. Expect SportMax, MaxMara, Kenzo shoes, Marc Aurel and 120% Linen.

French Connection/ Nicole Farhi Factory Outlet

75–83 Fairfield Road E3
Tel: 0181 981 3931

Open: Tues–Wed 10am–3pm, Thurs 11am–6.30pm, Fri 10am–5.30pm and Sat 10am–3pm

If you're a fan of French Connection or Nicole Farhi, then you'll adore the factory outlet which sells women's and men's old stock, cancelled orders, seconds, samples and one-off ideas which never made it into production from current and recent collections. It's the best bit of Bow by far.

In Wear

100 Garrett Lane SW18
Tel: 0181 871 2155

Open: Mon–Fri 10am–5pm and Sat 10am–4pm

Casual women's and menswear from In Wear and Matinique. You will get up to 70% off the usual prices for the cost of a bus fare to Wandsworth.

Joseph Clearance Shop

53 King's Road SW3
Tel: 0171 730 7562

Open: Mon–Sat 10.30am–6.30pm, late night Wed till 7pm and Sun 12pm–5pm

Past seasons' collections from Joseph and his ever-increasing entourage of designer followers that includes Equipment, APC, Irie and Teenflo. Discounts depend on the age and condition of the stock, but whatever is available will probably be a great good buy.

Paul Smith Sale Shop

23 Avery Row W1
Tel: 0171 493 1287

Open: Mon–Sat 10am–6pm and late night Thurs till 7pm

Last season's stock sold at a knock-down price in a hip three-floor store in the heart of the West End. If you want the label without the loaded prices, try here first.

Whistles Sale Shop

25 King's Road SW3
Tel: 0171 730 1181

Open: Mon–Tues 10am–6pm, late night Wed till 7pm and Thurs–Sat 10am–6.30pm

If you want to pick up a piece of wonderful Whistles at a fraction of the price make this store your first destination. The worthwhile stock includes press samples (after we've finished with them), end-of-line trouser suits, coats and evening dresses and occasional one-offs that have proved too expensive to put into production.

Kids' Clothes

Buckle My Shoe

18–19 St Christopher's Place W1
Tel: 0171 935 5589
Open: Mon–Sat 10am–6pm and late night Thurs till 7pm

A specialist children's shoe shop providing leading Italian high-fashion and traditional styles for discerning little feet. Trained staff will advise on the first walking shoe or stomping boots for toddlers to ensure each pair fits perfectly and has that all-important "growing room".

Also at: Brent Cross Shopping Centre, Hendon Way NW4, tel: 0181 202 4423.

French Connection

249 Regent Street W1
Tel: 0171 493 3124
Open: Mon–Sat 10am–6.30pm, late night Thurs till 8pm and Sun 12pm–6pm

Mum shops in French Connection? Then you can be assured of instant street cred here. Mirroring the trends in adult fashion, spring sees matched and mismatched bright beach colours in rough-and-tumble denim, tough towelling and soft cotton. For girls there are pretty patterned dresses, embroidered cardigans, bootcut stretch trousers, and gingham tie shirts; the boys can mimic big brother in skate shorts, nylon-coated drill jeans and jackets and ethnic-print shirts.

Jakss

319 Upper Street N1
Tel: 0171 359 4942
Open: Mon–Fri 10am–5.30pm and Sat 10.30pm–6pm

Jakss has by far the best selection of designer childrenswear in London catering for fashion-conscious babies, toddlers and teenagers. Labels read like a miniature *Who's Who* in fashion and include Oilily, US style from Donna Karan, Paul Smith, Lacoste, Calvin Klein and the adorable Baby Levi's. Established in 1974, the store is firmly rooted in both Islington and the Roman Road, so you can rely on a steady supply of groovy get up for label-crazy kids.

Also at: 463 and 469 Roman Road E3, tel: 0181 981 2233.

Oilily

9 Sloane Street SW1
Tel: 0171 823 2505
Open: Mon–Sat 10am–6pm and late night Wed till 7pm

With 26 years of experience, and an 80,000-strong fan club of mini customers, Oilily is well placed to design and make clothes that are as popular with kids as with parents. The colours are fun, the details practical – and the fan club receives letters and catalogues in the post.

Paul Smith Childrenswear

44 Floral Street WC2
Tel: 0171 379 7133
Open: Mon–Wed, Fri 10.30am–6.30pm, late night Thurs till 7pm and Sat 10am–6.30pm

Next-door to the grown-up world of Paul Smith lies the down-sized version (on the site of the old Paul Smith Jeans shop) – the only designer childrenswear label to warrant a stand-alone store. This season, cool kids can expect Sixties Californian beach chic characterised by seersucker ginghams, Madras checks, jacquard patterns and vivid prints. Girls can dress up in A-line coats and shifts, shirt dresses, shorts and short-sleeve shirts, while the boys have a choice of bright striped jersey, Seventies-inspired polos and towelling tops. A hint of Smithy humour is added in the shape of 3-D badges and heat-sealed patches containing toys.

Sasti

Unit 23 Portobello Green Arcade, 281 Portobello Road W10
Tel: 0181 960 1125
Open: Mon–Fri 10.30am–6pm and Sat 10am–6pm

This unit opened in March 1995 with the help of the Princes Youth Business Trust and provides fun and funky hand-made designs (adorable stuff such as fake fur coats with ears and knitted pixie hats). Wild Child is a range of bright and practical trousers, waistcoats, pinafores and playsuits, with prices as low as £12.

Tartine et Chocolat

66 South Molton Street W1
Tel: 0171 629 7233
Open: Mon–Sat 10am–6pm and late night Thurs till 7pm

Catherine Parvin's French company produces elegant, nostalgic childrenswear in sophisticated colours (chocolate and navy with tartans and checks). With five children herself, she has a child's-eye view of the world, reflected in her range of toys, accessories, nursery linen and even a kids' perfume, "Ptisenbon" (loosely translated as "little ones that smell nice") for 6–12-year-old girls. The clothes, though, are for well-behaved children who never splash in puddles or roll in the grass; it is the kind of gear that they will quite probably want to take off immediately. But their grannies will love it.

Tots in the Terrace

39 Turnham Green Terrace W4
Tel: 0181 995 0520
Open: Mon–Sat 10am–6pm and Sun 12pm–5pm

This little shop for little people is enough to make even the most hardened career girl rush off to check the biological clock. The stock from Hummelsheim, Oilily, Oshkosh B'Gosh, Babi Mini and Portofino is for 0–14-year-olds and includes dresses, trousers, shirts, accessories and swimwear. Some of it is just too cute for words.

What a Circus

8–10 King's Walk Shopping Mall, 122 King's Road SW3
Tel: 0171 584 0217
Open: Mon–Fri 10am–6pm and Sat 10am–6.30pm

What a Circus was opened in February 1996 (by Chris Tarrant) and is much more than just a clothes shop for kids. It has a tented ceiling, a circus ring, a box-office pay area and interactive activity boards to keep the kids entertained while you look round; the staff dress as clowns, toys litter the floor and there are nappy-changing and breast-feeding facilities on site. The clothes are as exciting and colourful as the store itself, with branded childrenswear for newborns to ten-year-olds (look out for Lego clothes), gift ideas (musical ice-cream scoops, Sleepy and Happy aromatherapy ointments) and the What a Circus own-brand T-shirts, sweatshirts, polo tops and caps. If you would like to know a little more, contact the Internet site at: http://www.kidbase.co.uk/kid.

Young England

47 Elizabeth Street SW1
Tel: 0171 259 9003
Open: Mon–Fri 10am–5.30pm and Sat 10am–3pm

Glamorously groomed children are at home in Young England, the Elizabeth Street store for aspiring social climbers. Nanny Barnes, who helps to keep the aristocratic clientele in check, is on hand to offer advice on choosing anything from layette and christening gowns to grown-up party frocks and tailored coats. The clothes (made in England) are exquisitely simple with traditional hand-smocked detailing, making them understandably expensive.

Wedding Dresses

Caroline Castigliano

62 Berners Street W1
Tel: 0171 636 8212
Open: by appointment

After launching her own sportswear label in the United States in the Eighties Caroline Castigliano turned her hand to bridal wear with a shop in Esher. Soon after, she took over the bridal room in Liberty and opened her second shop in Chiltern Street. This is now her flagship store; the Chiltern Street shop stocks "Caroline Castigliano Favorita" to cater for sizes 16–20.

Also at: 54 Chiltern Street W1, tel: 0171 935 9756, and 136 High Street, Esher KT10, tel: 01372 469 749.

Catherine Walker

The Conservatory, 46 Fulham Road SW3
Tel: 0171 581 8811
Open: Mon–Sat 10am–6pm and at other times by appointment

Lady Helen Windsor and Jemima Khan share the secret of Catherine Walker. Originally a children's, ladies and couture designer she has become more famous for her fluid wedding outfits, hand-embroidered with individual pearls and crystals. Her shop – formerly the conservatory to South Kensington Manor – is a little slice of tranquility in which to find a perfectly fitted dress. An added feature of the business is the "once worn" section, where customers can pick up a second-hand dress for significantly less than the expected £2,000 price tag.

Couture at: 65 Sydney Street SW3, tel: 0171 352 4626.

Deborah Milner

First floor, 22 Lupus Street SW1
Tel: 0171 821 6478
Open: by appointment

Milner's is a one-off operation for women who want to build on a dream for the big day. She recently moved from her atelier in Elizabeth Street to the more tranquil, less accessible quarters of Pimlico. There are few samples in her little workroom, but bags of style and a more fashion-conscious approach than at many bridal design boutiques.

Droopy and Browns

99 St Martin's Lane WC2
Tel: 0171 379 4514
Open: Mon–Wed 10.30am–6.30pm, late night Thurs till 7.30pm, Fri 10.30am–7pm and Sat 9.30am–5.30pm

Exclusive designs from Angela Holmes, who set up shop in York in 1972. Individually made hats, veils and headdresses are on offer alongside classic sheath dresses or lavish, full-skirted gowns in damask, organza or fairy-tale silk crepe.

Hourglass

5 Sheen Road, Richmond TW9
Tel: 0181 332 0166
Open: Mon–Sat 11am–6pm, appointments advisable

Corsetry is a major feature of Sarah Whitworth's designs in both her ready-to-wear and made-to-measure collections. A rapidly expanding feature of the shop is the eveningwear – priced from £300 to £500 and complementary accessories including solid silver tiaras which can be set with the stones of your choice.

Nazareth Walsh

33 Clerkenwell Green EC1
Tel: 0171 608 1847
Open: Mon–Fri 10.30am–5.30pm (closed Tues) and Sat by appointment

Made-to-measure dresses in traditional fabrics are a Nazareth Walsh speciality. After 12 years in Clerkenwell, the shop has a reputation for adaptability and the girls will build on the original framework to make a dress to suit your exact requirements. Evening dresses can also be bought off-the-peg or made-to-measure.

Neil Cunningham

28 Sackville Street W1
Tel: 0171 437 5793
Open: Mon–Sat 10am–5.30pm

Neil Cunningham's flattering dresses reinterpret the idea of the modern wedding in their form and fit. Making the Sindy Wedding Trousseau on behalf of Hasbro several years ago proved that he's an adaptable cove. Now that Neil has his own store in the heart of Mayfair he can cater for your requirements as well as Sindy's, both in wedding dresses and in his glamorous evening wear which was added in 1995.

Phillipa Lepley

494 Fulham Road SW6
Tel: 0171 386 0927
Open: by appointment

Lepley designs stunning couture dresses in natural fibres (average price, £2,800), which can be tried on at leisure in a purpose-built, light-filled conservatory. Hand-made shoes, bags, hats, veils, going-away suits and cocktail dresses are also available.

Rebecca Street

294 Upper Street N1
Tel: 0171 354 9955
Open: Tues–Sat 10am–6pm and late night Wed till 7.30pm

Simplicity is the key at Rebecca Street, whose sculpted and finely detailed dresses have to be tried on before you can appreciate their true elegance. As well as the dresses there are complementary accessories from young British designers such as Claire Norwood (shoes) and Malcolm Morris (tiaras and made-to-measure jewellery). If you can't find exactly what you want, most designs can be made in a variety of different fabrics, colours and lengths.

Virgin Bride

Grand Buildings, Northumberland Avenue WC2
Tel: 0171 321 0866
Open: Tues–Sat 10am–6pm and late night Thurs till 8pm

For anyone who has tried to organise a wedding and hold down a full-time job at the same time, Virgin Bride will come as welcome relief. The new store is the brainchild of Ailsa Petchey, former Virgin air hostess, who, after a fruitful chat with Richard Branson, came up with the idea for a "one-stop" wedding shop. Covering 10,000 square feet, the store offers mother-of-the-bride outfits, hair and beauty makeovers, stationery, honeymoon bookings (flying with you-know-who) and of course the all-important dress, all under one roof. The ranges are led by Beverley Summers, whose detailed bridal dresses can be short, long, flirty, fancy – collection or couture. Duchesse satin and silk dupion predominate, though velvet and brocade individual roses add a finishing flourish.

Coffee Shops

Brent Cross Ponti's Lavazza

The Food Gallery, Brent Cross Shopping Centre, Hendon Way NW4

Open: Mon–Fri 9.30am–8pm, Sat 8.30am–6pm and Sun 10.30am–5pm

"The Italians' favourite coffee" now has its very own coffee shop. Situated among the hustle and bustle of Brent Cross, it is packed with ladies who lunch (and shop) on well-earned breaks from their spending sprees. As well as the expected espressos and cappuccinos (as good as any you'll find in Italy), there are Italian-style snacks and a full range of take-home blends, espresso machines and coffee pots.

Camden Primrose Patisserie

136 Regents Park Road NW1

Open: 8.30am–9pm seven days a week

With a reputation for a mean apple crumble and a loyal local following, the Primrose Patisserie is a welcoming (and busy at the quietest of times) coffee stop. A stone's throw from Camden, but a world away from the market hubub, the friendly staff offer tea, coffee, cakes, sandwiches – all home-cooked in their bakery. For a take-home treat, you can buy a whole apple tart for £14.

City and East End St John's Café

12 Jerusalem Passage EC1

Open: Mon-Fri 7am-5.30pm

This cosy little Clerkenwell café is popular with office and factory workers. It's slightly off the beaten track but well worth finding. The coffee is great, as is the family atmosphere provided by Vince Sartori whose grandfather opened the café in 1916. The no-nonsense food includes fried eggs and bacon, pasta and fish dishes. Prices are among the cheapest you will find anywhere, with breakfast starting at £1.50, tea at 20p, and sandwiches from 70p.

Covent Garden Neal's Yard Beach Café

13 Neal's Yard WC2

Open: Mon-Fri, Sun 11am-7pm and Sat 10am-8pm

A little slice of Fifties Miami in Covent Garden, the Beach Café has sea-and-sand decor and sunny staff to match. They do a great line in ice cream and smoothies, from £2.95. If you can't make up your mind combine the two with a Caffe Scecherato – espresso coffee, caffe latte ice cream and milk, £2.50.

Hampstead The Coffee Cup

74 High Street Hampstead NW3

Tel: 0171 435 7565

Open: Mon–Fri 8am–10pm and Sat–Sun 9am–10pm

More of a lounge than a café, The Coffee Cup is a part of Hampstead society with regular customers meeting up every day for breakfast. For serious shoppers, every type of coffee is available with raisin toast and croissants on the side.

Islington Gill Wing Café

300 St Paul's Road N1

Open: 8am–11pm seven days a week

Part of the Gill Wing Islington empire, this is a good place to head for when the shops prove too much. As well as liquid refreshment, the café is known for its food, especially the sausages. The café turns into a jazz bar downstairs, open till 11pm with a constantly changing line-up of musicians and menus.

Knightsbridge Gloriette

128 Brompton Road SW3

Open: Mon–Sat 7am–8pm and Sun 9am–6pm

Collapse with your Harrods bags and try some of the most mor-ish coffee and patisserie around. Try Eiskaffe – a long, refreshing iced coffee with a lavish scoop of vanilla ice cream topped with whipped cream, or go for Caramel Latte Macchiato – a single espresso within a glass of caramel foamed milk.

Notting Hill Portobello Café

305 Portobello Road W10

Open: Mon–Thurs, Sun 10am–10pm and Fri–Sat 9am–10pm

"The best breakfast on Portobello Road", served all day, every day. If you're visiting the markets at the weekend then this is the obvious stop for anything from a pot of tea to a Sunday brunch or lunch. In summer, the garden is open so you can sit and soak up the sun while sipping your Mocha.

Soho Bar Italia

22 Frith Street W1

Open: 24 hours a day, seven days a week

Truly an open-all-hours coffee shop, this is also one of the most famous cafés in the capital. Immortalised by Pulp, favoured by clubbers, shoppers and those with a nose for a fine cappuccino, Bar Italia is busy at all times – especially in the summer when visitors spill out on to the pavements.

Soho The Living Room

3 Bateman Street W1

Tel: 0171 437 4827

Open: Mon–Fri 10.30am–12am, Sat 11am–12am and Sun 12pm–11pm

Ever-so-trendy Soho café that is something of a home from home. With battered sofas, compulsory passive smoking and permanent art exhibitions, you may be forgiven for feeling you have wandered out of London into Amsterdam.

Shop Assistance

Best places for...

Bags
Anya Hindmarch
Bill Amberg
Harvey Nichols
Fenwick
Selina Blow

Beaching it
Sam de Teran
Benetton

Bumping into designers
The Cross
Portobello Market
Richard James
Vent

Bumping into fashion editors
Blackout II
Harvey Nichols
Joseph
Space NK
Steinberg & Tolkein

Changing rooms
Clusaz
Guess?
Siena

Club gear
Bond
Duffer of St George
Shop
Slam City Skates

Cocktail dresses
Anna Molinari
Dorothy Perkins
Monsoon
Principles

Fashion food
Armani Express
Café 100 in Aquascutum
DKNY
Joe's in Fenwick
Liberty (basement)
Nicole's at Nicole Farhi
Space NK

Generous sizes
French Connection
Hobbs
Marks and Spencer
Nicole Farhi

Great coats
Jaeger
Jigsaw
Marks and Spencer
MaxMara

Hanging out
Bon Chic Bon Genre (*Hello*! readers only)
DKNY
Hype DF
Low Pressure
Shop
Slam City Skates
Squire

Helpful shop assistants
Bizoo
Galerie Gaultier
Le Coin
Paul Smith
Question Air
Rigby & Peller

Luxury lingerie
Agent Provocateur
Boisvert
Janet Reger
Femme Fatale
Fenwick

Office suits
Galicia
Jigsaw
Wardrobe

One-stop shopping
Anna, NW1
Ground Zero
Hype DF
Liberty
Matches
Selfridges
Wardrobe

Oscars dresses
Amanda Wakeley
Valentino

Pyjamas and nighties
The Gap
Laurence Tavernier
Lord's
Margaret Howell

Sofa wear
Amanda Wakeley
Betty Jackson
Muji
Nicole Farhi

Sports kit
DKNY
Lillywhites
Sports Locker

Smart days
Paddy Campbell
Selfridges
Teenflo

Weekends
Callaghans
The Gap
Nicole Farhi
Racing Green

Index by Name

Numbers in italics refer to main shop review where there is more than one page reference

Index by Area

All Over the Shop

Bond Street

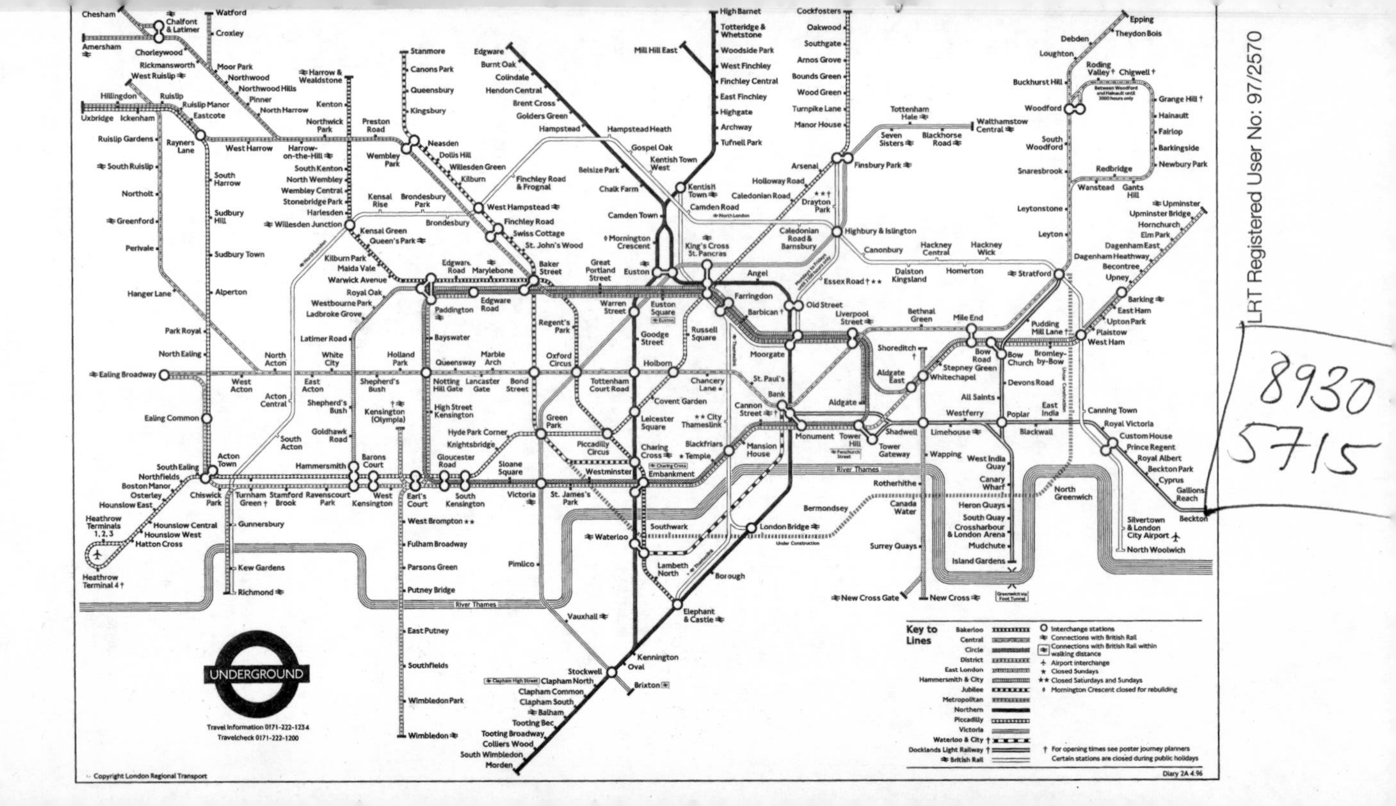

Chesham
Chalfont & Latimer
Watford
Croxley
Amersham
Chorleywood
Rickmansworth
Moor Park
Northwood
Northwood Hills
Pinner
North Harrow
West Ruislip
Hillingdon
Ruislip
Ruislip Manor
Eastcote
Uxbridge
Ickenham
Ruislip Gardens
Rayners Lane
West Harrow
Harrow & Wealdstone
Kenton
Northwick Park
Preston Road
Harrow-on-the-Hill
South Ruislip
South Harrow
Northolt
Greenford
Perivale
Sudbury Hill
Sudbury Town
Hanger Lane
Alperton
Park Royal
North Ealing
Ealing Broadway
West Acton
North Acton
East Acton
Acton Central
Ealing Common
South Acton
Acton Town
South Ealing
Northfields
Boston Manor
Osterley
Hounslow East
Hounslow Central
Hounslow West
Hatton Cross
Heathrow Terminals 1, 2, 3
Heathrow Terminal 4 †
Chiswick Park
Turnham Green †
Stamford Brook
Ravenscourt Park
Gunnersbury
Kew Gardens
Richmond
Stanmore
Canons Park
Queensbury
Kingsbury
Wembley Park
Neasden
Dollis Hill
Willesden Green
Kilburn
South Kenton
North Wembley
Wembley Central
Stonebridge Park
Harlesden
Willesden Junction
Kensal Rise
Brondesbury Park
Brondesbury
Kensal Green
Queen's Park
Kilburn Park
Maida Vale
Warwick Avenue
Royal Oak
Westbourne Park
Ladbroke Grove
Latimer Road
White City
Holland Park
Shepherd's Bush
Kensington (Olympia)
Goldhawk Road
Hammersmith
Barons Court
West Kensington
Earl's Court
West Brompton ★★
Fulham Broadway
Parsons Green
Putney Bridge
East Putney
Southfields
Wimbledon Park
Wimbledon
River Thames
Edgware
Burnt Oak
Colindale
Hendon Central
Brent Cross
Golders Green
Hampstead
Hampstead Heath
Gospel Oak
Belsize Park
Chalk Farm
Kentish Town West
Kentish Town
Camden Town
Camden Road
West Hampstead
Finchley Road & Frognal
Finchley Road
Swiss Cottage
St. John's Wood
Edgware Road
Marylebone
Baker Street
Great Portland Street
Euston
♦ Mornington Crescent
King's Cross St. Pancras
Paddington
Bayswater
Queensway
Notting Hill Gate
Lancaster Gate
Marble Arch
Bond Street
High Street Kensington
Gloucester Road
South Kensington
Sloane Square
Victoria
Hyde Park Corner
Knightsbridge
Green Park
Regent's Park
Oxford Circus
Warren Street
Euston Square
Goodge Street
Tottenham Court Road
Holborn
Russell Square
Covent Garden
Leicester Square
Piccadilly Circus
Charing Cross
Embankment
Westminster
St. James's Park
★ Temple
Blackfriars
Mansion House
Chancery Lane ★
★★ City Thameslink
St. Paul's
Bank
Cannon Street ★†
Monument
Tower Hill
Fenchurch Street
Tower Gateway
Aldgate
Aldgate East
Farringdon
Barbican †
Moorgate
Liverpool Street
Old Street
Angel
Essex Road †★★
Waterloo
Southwark
Lambeth North
Elephant & Castle
Borough
London Bridge
Bermondsey
Pimlico
Vauxhall
Kennington
Oval
Stockwell
Brixton
Clapham High Street
Clapham North
Clapham Common
Clapham South
Balham
Tooting Bec
Tooting Broadway
Colliers Wood
South Wimbledon
Morden
Mill Hill East
High Barnet
Totteridge & Whetstone
Woodside Park
West Finchley
Finchley Central
East Finchley
Highgate
Archway
Tufnell Park
Cockfosters
Oakwood
Southgate
Arnos Grove
Bounds Green
Wood Green
Turnpike Lane
Manor House
Arsenal
Holloway Road
Caledonian Road
Drayton Park
Caledonian Road & Barnsbury
Highbury & Islington
Finsbury Park
Seven Sisters
Tottenham Hale
Blackhorse Road
Walthamstow Central
Canonbury
Dalston Kingsland
Hackney Central
Hackney Wick
Homerton
Stratford
Bethnal Green
Mile End
Shoreditch
Whitechapel
Stepney Green
Bow Road
Bow Church
Bromley-by-Bow
Devons Road
All Saints
Pudding Mill Lane †
Shadwell
Limehouse
Westferry
Poplar
East India
Blackwall
Wapping
Rotherhithe
Canada Water
Surrey Quays
New Cross Gate
New Cross
West India Quay
Canary Wharf
Heron Quays
South Quay
Crossharbour & London Arena
Mudchute
Island Gardens
Greenwich via Foot Tunnel
North Greenwich
Canning Town
Royal Victoria
Custom House
Prince Regent
Royal Albert
Beckton Park
Cyprus
Gallions Reach
Beckton
Silvertown & London City Airport
North Woolwich
Under Construction
West Ham
Plaistow
Upton Park
East Ham
Barking
Upney
Becontree
Dagenham Heathway
Dagenham East
Elm Park
Hornchurch
Upminster Bridge
Upminster
Epping
Theydon Bois
Debden
Loughton
Buckhurst Hill
Roding Valley †
Chigwell †
Grange Hill †
Hainault
Fairlop
Barkingside
Newbury Park
Between Woodford and Hainault until 2000 hours only
Woodford
South Woodford
Snaresbrook
Redbridge
Wanstead
Gants Hill
Leytonstone
Leyton
UNDERGROUND
Travel Information 0171-222-1234
Travelcheck 0171-222-1200
Key to Lines
Bakerloo
Central
Circle
District
East London
Hammersmith & City
Jubilee
Metropolitan
Northern
Piccadilly
Victoria
Waterloo & City †
Docklands Light Railway †
British Rail
Interchange stations
Connections with British Rail
Connections with British Rail within walking distance
Airport interchange
★ Closed Sundays
★★ Closed Saturdays and Sundays
♦ Mornington Crescent closed for rebuilding
† For opening times see poster journey planners
Certain stations are closed during public holidays
Diary 2A 4.96